HOOKED on LITERATURE!

Ready-to-Use
Activities & Materials
to Spark Students' Interest
in Literature,
Grades 9 & Up

JACK UMSTATTER

**THE CENTER FOR APPLIED
RESEARCH IN EDUCATION**
West Nyack, New York 10995

Library of Congress Cataloging-in-Publication Data

Umstatter, Jack.
    Hooked on literature! : ready-to-use activities and materials to
spark students' interest in literature, grades 9 and up / by Jack
Umstatter.
        p.   cm.
    Includes bibliographical references.
    ISBN 0-87628-546-9
    1. Literature—Study and teaching (Higher)   I. Title.
PN59.U67   1994
809—dc20   93-46483
                                                                                  CIP

C5469-6

ISBN 0-87628-546-9

**The Center for Applied Research
in Education,** Professional Publishing
West Nyack, New York 10995

Simon & Schuster, A Paramount Communications Company

Printed in the United States of America

DEDICATION

Thanks to Chris, Kate, Maureen, John, Mary, Jim, Martha, Nana, and Priscilla for their support, and to the many special students who inspired this book.

About the Author

Jack Umstatter has taught English and literature on both the junior and senior high school levels in the West Islip, New York, public schools since 1972 and education and literature at Dowling College in Oakdale, New York, for the past five years.

Mr. Umstatter graduated from Manhattan College with a B.A. in English and completed his M.A. in English at S.U.N.Y.-Stony Brook. He earned his Educational Administration degree at Long Island University.

A member of Phi Delta Kappa and the National Council of Teachers of English, Mr. Umstatter has been selected West Islip High School's Teacher of the Year several times and most recently was elected to *Who's Who Among America's Teachers*. He has taught all levels of secondary English classes including the Honors and the Advanced Placement Literature classes. As coach of the high school's Academic Team, the Brainstormers, he led the team in capturing the Long Island and New York State championships when competing in the American Scholastic Competition Network National Tournament of Champions in Lake Forest, Illinois.

About This Resource

You are truly one of a unique breed. Much is demanded of you as an English teacher who teaches literature as well as a multitude of other language-related skills. You are asked to be inspirational, insightful, entertaining, and so much more. Finding the time to do research on literary topics or develop interesting literature lessons seems more difficult than ever. Hercules probably had it easier!

Along with the broad demands of teaching English, you probably have a daily scenario that looks like this. Today, besides teaching your regular classes, you met with your homeroom, monitored a noisy lunchroom, or sat on hall duty. Then you spent your prep and lunch periods correcting tests, administering make-up exams, and giving extra help to your students. After the last period you walked out of your classroom with a couple of sets of essays in your briefcase. Tonight, you will prepare a test on the novel your students are currently reading, research next week's lessons, correct yesterday's quizzes and try to find time to get to those essays. You also have family commitments (*most* teachers do!), probably coach a team, direct a play, or head the school paper, literary magazine, or yearbook (*many* English teachers do!), and certainly have other responsibilities just as other human beings have (*all* English teachers do!). Needless to say, your time is precious.

With all that in mind, I designed *Hooked on Literature!* as a creative, practical, and informative resource to assist you, the high school or college literature teacher, in stimulating your students' interest and knowledge in the world you love—**literature**. Organized into nine sections that cover literature from the classics to the contemporary, the book is an easy-to-use resource of ideas and activities that will make teaching literature more effective and enjoyable for you and your students. These classroom-tested exercises, which have received very positive student responses, will inform and challenge your students as they gain greater literary knowledge and appreciation. The Table of Contents provides a quick and convenient guide to locating each activity's questions and answers.

You can choose the activity's implementation. With thousands of questions found in more than 150 ready-for-use activities, you can select pages for a unit's introduction or review as an individual, small group/cooperative learning, or entire-class activity. You may want to give some of the materials as homework assignments or research-based activities to promote more improved and effective library skills. They're also useful as springboards for discussions that deal with these literary topics or for class and school literature bees or similar contests. Additionally, a school's Academic Team will find these materials beneficial in preparing for local, statewide, and even national competitions.

Use these productive, educational, and enjoyable units of instructional activities when needed within your literature curriculum or when developing a new curriculum. They enhance literature study and promote student involvement and interest in literature. Just ask the teachers and kids who have used them!

Jack Umstatter

Acknowledgements

I especially thank my wife, Chris, and daughters, Kate and Maureen, for being there when I needed them.

I'd also like to thank Joe Tessitore, Win Huppuch, and Connie Kallback for their confidence, support, and guidance in this labor of love.

Some of the activities were created with software developed by WISCO Computing in Wisconsin Rapids, Wisconsin, who has given permission to use it.

To the English teachers everywhere who inspire their students to read, learn, enjoy, and dream, I acknowledge your skills and pay tribute to your wonderful efforts.

Finally, my thanks to all those students who have made my years in the classroom so meaningful and inspirational.

Table of Contents

SECTION 2:   CHARACTERS—LITERATURE'S LEGACIES—57

SECTION 3:   TIMING IS EVERYTHING—81

SECTION 4: NOVELS—TALES TO REMEMBER—119

ANSWER KEYS TO ACTIVITIES—285

LITERATURE ACTIVITIES

SECTION 1

AUTHORS WHO MAKE US LAUGH AND CRY

SOME AMERICAN AUTHORS BORN BEFORE 1800

Fill in the names of these thirteen American authors who were born before 1800. Their birth and death dates and one of their important works are given.

1. ———————————————————————— 1579–1631 *The General History of Virginia, New England, and the Summer Isles*

2. ———————————————————————— 1590–1657 *Of Plymouth Plantation*

3. ———————————————————————— 1612–1672 *The Tenth Muse Lately Sprung Up in America*

4. ———————————————————————— 1631–1705 "The Day of Doom"

5. ———————————————————————— 1642–1729 *Preparatory Meditations*

6. ———————————————————————— 1674–1744 *The History of the Dividing Line*

7. ———————————————————————— 1703–1758 *The Nature of True Virtue*

8. ———————————————————————— 1706–1790 *Poor Richard's Almanack*

9. ———————————————————————— 1753–1784 *Poems on Various Subjects*

10. ——————————————————————— 1779–1843 *The Star-Spangled Banner*

11. ——————————————————————— 1779–1863 *'Twas the Night Before Christmas*

12. ——————————————————————— 1783–1859 *The Legend of Sleepy Hollow*

13. ——————————————————————— 1789–1851 *The Last of the Mohicans*

SOME AMERICAN AUTHORS BORN DURING THE 1800s

Identify the forty-three American authors whose life spans and works are listed next to the answer spaces.

1. _____ 1803–1882 *Essays, First and Second Series*

2. _____ 1804–1864 *The Scarlet Letter*

3. _____ 1807–1892 "The Barefoot Boy"

4. _____ 1809–1849 "The Raven"

5. _____ 1811–1896 *Uncle Tom's Cabin*

6. _____ 1817–1862 *Walden*

7. _____ 1819–1892 *Leaves of Grass*

8. _____ 1819–1891 *Billy Budd*

9. _____ 1830–1886 "Because I Could Not Stop for Death"

10. _____ 1832–1888 *Little Women*

11. _____ 1832–1899 *Ragged Dick Series*

12. _____ 1835–1910 *Tom Sawyer*

13. _____ 1837–1920 *The Rise of Silas Lapham*

14. _____ 1843–1916 *The Portrait of a Lady*

15. _____ 1851–1904 *The Awakening*

16. _____ 1862–1910 *The Four Million*

17. _____ 1862–1937 *The Age of Innocence*

18. _____ 1862–1930 *Nancy Drew Series*

19. _____ 1867–1957 *Little House in the Big Woods*

20. _____ 1869–1946 *Seventeen*

21. _____ 1871–1945 *An American Tragedy*

22. _____ 1871–1900 *The Red Badge of Courage*

23. _____ 1873–1947 *A Lost Lady*

24. _____ 1874–1935 *Life with Father*

25. _____ 1874–1963 "Mending Wall"

SOME AMERICAN AUTHORS BORN DURING THE 1800s (continued)

26. _____ 1874–1946 *The Autobiography of Alice B. Toklas*

27. _____ 1875–1939 *Riders of the Purple Sage*

28. _____ 1876–1916 *The Call of the Wild*

29. _____ 1876–1941 *Winesburg, Ohio*

30. _____ 1878–1967 *Chicago Poems*

31. _____ 1878–1968 *The Jungle*

32. _____ 1885–1951 *Main Street*

33. _____ 1887–1968 *So Big*

34. _____ 1888–1959 *The Big Sleep*

35. _____ 1890–1980 *Ship of Fools*

36. _____ 1892–1973 *The Good Earth*

37. _____ 1894–1961 *The Maltese Falcon*

38. _____ 1896–1940 *The Great Gatsby*

39. _____ 1896–1953 *The Yearling*

40. _____ 1897–1975 *The Skin of Our Teeth*

41. _____ 1897–1962 *As I Lay Dying*

42. _____ 1899–1985 *Charlotte's Web*

43. _____ 1899–1961 *The Old Man and the Sea*

SOME AMERICAN AUTHORS BORN DURING THE 1900s

Using the life spans and works given to you, identify these fifty-eight American authors born during the 1900s.

1. _____ 1900–1949 *Gone with the Wind*

2. _____ 1900–1938 *You Can't Go Home Again*

3. _____ 1901–1960 *Their Eyes Were Watching God*

4. _____ 1902–1968 *The Grapes of Wrath*

5. _____ 1903–1940 *Miss Lonelyhearts*

6. _____ 1903–1989 *Lust for Life*

7. _____ 1903–1987 *Tobacco Road*

8. _____ 1904–1991 *Green Eggs and Ham*

9. _____ 1905–1982 *Atlas Shrugged*

10. _____ 1905–1989 *All the King's Men*

11. _____ 1905–1984 *Watch on the Rhine*

12. _____ 1907– *Poland*

13. _____ 1907– *Stranger in a Strange Land*

14. _____ 1908–1981 *The Human Comedy*

15. _____ 1908–1960 *Black Boy*

16. _____ 1911–1983 *A Streetcar Named Desire*

17. _____ 1912–1982 *The Wapshot Chronicle*

18. _____ 1912– *Hard Times*

19. _____ 1913–1973 *Picnic*

20. _____ 1914–1986 *The Natural*

21. _____ 1914– *A Bell for Adano*

22. _____ 1914– *Invisible Man*

23. _____ 1914– *The Miracle Worker*

24. _____ 1916–1990 *The Thanatos Syndrome*

25. _____ 1917–1967 *The Heart Is a Lonely Hunter*

26. _____ 1919– *Franny and Zooey*

SOME AMERICAN AUTHORS BORN DURING THE 1900s (continued)

27. _____ 1919–1965 "The Lottery"

28. _____ 1920–1992 *The Intelligent Man's Guide to Science*

29. _____ 1920– *The Martian Chronicles*

30. _____ 1921–1992 *The Autobiography of Malcolm X*

31. _____ 1922– *Slaughterhouse-Five*

32. _____ 1922–1969 *On the Road*

33. _____ 1923– *Catch-22*

34. _____ 1923– *The Naked and the Dead*

35. _____ 1924–1987 *Go Tell It on the Mountain*

36. _____ 1924–1984 *Breakfast at Tiffany's*

37. _____ 1925– *The Confessions of Nat Turner*

38. _____ 1926– *To Kill a Mockingbird*

39. _____ 1926– *A Separate Peace*

40. _____ 1928– *Night*

41. _____ 1928– *The Zoo Story*

42. _____ 1929– *The Promise*

43. _____ 1929– *Rosemary's Baby*

44. _____ 1930– *The End of the Road*

45. _____ 1930–1965 *A Raisin in the Sun*

46. _____ 1931– *Song of Solomon*

47. _____ 1931– *Bonfire of the Vanities*

48. _____ 1932– *Rabbit, Run*

49. _____ 1932–1963 "Daddy"

50. _____ 1933– *Portnoy's Complaint*

51. _____ 1936– *The Effect of Gamma Rays on Man-in-the-Moon Marigolds*

52. _____ 1937– *The Crying of Lot 49*

53. _____ 1941– *Dinner at the Homesick Restaurant*

54. _____ 1942– *Jurassic Park*

55. _____ 1944– *The Color Purple*

56. _____ 1947– *The Hunt for Red October*

57. _____ 1950– *The Outsiders*

58. _____ 1955– *The Great Santini*

SOME BRITISH AUTHORS BORN BEFORE 1800

Using the life spans and works given to you, identify these twenty British authors who were born before 1800.

1. _____ 1340–1400 *The Canterbury Tales*

2. _____ c. 1408–1471 *Morte d'Arthur*

3. _____ 1552–1599 *The Faerie Queene*

4. _____ 1564–1616 *Romeo and Juliet*

5. _____ 1572–1631 "Death Be Not Proud"

6. _____ 1608–1674 *Paradise Lost*

7. _____ 1660–1731 *Robinson Crusoe*

8. _____ 1667–1745 *A Modest Proposal*

9. _____ 1688–1744 *The Rape of the Lock*

10. _____ 1707–1754 *Tom Jones*

11. _____ 1716–1771 "Elegy Written in a Country Churchyard"

12. _____ 1740–1795 *The Life of Samuel Johnson*

13. _____ 1751–1816 *The Rivals*

14. _____ 1757–1827 "The Lamb"

15. _____ 1770–1850 "Tintern Abbey"

16. _____ 1772–1834 "The Rime of the Ancient Mariner"

17. _____ 1775–1817 *Pride and Prejudice*

18. _____ 1788–1824 *Don Juan*

19. _____ 1795–1821 "Ode on a Grecian Urn"

20. _____ 1797–1851 *Frankenstein*

SOME BRITISH AUTHORS BORN DURING THE 1800s

Identify the twenty-seven British authors whose life spans and works are listed next to the blank spaces.

1. _____ 1806–1861 *Sonnets from the Portuguese*

2. _____ 1809–1892 *Idylls of the King*

3. _____ 1811–1863 *Vanity Fair*

4. _____ 1812–1870 *David Copperfield*

5. _____ 1816–1855 *Jane Eyre*

6. _____ 1818–1848 *Wuthering Heights*

7. _____ 1819–1880 *Silas Marner*

8. _____ 1832–1898 *Through the Looking Glass*

9. _____ 1840–1928 *Jude the Obscure*

10. _____ 1847–1912 *Dracula*

11. _____ 1854–1900 *The Picture of Dorian Gray*

12. _____ 1856–1950 *Saint Joan*

13. _____ 1857–1924 *Heart of Darkness*

14. _____ 1859–1930 *The Memoirs of Sherlock Holmes*

15. _____ 1865–1936 "If"

16. _____ 1866–1943 *The Tale of Peter Rabbit*

17. _____ 1871–1909 *The Playboy of the Western World*

18. _____ 1874–1965 *Of Human Bondage*

19. _____ 1879–1970 *Howards End*

20. _____ 1882–1941 *Finnegan's Wake*

21. _____ 1882–1956 *Winnie-the-Pooh*

22. _____ 1882–1941 *To the Lighthouse*

23. _____ 1885–1930 *Sons and Lovers*

24. _____ 1888–1965 *Murder in the Cathedral*

25. _____ 1890–1976 *And Then There Were None*

26. _____ 1892–1973 *The Fellowship of the Rings*

27. _____ 1898–1963 *The Lion, the Witch, and the Wardrobe*

Name _____ Date _____ Period _____

SOME BRITISH AUTHORS BORN DURING THE 1900s

Using the life spans and the works given, identify the twenty British authors born during the 1900s.

1. _____ 1900–1954 *The Lost Horizon*

2. _____ 1903–1950 *Nineteen Eighty-Four*

3. _____ 1903–1966 *The Loved One*

4. _____ 1905–1983 *The King Must Die*

5. _____ 1906–1989 *Waiting for Godot*

6. _____ 1907–1989 *Rebecca*

7. _____ 1907–1973 "Musee des Beaux Arts"

8. _____ 1911–1993 *Lord of the Flies*

9. _____ 1914–1953 *Portrait of the Artist as a Young Dog*

10. _____ 1916– *All Things Bright and Beautiful*

11. _____ 1916–1990 "Beware of the Dog"

12. _____ 1917– *A Clockwork Orange*

13. _____ 1919– "Through the Tunnel"

14. _____ 1926– *Equus*

15. _____ 1930– *The Hawk in the Rain*

16. _____ 1930– *The Birthday Party*

17. _____ 1931– *The Spy Who Came in from the Cold*

18. _____ 1936– *Butley*

19. _____ 1937– *Rosencrantz and Guildenstern Are Dead*

20. _____ 1939– *The Good Soldier*

SOME WORLD AUTHORS BORN BEFORE 1800

Using the life spans and the works given, identify the twenty-five world authors born before 1800.

1. _____ 700 B.C. *Iliad*

2. _____ 525 B.C.–456 B.C. *Oresteia*

3. _____ 518 B.C.–438 B.C. *Epinicia*

4. _____ 496 B.C.–406 B.C. *Oedipus Rex*

5. _____ 485 B.C.–406 B.C. *Medea*

6. _____ 427 B.C.–348 B.C. *The Republic*

7. _____ 70 B.C.–19 B.C. *Georgics*

8. _____ 43 B.C.–17 A.D. *Metamorphoses*

9. _____ c. 48–c. 122 *Parallel Lives*

10. _____ 701–762 *The River-Merchant's Wife*

11. _____ 1048?–1122 *The Rubáiyát*

12. _____ 1265–1321 *The Divine Comedy*

13. _____ 1304–1374 *Sonnets to Laura*

14. _____ 1313–1375 *Decameron*

15. _____ 1533–1592 *Essays* (French)

16. _____ 1547–1616 *Don Quixote*

17. _____ 1562–1635 *El cabellero de Olmedo*

18. _____ 1621–1695 *Fables Choisies, Mises en Vers*

19. _____ 1622–1673 *Tartuffe*

20. _____ 1639–1699 *Britannicus*

21. _____ 1644–1694 *The Sun Path*

22. _____ 1694–1778 *Candide*

23. _____ 1749–1832 *Faust*

24. _____ 1785–1863 and 1786–1859 Fairy Tales

25. _____ 1799–1850 *La Comédie Humaine*

SOME WORLD AUTHORS BORN DURING THE 1800s

Using the life spans and the works given, identify these twenty-two world authors born during the 1800s.

1. _____ 1802–1870 *The Three Musketeers*

2. _____ 1802–1885 *Les Misérables*

3. _____ 1805–1875 "The Emperor's Clothes"

4. _____ 1821–1880 *Madame Bovary*

5. _____ 1821–1881 *Crime and Punishment*

6. _____ 1828–1910 *War and Peace*

7. _____ 1828–1906 *An Enemy of the People*

8. _____ 1828–1905 *The Time Machine*

9. _____ 1850–1894 *Kidnapped*

10. _____ 1860–1904 *The Cherry Orchard*

11. _____ 1860–1937 *Peter Pan*

12. _____ 1867–1937 *Six Characters in Search of an Author*

13. _____ 1868–1918 *Cyrano de Bergerac*

14. _____ 1873–1954 *Gigi*

15. _____ 1875–1955 *Death in Venice*

16. _____ 1875–1950 *Tarzan*

17. _____ 1877–1962 *Siddhartha*

18. _____ 1883–1931 *The Prophet*

19. _____ 1883–1924 *The Trial*

20. _____ 1883–1957 *Zorba the Greek*

21. _____ 1890–1960 *Doctor Zhivago*

22. _____ 1898–1970 *All Quiet on the Western Front*

SOME WORLD AUTHORS BORN DURING THE 1900s

Fill in the names of the fourteen world authors whose life spans and works are listed after the blanks.

1. _____ 1900–1944 *The Little Prince*

2. _____ 1903–1988 *Cry, the Beloved Country*

3. _____ 1905–1980 *No Exit*

4. _____ 1910– *Antigone*

5. _____ 1912– *The Bald Soprano*

6. _____ 1913–1960 *The Stranger*

7. _____ 1916– *The Shoes of the Fisherman*

8. _____ 1918– *The Gulag Archipelago*

9. _____ 1928– *One Hundred Years of Solitude*

10. _____ 1931– *The Apprenticeship of Duddy Kravitz*

11. _____ 1933– *Being There*

12. _____ 1933– "Babi Yar"

13. _____ 1936– *The Garden Party*

14. _____ 1937– *The Thorn Birds*

AUTHORS AND THEIR INITIALS

Well-known authors are listed here with their initials and last names. Write the names that belong to the initials on the line following the name.

1. A. R. Ammons _____

2. W. H. Auden _____

3. J. M. Barrie _____

4. H. E. Bates _____

5. L. Frank Baum _____

6. G. K. Chesterton _____

7. J. R. R. Tolkien _____

8. J. D. Salinger _____

9. C. L. Lewis _____

10. A. J. Cronin _____

11. e. e. cummings _____

12. G. W. Curtis _____

13. C. Day Lewis _____

14. T. S. Eliot _____

15. E. M. Forster _____

16. A. B. Guthrie _____

17. A. E. Housman _____

18. W. Somerset Maugham _____

19. H. L. Mencken _____

20. J. B. Priestly _____

21. B. F. Skinner _____

22. C. P. Snow _____

23. H. G. Wells _____

24. Morris L. West _____

25. E. B. White _____

AUTHORS AND THEIR INITIALS (continued)

26. T. H. White _____

27. Pearl S. Buck _____

28. W. E. B. Du Bois _____

29. F. Scott Fitzgerald _____

30. D. H. Lawrence _____

31. A. A. Milne _____

32. Dorothy L. Sayers _____

33. P. G. Wodehouse _____

34. George M. Cohan _____

35. George S. Kaufman _____

36. J. M. Synge _____

AMERICAN AUTHORS AND GEOGRAPHY

How familiar are you with the favorite settings of some American authors? Here is your opportunity to show your geographic and literary savoir-faire and learn a thing or two at the same time.

Below are categorized six North American geographical sections. Identify the section that served as the primary setting of some of the authors' major works, although each could certainly have written about other sections.

EAST . . . New York, New Jersey, Pennsylvania, Delaware, Maryland

NORTHEAST . . . Maine, Vermont, New Hampshire, Massachusetts, Connecticut, Rhode Island

SOUTH . . . Virginia, West Virginia, Kentucky, Tennessee, Mississippi, Alabama, Florida, Georgia, North Carolina, South Carolina

MIDWEST . . . Missouri, Kansas, Nebraska, Iowa, South Dakota, North Dakota, Minnesota, Wisconsin, Illinois, Indiana, Michigan, Ohio

WEST . . . Oregon, Idaho, Washington, Montana, Wyoming, Utah, Colorado, New Mexico, Alaska, Hawaii

SOUTHWEST . . . California, Arizona, Nevada, Texas, Louisiana, Oklahoma, Arkansas

AMERICAN AUTHORS AND GEOGRAPHY (continued)

Geographical Section	Author	Major Work(s)
1. _____	Sinclair Lewis	_____
2. _____	Willa Cather	_____
3. _____	Nathaniel Hawthorne	_____
4. _____	Robert Frost	_____
5. _____	Tennessee Williams	_____
6. _____	DuBose Heyward	_____
7. _____	Ellen Glasgow	_____
8. _____	Bronson Alcott	_____
9. _____	Edgar Lee Masters	_____
10. _____	Erskine Caldwell	_____
11. _____	Hamlin Garland	_____
12. _____	Washington Irving	_____
13. _____	Sarah Orne Jewett	_____
14. _____	Jack London	_____
15. _____	Ken Kesey	_____
16. _____	Sidney Lanier	_____
17. _____	Carson McCullers	_____
18. _____	Katherine Anne Porter	_____
19. _____	Marjorie K. Rawlings	_____
20. _____	Flannery O'Connor	_____
21. _____	Theodore Dreiser	_____
22. _____	Mark Twain	_____
23. _____	Henry David Thoreau	_____
24. _____	Eudora Welty	_____
25. _____	James Whitcomb Riley	_____

DO YOU KNOW THEIR FAMOUS CONTEMPORARIES?

Write the letter of the correct answer next to each question.

1. Wilkie Collins, the famous mystery writer, was born in 1824. Also born that year was:
   a. Horace Mann
   b. Alexander Dumas
   c. Dred Scott

2. Both these writers were born in 1850:
   a. Guy de Maupassant and Robert Louis Stevenson
   b. W. H. Auden and T. S. Eliot
   c. Thomas Hardy and Emile Zola

3. Lewis Carroll and Louisa May Alcott were born in the year:
   a. 1895
   b. 1864
   c. 1832

4. D. H. Lawrence, Sinclair Lewis, and Ezra Pound were born in the year:
   a. 1885
   b. 1900
   c. 1834

5. Three famous writers, all born in 1811, are Harriet Beecher Stowe, Horace Greeley, and:
   a. Nathaniel Hawthorne
   b. William Makepeace Thackeray
   c. Hans Christian Andersen

6. John Steinbeck, Charles Lindbergh, Alan Paton, Graham Greene, and Evelyn Waugh were born during the term of which United States President?
   a. Theodore Roosevelt
   b. Woodrow Wilson
   c. Calvin Coolidge

7. Edgar Lee Masters' poetic contemporary was:
   a. Dylan Thomas
   b. E. A. Robinson
   c. W. H. Auden

8. Emily Dickinson (1830–1886), had she chosen to do so, could have spoken with all of the following except:
   a. Jules Verne
   b. Henrik Ibsen
   c. T. S. Eliot
   d. Leo Tolstoy

9. Which two lived in the same century?
   a. Friedrich Nietzsche and James Boswell
   b. Rachel Carson and Aleksandr Solzhenitsyn
   c. Eugene Ionesco and Thomas Huxley

10. Who is not a contemporary of the others?
    a. John Keats
    b. Percy Bysshe Shelley
    c. Alexander Pushkin
    d. James Barrie

11. All of the following happened in the year 1949 except:
    a. George Orwell's *Nineteen Eighty-Four* was published.
    b. Arthur Miller's *Death of a Salesman* was produced.
    c. William Faulkner won the Nobel Prize for Literature.
    d. Robert Penn Warren was appointed the first official Poet Laureate of the United States.

12. Which of these writers did not write during the same era as the others?
    a. H. G. Wells
    b. Thomas Hardy
    c. Samuel Richardson
    d. Oscar Wilde

13. Identify the year in which all these works were published: Mailer's *The Executioner's Song,* Le Carre's *Smiley's People,* and Tom Wolfe's *The Right Stuff?*
    a. 1980
    b. 1933
    c. 1877
    d. 1957

14. John Fitzgerald Kennedy won the U.S. Presidential election in 1960. Which two authors died that same year?
    a. William Faulkner and George Bernard Shaw
    b. Zora Neale Hurston and Richard Wright
    c. John Steinbeck and Edgar Lee Masters
    d. T. S. Eliot and Carl Sandburg

15. Which pair of authors was alive to hear firsthand about the American Revolution?
    a. Voltaire and Goethe
    b. Dickens and D. H. Lawrence
    c. Petrarch and Colette
    d. Byron and Donne

AMERICAN AUTHORS' FAMOUS AND NOT SO FAMOUS FIRSTS
(PART ONE)

There are those times when a first-time author hits the nail on the head and finds success on his initial literary venture. Then there are other fledglings who need a bit more time and experience before they hit the big time. Here are some early writings by famous American authors and some of their later literary endeavors. See if you can match the authors with their works. Use the following list of authors to answer the first forty questions. Put the letter or letters of the author in the blanks provided for numbers 1–40.

A. Louisa May Alcott
B. Sherwood Anderson
C. John Barth
D. Truman Capote
E. Willa Cather
F. James Fenimore Cooper
G. James Gould Cozzens
H. Stephen Crane
I. Clarence Day
J. James Dickey
K. Theodore Dreiser
L. William Faulkner
M. F. Scott Fitzgerald
N. Robert Frost

O. Nathaniel Hawthorne
P. Ernest Hemingway
Q. O. Henry
R. William Dean Howells
S. Sinclair Lewis
T. Bernard Malamud
U. Edgar Lee Masters
V. Herman Melville
W. Frank Norris
X. Eugene O'Neill
Y. Sylvia Plath
Z. Edgar Allan Poe
aa. Philip Roth
bb. Karl Shapiro

cc. Gertrude Stein
dd. William Styron
ee. Henry David Thoreau
ff. James Thurber
gg. Mark Twain
hh. Kurt Vonnegut
ii. Robert Penn Warren
jj. Edith Wharton
kk. Nathanael West
ll. Walt Whitman
mm. Tennessee Williams
nn. Thomas Wolfe

EARLIER WRITING

_____ 1. *Cabbages and Kings*

_____ 2. *The Natural*

_____ 3. *Goodbye, Columbus*

_____ 4. *Windy McPherson's Son*

_____ 5. *Other Voices, Other Rooms*

_____ 6. *Maggie: A Girl on the Streets*

_____ 7. *Flower Fables*

_____ 8. *A Winter Ship*

_____ 9. *The Marble Faun*

_____ 10. *April Twilights*

_____ 11. *Sister Carrie*

_____ 12. *The Floating Opera*

MORE FAMOUS LATER WORK

The Ransom of Red Chief

The Fixer

Portnoy's Complaint

Winesburg, Ohio

In Cold Blood

The Red Badge of Courage

Little Women

The Bell Jar

As I Lay Dying

My Antonia

An American Tragedy

The Sot-Weed Factor

_____	13.	*The '96 Half-Way Book*	*Life with Father*
_____	14.	*Poets of Today VII*	*Deliverance*
_____	15.	*Twilight*	*"The Death of the Hired Man"*
_____	16.	*Fanshawe*	*The Scarlet Letter*
_____	17.	*Confusion*	*Guard of Honor*
_____	18.	*Precaution*	*The Last of the Mohicans*
_____	19.	*Battle of Angels*	*The Glass Menagerie*
_____	20.	*John Brown*	*All the King's Men*
_____	21.	*Verses*	*Ethan Frome*
_____	22.	*The Crisis in Industry*	*Look Homeward, Angel*
_____	23.	*Three Lives*	*The Autobiography of Alice B. Toklas*
_____	24.	*Lie Down in Darkness*	*Sophie's Choice*
_____	25.	*Tamerlane and Other Poems*	*"The Raven"*
_____	26.	*Typee*	*Moby Dick*
_____	27.	*The Dream Life of Balso Snell*	*Miss Lonelyhearts*
_____	28.	*The Celebrated Jumping Frog of Calaveras County*	*Huck Finn*
_____	29.	*Player Piano*	*Slaughterhouse-Five*
_____	30.	*Franklin Evans; Or, The Inebriate*	*Leaves of Grass*
_____	31.	*Yvernelle A Legend of Feudal France*	*The Octopus*
_____	32.	*Thirst*	*The Hairy Ape*
_____	33.	*A Book of Verses*	*Spoon River Anthology*
_____	34.	*Hike and the Aeroplane*	*Babbitt*
_____	35.	*Poems of Two Friends*	*The Rise of Silas Lapham*
_____	36.	*Poems*	*V-Letter and Other Poems*
_____	37.	*Is Sex Necessary?*	*"The Secret Life of Walter Mitty"*
_____	38.	*This Side of Paradise*	*The Great Gatsby*
_____	39.	*Three Stories and Ten Poems*	*The Old Man and the Sea*
_____	40.	*A Week on the Concord and Merrimack Rivers*	*Walden*

AMERICAN AUTHORS' FAMOUS AND NOT SO FAMOUS FIRSTS
(PART TWO)

Now here's the easy part. These authors might have accomplished their most famous writing the first time around. List the author's name next to his or her work.

FAMOUS BOOK	AUTHOR
41. *Go Tell It on the Mountain*	_____
42. *Tarzan of The Apes*	_____
43. *Invisible Man*	_____
44. *Catch-22*	_____
45. *From Here to Eternity*	_____
46. *One Flew Over the Cuckoo's Nest*	_____
47. *To Kill a Mockingbird*	_____
48. *The Naked and the Dead*	_____
49. *The Heart Is a Lonely Hunter*	_____
50. *Gone with the Wind*	_____
51. *The Catcher in the Rye*	_____

HOW NOBEL OF YOU!

The following authors have been recipients of the Nobel Prize for Literature. The year of the award is next to each author. Match the authors, listed chronologically according to the date of their award, with their literary work(s). Some titles were written before and some were written after the year of the author's award.

AUTHORS

WORKS

1. _____ Rudyard Kipling   1907

A. *Siddhartha, Steppenwolf, Demian*

2. _____ W. B. Yeats   1923

B. *Death in Venice*

3. _____ George Bernard Shaw   1925

C. *One Hundred Years of Solitude*

4. _____ Thomas Mann   1929

D. *The Old Man and the Sea*

5. _____ Sinclair Lewis   1930

E. *The Stranger, The Plague*

6. _____ John Galsworthy   1932

F. *Babbitt, Arrowsmith*

7. _____ Luigi Pirandello   1934

G. *The Jungle Book*

8. _____ Eugene O'Neill   1936

H. *Murder in the Cathedral*

9. _____ Pearl S. Buck   1938

I. *St. Joan*

10. _____ Herman Hesse   1946

J. *Lord of the Flies*

11. _____ T. S. Eliot   1948

K. *The Grapes of Wrath*

12. _____ William Faulkner   1949

L. *The Good Earth*

13. _____ Ernest Hemingway   1954

M. *Long Day's Journey into Night*

14. _____ Albert Camus   1957

N. *Doctor Zhivago*

15. _____ Boris Pasternak   1958

O. *No Exit*

16. _____ John Steinbeck   1962

P. *The Forsyte Saga*

17. _____ Jean Paul Sartre   1964

Q. *The Wild Swans at Coole*

18. _____ Samuel Beckett   1969

R. *Six Characters in Search of an Author*

19. _____ Gabriel García Márquez   1982

S. *As I Lay Dying*

20. _____ William Golding   1983

T. *Waiting for Godot*

HIDDEN AUTHORS

For each numbered question, identify the authors of four different pieces of literature. The circled letters will furnish the letters (in order) of the hidden author. Finally, match that author with his or her literary work from the twenty listed immediately below. The first one is done for you.

LITERARY WORKS

As I Lay Dying
Beloved
Black Boy
The Chosen
Death on the Nile
Fanshawe
Giant

In Our Time
Lie Down in Darkness
The Lost Horizon
Of Mice and Men
Poland
A Raisin in the Sun
Sister Carrie

Songs of Innocence
Sons and Lovers
Tobacco Road
Vanity Fair
Walden
Winesburg, Ohio

TITLE	AUTHOR

1. *Ben Hur* W A (L) L (A) C E

   The Age of Innocence (W) H A (R) T O N

   Don Quixote C (E) R V A (N) T E S

   Father Brown Stories (C) H E S T (E) R T O N

   The hidden author is **Lawrence** who wrote *Sons and Lovers.*

2. *Little Foxes* ◯ ◯ _ _ ◯ _ _

   Come Back, Little Sheba ◯ ◯ ◯ _

   "My Last Duchess" _ _ _ ◯ _ _ _ _

   Life with Father _ ◯ ◯

   The hidden author is _____ who wrote _____.

3. *The Skin of Our Teeth* _ _ _ ◯ _ ◯

   Babbitt _ ◯ _ ◯ _

   Abe Lincoln in Illinois ◯ _ ◯ _ _ _ _ _

   Ships of Fools _ _ ◯ _ _ _

   The hidden author is _____ who wrote _____.

4. *Portnoy's Complaint* _ _ ◯ ◯

   Nineteen Eighty-Four ◯ ◯ _ _ _ _

   The Picture of Dorian Gray _ _ _ _ _ ◯

   Pride and Prejudice ◯ ◯ _ _ _ _

   The hidden author is _____ who wrote _____.

HIDDEN AUTHORS (continued)

5. *Metamorphosis* _ _ ◯ _ ◯

   The Member of the Wedding _ _ _ ◯ ◯ _ _ _ _ _

   A Separate Peace ◯ ◯ _ _ _ _ _ _

   This Side of Paradise _ _ _ _ _ ◯ ◯ _ _ _

   The hidden author is _____ who wrote _____.

6. *All the King's Men* ◯ _ _ ◯ _ _

   All My Sons _ ◯ _ _ _ _

   Faust ◯ _ _ _ ◯ _

   A Tree Grows in Brooklyn _ _ _ ◯ _

   The hidden author is _____ who wrote _____.

7. *Pygmalion* _ ◯ ◯ ◯

   Little Women _ _ _ _ ◯ _

   The Rise of Silas Lapham ◯ ◯ _ _ _ _ _ _

   The Red Badge of Courage _ ◯ _ ◯ ◯

   The hidden author is _____ who wrote _____.

8. *The Friendly Persuasion* _ _ ◯ ◯

   One Flew Over the Cuckoo's Nest _ _ _ _ ◯

   Don Juan _ _ ◯ ◯ _

   The Octopus ◯ _ _ _ _ _

   The hidden author is _____ who wrote _____.

9. *Gulliver's Travels* ◯ _ _ _ ◯

   Silas Marner ◯ _ ◯ _ _

   A Gift from the Sea _ _ ◯ _ ◯ ◯ _ _ _

   "Because I Could Not Stop for Death" _ _ ◯ ◯ _ _ _ _ _

   The hidden author is _____ who wrote _____.

10. *Paradise Lost* ◯ ◯ _ _ _ _ _

    "The Enormous Radio" ◯ ◯ ◯ _ _ _ _

    Leaves of Grass _ _ _ _ _ _ ◯

    Hiroshima _ ◯ ◯ _ _ _

    The hidden author is _____ who wrote _____.

HIDDEN AUTHORS (continued)

11. *The Human Comedy* _ ◯ _ _ _ ◯

    The Brothers Karamazov ◯ _ _ _ _ _ ◯ _ _ _ _

    "Tintern Abbey" _ _ ◯ _ ◯ _ _ _ _ _

    Cyrano de Bergerac _ ◯ _ _ _ ◯ _

    The hidden author is _____ who wrote _____.

12. *The Zoo Story* _ _ ◯ _ _

    The Life of Samuel Johnson, LL.D. _ _ _ _ _ ◯ _

    Seventeen _ ◯ _ ◯ _ _ _ _ _ _

    Night _ _ _ _ ◯ _

    The hidden author is _____ who wrote _____.

13. "The Gold Bug" ◯ _ _

    "The Death of the Hired Man" _ _ ◯ _ ◯

    The Awakening _ _ ◯ _ _ _

    The Cherry Orchard _ _ _ ◯ _ _ _

    The hidden author is _____ who wrote _____.

14. *The Misanthrope* ◯ ◯ _ _ _ _ _

    Dandelion Wine _ ◯ _ _ _ _ ◯ _

    The Night of the Iguana _ ◯ _ _ _ _ _ ◯

    The Miracle Worker _ _ _ _ ◯ ◯

    The hidden author is _____ who wrote _____.

15. *The Rivals* _ ◯ _ _ ◯ _ _ _

    Franny and Zooey _ _ ◯ _ _ _ _ _

    Slaughterhouse-Five _ _ _ _ _ _ _ ◯

    The Sea Wolf _ ◯ ◯ _ _ _

    The hidden author is _____ who wrote _____.

16. *Gone with the Wind* _ _ ◯ _ ◯ _ _ _

    On the Road _ _ _ _ _ ◯ ◯

    Bleak House _ _ _ ◯ ◯ _ _

    "Elegy in a Country Churchyard" _ ◯ ◯ ◯

    The hidden author is _____ who wrote _____.

HIDDEN AUTHORS (continued)

17. *The Scarlet Letter* ◯ ◯ _ _ _ _ _ ◯ _

    Tarzan of the Apes _ _ _ _ _ _ _ _ ◯

    "The Secret Life of Walter Mitty" _ _ _ _ ◯ ◯ ◯

    The Prince of Tides _ _ _ ◯ _ ◯

    The hidden author is _____ who wrote _____.

18. *The Crying of Lot 49* _ _ _ ◯ ◯ _ _

    All Creatures Great and Small _ _ ◯ _ ◯ _ _

    Kidnapped ◯ ◯ _ _ _ _ _ _

    Rabbit, Run _ _ _ ◯ _ ◯

    The hidden author is _____ who wrote _____.

19. *Breakfast at Tiffany's* ◯ ◯ _ _ _ _

    Tom Jones _ _ _ ◯ ◯ _ _ _

    The Color Purple ◯ _ _ _ ◯ _

    Catch-22 _ _ ◯ ◯ _ _

    The hidden author is _____ who wrote _____.

20. *Robinson Crusoe* _ _ ◯ _ ◯

    Jane Eyre _ ◯ _ _ _ _

    Madame Bovary _ _ _ _ ◯ ◯ _ _

    No Exit _ _ _ _ ◯ _

    The hidden author is _____ who wrote _____.

LITERARY LICENSE PLATES

Here are license plates designed for some of the authors found in this resource. Pretend for the time being that each author has a vehicle that requires a license plate. The plates are take-offs on the author's name, works, settings, or characters. See how many of these plates you can correctly connect to their authors. Each author is used only once.

1. _____ LTTLWMN

2. _____ CVL DIS

3. _____ AL B. TROS

4. _____ C-P HA-LO

5. _____ NO EXIT

6. _____ C WOLF

7. _____ SIGH LESS, LAUGH HIM!

8. _____ HERO SHE MA

9. _____ J.N. AIR

10. _____ 1984

11. _____ DR. Z

12. _____ FRANK N. STEIN

13. _____ SEE RAN OH!

14. _____ IF

15. _____ MISS N. TROP

16. _____ 80 DAZE

17. _____ THE PROFIT

18. _____ THE 4,000,000

19. _____ DOCK TOUR ZOOS

20. _____ JUNE 0

21. _____ ON / ROAD

22. _____ RICHARD III

23. _____ BILL E. BUDD

LITERARY LICENSE PLATES (continued)

24. _____ CAN DEED

25. _____ ALAS! BE TOKE LASS!

26. _____ U-MAN, CALM EDDY

27. _____ BE LOVE ED

28. _____ DON KEY HOE TEE

29. _____ CATCH-22

30. _____ ED A. PUSS

31. _____ MR. CHIPS

32. _____ WIN E.

33. _____ 7THEBES

34. _____ ¢¢¢ & Sensibility

35. _____ THE STRANGER

36. _____ UTOPIA

37. _____ CHILDE HAROLD

38. _____ HEDDA

39. _____ June 16, 1904

40. _____ 17

41. _____ HUNCHBACK

42. _____ LADY CHATTERLEY

43. _____ EREWHON

44. _____ BABBITT

45. _____ GO-DOUGH

46. _____ EVANGELINE

47. _____ CRUSOE

48. _____ TROJAN WAR

49. _____ HOLDEN

50. _____ PETER PAN

51. _____ THE PRINCE

52. _____ JABBERWOCKY

53. _____ HOW GREEN!

LITERARY LICENSE PLATES (continued)

54. _____ SPOON RIVER

55. _____ PLAYBOY

56. _____ LOMAN

57. _____ SCARLETT

58. _____ TO BACK OH RD.

59. _____ OCTOPUS

60. _____ LONG DAY'S JOURNEY

61. _____ 6 CHARACTERS

62. _____ OUR TOWN

63. _____ WILD SWANS

64. _____ GATSBY

65. _____ XMAS CAROL

66. _____ PORGY

67. _____ FAUST

68. _____ THE HORROR! THE HORROR!

69. _____ ALL QUIET

70. _____ PATHFINDER

71. _____ UNCLE REMUS

72. _____ A LOST LADY

73. _____ THE FAERIE QUEENE

74. _____ THE BELLE OF AMHERST

75. _____ TOM JONES

76. _____ THE YEARLING

77. _____ HUCK

78. _____ IVANHOE

79. _____ MRS. MALAPROP

80. _____ CANTERBURY

81. _____ PURPLE SAGE

82. _____ YOKNAPATAWPHA

83. _____ SAINT JOAN

LITERARY LICENSE PLATES (continued)

84. _____ TESS & JUDE

85. _____ KING COAL

86. _____ RED BADGE

87. _____ GRAPES OF WRATH

88. _____ 7 GABLES

89. _____ DR. JEKYLL

90. _____ NICK ADAMS

91. _____ DRACULA

92. _____ STEPPENWOLF

93. _____ THE FROGS

94. _____ STREETCAR

95. _____ E. FROME

96. _____ DORIAN

97. _____ WAR & PEACE

98. _____ DR. MOREAU

99. _____ MISS LONELYHEARTS

100. _____ MRS. DALLOWAY

101. _____ THE PRELUDE

102. _____ STUDS LONIGAN

103. _____ U.T. CABIN

104. _____ SHERLOCK

THE PARADE OF AUTHORS (PART ONE)

Identify each of the fifty authors who wrote these pieces of literature.

1. _____ *Little Women, Little Men*

2. _____ *The Scarlet Letter, The House of the Seven Gables, Twice-Told Tales*

3. _____ *The Bell Jar, The Colossus, The Collected Poems*

4. _____ *Walden, Civil Disobedience*

5. _____ *Hawaii, Tales of the South Pacific, Chesapeake*

6. _____ *The Stranger, The Myth of Sisyphus and Other Essays, The Rebel, The Fall*

7. _____ *The Right Stuff, The Bonfire of the Vanities*

8. _____ *Lyrical Ballads, The Poetical Works, "Kubla Kahn"*

9. _____ *Cry, the Beloved Country*

10. _____ *One Hundred Years of Solitude, Love in the Time of Cholera*

11. _____ *Gulliver's Travels, "A Modest Proposal"*

12. _____ *Robinson Crusoe, Moll Flanders, A Journal of the Plague Year*

13. _____ *The Color Purple, Once, Meridian*

14. _____ *Alice's Adventures in Wonderland, Through the Looking Glass*

15. _____ *Pride and Prejudice, Sense and Sensibility, Mansfield Park*

16. _____ *Promises, All the King's Men*

17. _____ *The Grapes of Wrath, East of Eden, Tortilla Flat*

18. _____ *Arrowsmith, Main Street, Babbitt, Elmer Gantry*

19. _____ *The Sketch Book of Geoffrey Crayon, Gent., A History of New York*

20. _____ *The Catcher in the Rye, Franny and Zooey*

21. _____ *Couples; The Witches of Eastwick; Rabbit Redux; Rabbit, Run*

22. _____ *The Rise of Silas Lapham, A Modern Instance*

23. _____ *The Pathfinder, The Deerslayer, The Last of the Mohicans*

24. _____ *Chimera, The Sot Weed Factor, Giles Goat-Boy*

25. _____ *The Waste Land, Murder in the Cathedral, The Cocktail Party*

26. _____ *Tarzan of the Apes*

27. _____ *Decameron, Filostrato*

28. _____ *The Canterbury Tales*

29. _____ *Black Boy, Native Son, The Outsider*

30. _____ *Twenty Thousand Leagues Under the Sea, The Time Machine*

31. _____ *Barry Lyndon, Vanity Fair, Book of Snobs*

32. _____ *Lord of the Flies, The Spire, Pincher Martin*

33. _____ *Paradise Lost, Paradise Regained, Samson Agonistes*

34. _____ *Morte d'Arthur*

35. _____ *The Republic, Apologia*

36. _____ *The Age of Innocence, Ethan Frome, The House of Mirth*

37. _____ *The Sea-Wolf, The Call of the Wild, White Fang, Martin Eden*

38. _____ *Slaughterhouse-Five; or The Children's Crusade, Cat's Cradle*

39. _____ *Typee, Omoo, Billy Budd, Moby Dick*

40. _____ *Death in Venice, The Magic Mountain, Buddenbrooks*

41. _____ *Candide*

42. _____ *Pygmalion, Major Barbara, Saint Joan*

43. _____ *Anna Karenina, War and Peace*

44. _____ *An Essay on Criticism, The Rape of the Lock, An Essay on Man*

45. _____ *Adam Bede, Middlemarch, Silas Marner, The Mill on the Floss*

46. _____ *Droll Tales, The Human Comedy, Le Pere Goriot*

47. _____ *The Executioner's Song, The Naked and the Dead, Armies of the Night*

48. _____ *Go Tell It on the Mountain, Notes of a Native Son, Nobody Knows My Name*

49. _____ *A Bell for Adano, Hiroshima*

50. _____ *An American Tragedy, Sister Carrie*

THE PARADE OF AUTHORS (PART TWO)

Identify the fifty authors whose works are listed below.

1. _____ *Goodbye, Columbus, Portnoy's Complaint*

2. _____ *The Lottery, The Haunting of Hill House*

3. _____ *Ship of Fools, Flowering Judas, Collected Short Stories*

4. _____ *A Story Teller's Story; Winesburg, Ohio*

5. _____ *Self-Reliance, Society and Solitude*

6. _____ *O Pioneers!, My Antonia, Death Comes for the Archbishop*

7. _____ *A Farewell to Arms, The Old Man and the Sea, A Moveable Feast*

8. _____ *The Red Badge of Courage, Maggie: A Girl of the Streets*

9. _____ *Uncle Vanya, The Seagull, The Cherry Orchard, Three Sisters*

10. _____ *Of Human Bondage, The Razor's Edge, The Moon and Sixpence*

11. _____ *Faust Part I and Part II, The Sorrows of Young Werther*

12. _____ *The Iliad, The Odyssey*

13. _____ *The Count of Monte Cristo, The Three Musketeers*

14. _____ *The Return of the Native, Tess of the D'Urbervilles, Far from the Madding Crowd, Jude the Obscure*

15. _____ *Georgics, Aeneid*

16. _____ *The Playboy of the Western World, Riders to the Sea*

17. _____ *Songs and Sonnets, The Anniversaries, "Death Be Not Proud"*

18. _____ *Madame Bovary*

19. _____ *Leaves of Grass, "O Captain! My Captain," "Song of Myself"*

20. _____ *On the Road, Desolation Angels*

21. _____ *Gone with the Wind*

22. _____ *Three Lives, The Autobiography of Alice B. Toklas*

23. _____ *The Martian Chronicles, The Illustrated Man, Fahrenheit 451*

24. _____ *The Thin Man, The Maltese Falcon, The Glass Key*

25. _____ *The Time of Your Life, The Human Comedy*

THE PARADE OF AUTHORS (PART TWO) (continued)

26. _____ *Beloved, Tar Baby, Song of Solomon, The Bluest Eye*

27. _____ *Jane Eyre, The Professor*

28. _____ *Look Homeward, Angel; You Can't Go Home Again*

29. _____ *Don Quixote*

30. _____ *The Elements of Style, Charlotte's Web*

31. _____ *Imperial Woman, The Good Earth, A House Divided*

32. _____ *Starship Troopers, Stranger in a Strange Land*

33. _____ *Tender Is the Night, The Great Gatsby, The Last Tycoon*

34. _____ *The Wapshot Chronicle, Falconer, The Wapshot Scandal*

35. _____ *Songs of Innocence, Songs of Experience*

36. _____ *Claudine, Cheri, Gigi, Sido*

37. _____ *The Murder of Roger Ackroyd, Ten Little Indians (And Then There Were None)*

38. _____ *The Hunchback of Notre Dame, Les Misérables*

39. _____ *Parallel Lives, Moralia*

40. _____ *Tom Jones, Joseph Andrews*

41. _____ *The Idiot, Crime and Punishment, The Brothers Karamazov*

42. _____ *Nineteen Eighty-Four, Animal Farm*

43. _____ *The Picture of Dorian Gray, The Importance of Being Earnest*

44. _____ *Nausea, No Exit*

45. _____ *Under Milk Wood, A Child's Christmas in Wales, "Do Not Go Gentle into that Good Night"*

46. _____ *The Strange Case of Doctor Jekyll and Mr. Hyde, Kidnapped, Treasure Island*

47. _____ *Lord Jim, Heart of Darkness, The Secret Sharer*

48. _____ *Doctor Zhivago, Over the Barriers*

49. _____ *A Study in Scarlet, The Hound of the Baskervilles, The Adventures of Sherlock Holmes*

50. _____ *Childe Harold's Pilgrimage, Don Juan*

THE PARADE OF AUTHORS (PART THREE)

Identify the fifty authors whose works are listed below.

1. _____ *Demian, Siddhartha, Steppenwolf*

2. _____ *David Copperfield, Oliver Twist, Great Expectations*

3. _____ *The Lyrical Ballads, The Prelude*

4. _____ *Cyrano de Bergerac*

5. _____ *Frankenstein, or the Modern Prometheus*

6. _____ *Romeo and Juliet, Two Gentlemen of Verona, Macbeth, Hamlet*

7. _____ *Idylls of the King,* "The Charge of the Light Brigade"

8. _____ *Captains Courageous, The Jungle Book, Kim*

9. _____ *A Doll's House, The Master Builder, Peer Gynt*

10. _____ *Wuthering Heights*

11. _____ *Daisy Miller, The Portrait of a Lady, The American, The Ambassadors*

12. _____ *Their Eyes Were Watching God, Mules and Men*

13. _____ *Uncle Tom's Cabin*

14. _____ *Sophie's Choice, The Confessions of Nat Turner*

15. _____ *Sonnets from the Portuguese*

16. _____ *The Life of Samuel Johnson*

17. _____ *Women in Love, Sons and Lovers, Lady Chatterley's Lover*

18. _____ *Metamorphosis, The Trial, In the Penal Colony*

19. _____ *Finnegan's Wake, Portrait of the Artist as a Young Man, Dubliners, Ulysses*

20. _____ *The Crying of Lot 49, V, Gravity's Rainbow*

21. _____ *A Passage to India, Howards End, A Room with a View, The Longest Journey*

22. _____ *All Creatures Great and Small, All Things Wise and Wonderful*

23. _____ *The Zoo Story, Tiny Alice, Who's Afraid of Virginia Woolf?*

24. _____ *The Great Santini, Prince of Tides, The Lords of Discipline*

25. _____ *The Yearling*

26. _____ *The Effect of Gamma Rays on Man-in-the-Moon Marigolds, The Pigman*

27. _____ *The Agony and the Ecstasy, Lust for Life*

28. _____ *The Hobbit, The Lord of the Rings*

29. _____ *All Quiet on the Western Front*

30. _____ *The Big Sleep; The Long Goodbye; Farewell, My Lovely*

31. _____ *The Spy Who Came in from the Cold, The Perfect Spy*

32. _____ "The Purloined Letter," "The Fall of the House of Usher," "The Gold-Bug"

33. _____ *Foundation,* "Nightfall," *The Intelligent Man's Guide to Science*

34. _____ *Dracula*

35. _____ *Tom Swift, The Bobbsey Twins, The Hardy Boys, Nancy Drew*

36. _____ *Rebecca, My Cousin Rachel*

37. _____ *The Andromeda Strain, The Terminal Man, Jurassic Park*

38. _____ *Light in August, The Sound and the Fury, As I Lay Dying*

39. _____ *Invisible Man*

40. _____ *The Hunt for Red October, Clear and Present Danger*

41. _____ *Life with Father, Life with Mother*

42. _____ *The Children's Hour, The Little Foxes, Watch on the Rhine*

43. _____ *Ragged Dick, Tattered Tom*

44. _____ *In Cold Blood; Breakfast at Tiffany's; Other Voices, Other Rooms*

45. _____ *Breakfast at the Homesick Restaurant, The Accidental Tourist*

46. _____ *The Adventures of Huckleberry Finn, The Adventures of Tom Sawyer, A Connecticut Yankee in King Arthur's Court*

47. _____ *The Jungle, Oil!, King Coal, Dragon's Teeth*

48. _____ *Seventeen, Penrod, The Magnificent Ambersons, Alice Adams*

49. _____ *To the Lighthouse, Mrs. Dalloway*

50. _____ *Prometheus Bound, The Oresteia*

THE PARADE OF AUTHORS (PART FOUR)

Identify the fifty authors whose works are listed below.

1. _____ "The Ugly Duckling," "The Emperor's New Clothes," "The Princess and the Pea"

2. _____ *The Divine Comedy*

3. _____ *Tobacco Road, God's Little Acre*

4. _____ *So Big, Cimarron, Giant, Stage Door*

5. _____ *The Chosen, The Promise, My Name Is Asher Lev*

6. _____ *Little House in the Big Woods, Little House on the Prairie*

7. _____ *Night, The Golem, Souls on Fire*

8. _____ *Bridge of San Luis Rey, The Skin of Our Teeth, Our Town*

9. _____ *The Lion, the Witch, and the Wardrobe; The Chronicles of Narnia*

10. _____ *The Tale of Peter Rabbit, The Tailor of Gloucester, The Tale of Mrs. Tiggy-Winkle*

11. _____ *Tartuffe, The Misanthrope*

12. _____ *Oedipus Rex, Oedipus at Colonus, Antigone*

13. _____ *Around the World in Eighty Days, Twenty Thousand Leagues Under the Sea*

14. _____ *The Day of the Locust, Miss Lonelyhearts*

15. _____ *Peter Pan, The Little Minister, What Every Woman Knows*

16. _____ *Cat on a Hot Tin Roof, A Streetcar Named Desire, The Glass Menagerie*

17. _____ *Lost Horizon; Goodbye, Mr. Chips*

18. _____ "On Melancholy," "Ode on a Grecian Urn," "To a Nightingale"

19. _____ *The Faerie Queene*

20. _____ *Deenie, Superfudge, Blubber, Forever*

21. _____ *Roots, The Autobiography of Malcolm X*

22. _____ "The Death of the Hired Man," "Stopping by Woods on a Snowy Evening"

23. _____ *The Last Gentleman, Love in the Ruins, Lost in the Cosmos*

24. _____ *Chicago Poems; Smoke and Steel; Good Morning, America*

25. _____ *Hard Times, Division Street America, The Good War*

26. _____ *Zorba the Greek*

27. _____ *Medea, The Trojan Women, Electra*

28. _____ *The Prophet*

29. _____ *Six Characters in Search of an Author*

30. _____ *Tex; Rumble Fish; That Was Then, This Is Now; The Outsiders*

31. _____ *Cabbages and Kings, The Four Million,* "The Ransom of Red Chief"

32. _____ *How the Grinch Stole Christmas, The Cat in the Hat, Hop on Pop*

33. _____ *The Miracle Worker, Two for the Seesaw*

34. _____ *The Stepford Wives, Rosemary's Baby*

35. _____ "Barbara Frietchie," "The Barefoot Boy," "Snow-Bound"

36. _____ *The Little Prince; Wind, Sand, and Stars*

37. _____ *The Awakening*

38. _____ "Because I Could Not Stop for Death," "There is no frigate like a book," "There's been a death in the opposite house"

39. _____ *Catch-22, Something Happened, Good as Gold, God Knows*

40. _____ *Riders of the Purple Sage, The Last Plainsmen*

41. _____ *Come Back Little Sheba, Picnic, The Dark at the Top of the Stairs*

42. _____ *To Kill a Mockingbird*

43. _____ *Member of the Wedding, The Heart is a Lonely Hunter*

44. _____ *The Natural, The Assistant, The Fixer*

45. _____ *Atlas Shrugged, The Fountainhead*

46. _____ "Elegy Written in a Country Churchyard"

47. _____ *Winnie-the-Pooh*

48. _____ *The Rivals, The School for Scandal*

49. _____ *A Raisin in the Sun; To Be Young, Gifted and Black*

50. _____ *A Separate Peace, Phineas, Peace Breaks Out*

RIGHT FROM THE WRITER'S MOUTH
PART ONE

Make believe that the following quotes were taken from interviews with the various world authors, including novelists, playwrights, poets, essayists, and short-story writers. See if you can identify the author who is speaking in each of the quick biographies below by writing his or her name on the line following the quote.

1. My first novel (1951) captured an entire generation of young people as I told the story of a rather odd (in some people's opinion) young man who attends Pencey Prep. I am rather reclusive and if you have ever read an interview with me, you're lucky. . . . There aren't that many!

   _____

2. I was born in England in 1812 and worked in a blacking factory before my teens. You might know my novels for their sympathetic look at youngsters who had it pretty tough growing up. If you like, call me BOZ.

   _____

3. My family participated in the Salem witch trials. My schoolmates at Bowdoin College included Franklin Pierce and Henry Wadsworth Longfellow. I brought the story of Hester Prynne and her memorable "A" to life.

   _____

4. I'm an Irishman who experimented with various narrative techniques. Some called my works masterpieces while others saw very little literary value in them. My works dealt primarily with Dublin and its people although my wife Nora, our family, and I spent much of our lives outside Ireland. My *Ulysses* was banned.

   _____

5. In 1849 I was arrested for conspiring against the Russian government. Though I spent nearly five years in Siberia, this time allowed me to understand the process of expiation necessary for salvation. Raskolnikov is one of my most famous characters.

   _____

6. *Go Tell It on the Mountain,* my first novel (1953), was semiautobiographical. In my novels and essays I address the conditions of the black man. I passed away in 1987.

   _____

7. My real name was Teodor Josef Konrad Korzeniowski. I knew little English until I was about twenty years old. My experiences on the seas were the motivation for my works, which examine the loneliness of man and his conflicts with nature.

   _____

8. I am one of the great Athenian tragedians. I wrote more than one hundred plays and made major innovations for the Greek stage including the addition of a third actor and painted scenery. I died in my nineties.

   _____

9. My plays take a serious look at the American South. Two of my plays won Pulitzer Prizes. Who could ever forget Stanley Kowalski and Blanche DuBois? Did you know my real first name was Thomas?

_____

10. My novel won the 1968 Pulitzer Prize. In this book I looked at the 1831 slave rebellion in the state of Virginia. Equally stirring might be my book about the woman who had to choose which one of her children would be killed.

_____

11. Forever associated with New England, I recited "The Gift Outright" at President John F. Kennedy's inauguration. My writings earned me four Pulitzer Prizes. I felt that a poem was a "momentary stay against confusion."

_____

12. I was one of three sisters who went by the names Acton, Currer, and Ellis. My brother was an opium addict and an alcoholic who died at thirty-one. Though I caught a cold at his funeral and died several months later, I did leave the story of Heathcliff and Catherine for your enjoyment.

_____

13. I was an adventurous man who spent time at sea and in the Klondike. I was also a newspaper correspondent during the Russo-Japanese War. At one time I was one of the highest paid and most widely read novelists in the country. Several dogs and a nasty sea master are among my contributions to literary history.

_____

14. A major name in American drama, I wrote very serious drama including an autobiographical play about the Tyrone family. One of my plays was modeled after a play by the Greek playwright, Aeschylus. The 1936 Nobel Prize in Literature was mine.

_____

15. Since I wasn't doing too well as an eye doctor, I began to write mystery stories centering around a super sleuth. When I killed off this detective, the public hounded me to resurrect him. I gave in and wrote of his return. Though this detective never existed in real life, hundreds of letters arrive at his fictitious Baker Street address every year.

_____

16. Best known for my dark poetry, I published my sole novel, a story about the tendency to take one's life, under a pseudonym. I graduated from Smith College but chose to spend most of my adult life in England. My life ended tragically in 1963.

_____

17. In addition to at least two great novels, one of them dealing with Russia during the Napoleonic Wars, I also wrote moral and religious writings. I believed in the simple life and was so into this ascetic philosophy that I chose to leave my family and go to live in a monastery. I died on the way.

_____

18. I lived for the advancement of science! I am best known for my writings in the area of science fiction. Perhaps you have heard of my time traveler's adventures?

_____

19. I am a businessman who one day packed it all in to write. Known as "Jobby," I was a contributor to the Chicago literary renaissance along with Carl Sandburg and Theodore Dreiser. My book about a small Midwestern town in Ohio is my biggest literary claim to fame.

---

20. I am the Norwegian considered to be the father of modern drama. My "problem" plays made social-psychological realism an important dramatic component.

---

21. I was the Belle of Amherst. I dressed primarily in white but didn't go outside much. Since I wrote thousands of poems and locked them away, only a few were published while I was alive. I died in 1886 at the age of fifty-six.

---

22. Irish-born and Oxford-educated, I wrote poems, novels, and plays! I was known as a wit, a homosexual (for which I was jailed), and an eccentric. This incarceration may have contributed to my early death.

---

23. My stage manager saw no scenery and only several props in my most famous play, a Pulitzer Prize winner. I also won Pulitzer Prizes for another play and a novel published in 1927. One of my other plays became the musical *Hello, Dolly.*

---

24. Some people might remember me as Marilyn Monroe's husband, but please remember that I also had a number of plays that left my mark on the American theater. Writing primarily about the common man, I featured plays about wartime manufacturing, a worn-out over-the-road man, and witchcraft. *After the Fall* is thought to be autobiographical.

---

25. One would think that the combination of the great white whale and its well-known pursuer would be enough to give the public what it wanted. Some seventy years after its publication, my book finally received its just literary praise.

---

26. I was the one who found the English language so intriguing that I showed how GHOTI is pronounced the same way as you'd pronounce the word FISH. My plays covered such varied subjects as betting on a duchess, the world's oldest profession, and canonization. While pruning a tree at the age of ninety-four, I fell and died shortly thereafter.

---

27. You might not know that when President Lincoln met me, he said that I was the little lady who started the Civil War. As an abolitionist, I was proud to see that my antislavery book truly heightened the public's awareness of slavery in the United States.

---

28. I was a Scottish-born writer who was primarily a short-story writer though I wrote other forms of literature. If I told you my real name was Hector Hugh Munro, would that help you remember my pen name?

---

29. An avid anti-industrialist, I'm probably best known for writing books about the relationships between men and women. One of my novels had the U.S. ban lifted on it in 1959. How much of Paul Morel was me in one of my other famous novels? You'll have to find out for yourself.

---

30. I owned the Middle Ages as far as literature goes. I am called the Father of English poetry. I'm sorry that I never got to complete all those tales about those folks traveling to the holy shrine and back. Perhaps I bit off more than I could chew.

_____

31. An American playwright, I am primarily known as a leader of the Theater of the Absurd. My most successful play was set on a New England college campus where George and Martha lived.

_____

32. A certified lawyer, I wrote satirical pieces that made me famous in New York before my most famous short stories, contained in *The Sketch Book of Geoffrey Crayon, Gent.,* made my name even more recognizable. With my busy schedule, I was unable to sleep much, unlike my creation who slept for two decades.

_____

33. Many considered me the finest female dramatist of my time especially as I wrote plays that examined the psychological and social aspects of our existence. When I was twenty-nine years old, I wrote *The Children's Hour,* a play about a disturbed boarding-school student who makes a scathing accusation against two of the schoolmistresses. I died in 1984.

_____

34. The Bard of Avon. That says it all.

_____

35. Born in Ireland, I won the Nobel Prize for Literature in 1969. Primarily a playwright in the Theater of the Absurd, I addressed man's condition in a very pessimistic way. My characters, Krapp, Pozzo, Lucky, Gogo, and Didi, are searching for meaning in their existences.

_____

36. A Roman poet, I'm best known for my classic epic of Aeneas though I died before I could complete it.

_____

37. I was a short-story writer whose skill for creating surprise endings was admired greatly. When I served a few years in jail for embezzlement, I wrote "Whistling Dick's Christmas Stocking." *The Four Million* is a collection of my short stories featuring the common people of our society. My birth certificate of 1862 probably read *William Sidney Porter.*

_____

38. A sickly and disfigured child, I later became a renowned poet and satirist. I translated both the *Iliad* and the *Odyssey* after I had written *Pastorals* at the age of sixteen. I also wrote *An Essay on Criticism* and *The Rape of the Lock,* a mock-heroic poem, a year later.

_____

39. I was appointed the English poet laureate in the middle of the nineteenth century. Influenced greatly by the Romantics, I was regarded as the most popular Victorian poet. The death of my friend, Arthur Hallam, inspired me to compose "In Memoriam."

_____

40. I was a humorist who wrote short stories, essays, and created my own artwork. I worked for *The New Yorker* and editor Harold Ross for almost seven years. Though I died virtually blind, I left behind for your enjoyment the story of that lovable would-be-hero, Walter Mitty.

_____

41. I was born in Florence and was well versed in philosophy, theology, and poetry. Exiled from Florence, I lived in other Italian cities and wrote. My major work, an epic poem by the name of *Commedia,* was completed in 1321, the year I died. In this literary masterpiece I visit Hell, Purgatory, and Paradise.

42. Most of my novels are set in Yoknapatawpha County, Mississippi. My books examine the South and its past. I'm remembered stylistically for my stream-of-consciousness technique and my interior monologues. I won both a Nobel Prize for Literature in 1949 and a Pulitzer Prize for *The Rievers* in 1962.

43. My *A Modest Proposal* brought attention to the plight of the Irish of my time. My best-known satirical piece follows a ship's doctor on several voyages to lands such as Bobdingnag, Houyhnhmland, and Lilliput. I am buried in St. Patrick's Cathedral in Dublin.

44. *Utopia* was my creation. I had served under Henry VIII and I resigned from the Chancellor-ship in 1532 when Henry desired to head the Church of England. After incarceration in the Tower of London, I was beheaded. Canonized during the twentieth century, I see that you can read about me in the play, *A Man for All Seasons.*

45. My real last name was Foe, but I changed that in my adulthood. A writer of journals, pamphlets, and novels, I'm best remembered for my man who was accompanied by his man, Friday. I was a political activist who also satirized the English for their treatment of foreigners and the Church of England for its practices.

46. A Transcendentalist and naturalist who was Harvard-educated, I was a good friend of Ralph Waldo Emerson who, incidentally, owned land on Walden Pond. Since I refused to pay a tax while staying at Walden in the late 1840s, I was jailed. You can read about this experience in my essay "On the Duty of Civil Disobedience" in which my philosophy "that government is best which governs least" is discussed.

47. I was born in India to English parents. Known for my skill at writing short stories, poems, and novels, I was the first English writer to be awarded the Nobel Prize (1907). My 1899 poem entitled "White Man's Burden" concerns itself with imperialism.

48. I was a great English epic poet who wrote works such as "L'Allegro," "Il Penseroso," *Samson Agonistes,* and *Paradise Lost.* I was blind when I died in 1674.

49. Questions have arisen whether or not I, an Ionian poet who was supposedly blind, wrote the two great Greek epics. Don't get too worked up about all that stuff. Instead, enjoy the tales of the Trojan War and the return trip to Greece. Life's too short to argue about such trivial matters.

50. I was an important figure in the Harlem Renaissance of the 1920s. My skill at expressing the American black's situation through dialect and idiom was both admired and chastised.

RIGHT FROM THE WRITER'S MOUTH
(PART TWO)

Make believe that the following quotes were taken from interviews with various world authors including novelists, playwrights, poets, essayists, and short-story writers. Identify the author who is speaking in each of these quick biographies by writing his or her name on the line following the quote.

1. I was an English poet who lived from 1886 to 1967. My poetry exposed the atrocities of war. This feeling was partially due to my experiences in World War I in which I was wounded twice. *Siegfried's Journey* is quite autobiographical.

   _____

2. I was a popular French science-fiction writer whose stories were prophetic when we talk about the submarine, the flying machine, and space travel.

   _____

3. I created Hercule Poirot. My books have sold over 400 million copies. My play, *The Mousetrap,* was a long-running stage production. My disappearance has never really been totally explained. Was it a publicity stunt? I'll never tell!

   _____

4. Called "the most spiritual of artists," I was a famous eighteenth-century English poet who also illustrated his own works. I was a mystic, an engraver, and a leader in the Romantic movement. My two poems, "The Lamb" and "The Tiger," are classics.

   _____

5. My real name was Eric Blair. I was born in India and also served in Burma's Imperial Palace. Some of my writings expressed my abhorrence of totalitarianism. I was also known for coining the word doublespeak.

   _____

6. My adolescence along the banks of the Mississippi River served as a backdrop for three of my most famous novels. I am also remembered for my keen sense of humor and the colloquial speech found in my novels.

   _____

7. A poet, critic, and playwright, I was a leading literary figure of the early twentieth century. I was born in America but spent most of my years in England. *The Waste Land* and *Murder in the Cathedral* show the range of my literary abilities.

   _____

8. I am a female who loved capitalism. My two famous works defended my objective philosophy. I am against governmental restraint of self-motivated individuals. I bet many aren't sure how to pronounce my first name.

   _____

9. A Frenchman, I wrote several hundred popular historical plays and adventure novels. A group of writers did quite a bit of research to furnish plots for me. I then proceeded to rewrite these plots, often incurring the wrath of those who said I committed a literary sin by altering historical facts to suit my fancy.

   _____

© 1994 by The Center for Applied Research in Education

10. My tales of horror and mystery put me on the literary map forever. As an orphan, I was taken in by the John Allan family. For a time I attended West Point. My poem "Annabel Lee" was addressed to my deceased wife, a cousin whom I married when she was thirteen years old.

---

11. My novel won a Pulitzer Prize in 1983 and was made into a film a few years later. This book is told through letters sent by the protagonist, Celie, to God and to her sister. The novel concerns itself with black women and equality.

---

12. My *Complete Poems* received the Pulitzer Prize for Poetry in 1951. My simply poetry, free verse in style, addressed the Midwest (you recall "Chicago") and the emergence of early twentieth-century industrialism. I greatly admired the poetry of Walt Whitman and did extensive research on Abraham Lincoln.

---

13. The Nobel Prize winner of 1946, I was a German writer best noted for my novels about psychology, self-discovery, and spiritualism. My one novel, *Siddhartha,* shows fulfillment gained by listening to the beautiful words of the river.

---

14. I was an Algerian-born French existentialist famous for the philosophy of the absurd. My novel *The Stranger* begins with one of the most famous first lines of any literary work. I died in an automobile crash in 1960.

---

15. My 1954 composition *A Child's Christmas in Wales* is one of my more recognized literary efforts. My autobiographical sketches entitled *Portrait of the Artist as a Young Dog* shows my admiration for the skill of James Joyce. My exhortation to my father to fight death and exhibit that zest for life that characterized his years is found in the poem "Do Not Go Gentle into That Good Night."

---

16. Most of my poetry was written before I reached my fourth decade in life. My father was headmaster at Rugby, a prominent British public school. As a leading poet of the Victorian Age, I became well known for my reflective and sensitive poem, "Dover Beach."

---

17. A member of the "lost generation" and a leading spokesman for the Jazz Age, I became a renowned novelist and short-story writer, but I did have my difficulties as a Hollywood screenwriter. In *The Crack-Up* I describe how my wife's illness also brought many troubles for me. I was an alcoholic who died in 1940.

---

18. My 1925 novel was based on the real-life murder of Grace Brown by Chester Gillette in an upstate New York lake. Although some critics found my style rather crude, I felt that I told it as it is, naturalistically, in showing how social forces such as poverty and position can impact heavily and even trap the individual. Very few of you will forget the experiences that Carrie Meeber and George Hurstwood shared in my other famous novel.

---

19. Charles Lutwidge Dodgson is my real name! I was a professor who was inspired by Alice Littell to write stories and construct puzzles to amuse her. I was also a mathematics professor reputed to be quite boring at the task. I hope you enjoyed the "Jabberwocky" thing.

---

20. One of my novels so moved President Theodore Roosevelt that he invited me to the White House to talk to him about the subject of my book, the meat-packing industry. I also wrote novels based on such diverse subjects as the Teapot Dome Scandal and the Sacco-Vanzetti case. I died in 1968 at the age of 90.

_____

21. Some of my novels concerned themselves with the depressed economic classes of people. This concern began when I saw the farmers and the workers near my childhood Salinas, California, home. I won the Pulitzer Prize in 1940 and the Nobel Prize for Literature in 1962. My 1939 novel dealing with the plight of the Okies is probably my best-remembered work.

_____

22. A friend of Samuel Taylor Coleridge, I mystically celebrated nature through my poetry during England's Romantic Age. My poetry was criticized as being "unpoetic," yet I was still honored as England's poet laureate in 1843. As an older man, I lived in the Lake Country where I completed my famous *The Prelude*.

_____

23. My dramatic style is characterized by the term "comedy of menace." My plays feature the bizarre experiences, alienation, and isolation of the modern man within his environment. The most famous of my plays are *The Birthday Party* and *The Homecoming*.

_____

24. My novels focus on the shortcomings I found in American society as exemplified by Gopher Prairie, the setting for *Main Street*. In 1926 I refused to accept the Pulitzer Prize for *Arrowsmith* since I did not agree with the reasons why my novel was chosen for such an award.

_____

25. An English preacher, metaphysical poet, and later dean of St. Paul's Church, I wrote primarily love and religious poetry. The poems, "Woman's Constancy" and "The Canonization," are examples of my work.

_____

26. I was a highly regarded writer who wrote of provincial life in England. My life was far from exciting. I had very little contact with the literary people of my day, never married, and seldom ventured beyond my immediate surroundings. Despite all of these, I was able to depict diverse types of country people and their manners in an effective way.

_____

27. Born on Long Island, I became the Brooklyn *Eagle* editor before I founded the *Freeman,* my own paper. My 1855 publication, *Leaves of Grass,* a work featuring freedom and democracy concepts, was thought to be immoral by some critics.

_____

28. My *Beloved,* a look at black American slavery, received a Pulitzer Prize in 1988. In my novels I focus on the trials and tribulations of the black American woman. I was born Chloe Anthony Wofford.

_____

29. My family founded the village where the Baseball Hall of Fame is located. My frontier adventure stories were popular both in America and abroad. *The Leatherstocking Tales* and *Natty Bumpo* were my creations.

_____

30. My work, *Annie Allen,* won the 1950 Pulitzer Prize for poetry. As a black poetess, I express the concerns of the American blacks, especially those in my native Chicago. *In the Mecca* and *A Street in Bronzeville* are two of my more well-known writings.

31. An English philologist, medieval literature professor, and the creator of the world of Middle Earth, I was inspired by my studies at Oxford University to write the type of stories I did. My story, *The Simarillion,* was published after my death in 1973.

32. I was a French writer, dramatist, and philosopher whose real name was Francois Marie Arouet. Two of my acquaintances were Jonathan Swift and Alexander Pope. My satire and unorthodox concepts were renowned. My most famous work was *Candide.*

33. My religious pamphlet, *The Necessity of Atheism,* was enough to warrant my expulsion from Oxford. I married Mary Godwin who wrote *Frankenstein.* A philosophical poet who was a leader among the Romantic poets, I wrote "Ozymandias," *Prometheus Unbound,* and "Ode to the West Wind." Additionally, my 1821 publication, "Adonais," is an elegy commemorating the death of John Keats. I drowned when my yacht, the *Don Juan,* overturned in a storm.

34. My symbolically rich 1955 novel about a group of boys stranded on an island following an evacuation from their school was an immediate success first in my native England and shortly thereafter in the United States. I was awarded the Nobel Prize in Literature in 1983 and died ten years later.

35. An invalid and romantic love lyricist, I married another poet to whom I dedicated my most famous endeavor, *Sonnets from the Portuguese.* We were forced to elope to Italy because of my overbearing father. Perhaps this real-life romance of ours is as memorable as the famous poems we created.

36. Once a member of the Communist Party and then a convert to the Roman Catholic faith, I wrote heavily on the topics of moral and theological problems. Though I wrote plays and short stories as well, my best-known works are my novels such as *The Power and the Glory, A Burnt Out Case, The Heart of the Matter,* and *Brighton Rock,* which includes my memorable Pinkie.

37. When you hear the poems "Kubla Khan" and "The Rime of the Ancient Mariner," you think of me, a famed Romantic poet. I was one of fourteen children born into an English clergyman's family. My friend William Wordsworth and I published the *Lyrical Ballads.* Unfortunately, my personal life was not a very happy one since my marriage was unsuccessful and I was addicted to laudanum.

38. I guess you could say I came from good stock. My grandfather was a millionaire, my father was a philosopher-theologian, and my brother was a renowned psychologist. As a novelist, I was celebrated as a master technician. Some of my novels, including *The American, The Europeans,* and *The Portrait of a Lady,* explore the differences between the American innocence and the European experience. To make my writings realistic and unified, I wrote some of my more complex novels in a style coined "stream of consciousness" by my psychologist brother, William.

39. I wrote novels that featured the wealthy New York society. My literary mentor was Henry James. Though my novel of manners *The Age of Innocence* won the 1921 Pulitzer Prize for Fiction, my most well-known literary work might well be *Ethan Frome,* a story set in New England.

_____

40. In tune with my personal pessimism as experienced in my native Dorset (I call it Wessex in my books), the characters found in my British novels (of which I produced eleven in about two and a half decades) are often tragic victims of a cruel nature and an uncaring God. The later years of my literary career were taken up with my poetry.

_____

41. Although I was born in Albany, New York, in 1836, I loved to compose tales of the men of the mining areas of California. I found the flavor of these supposedly less-than-admirable men of this time intriguing. "The Outcasts of Poker Flat" and "The Luck of Roaring Camp" are two of my works.

_____

42. You know me better by my pen name than by my real name, Mary Ann, or Marian, Evans. My Victorian novel *Middlemarch* is considered a landmark in the fiction of nineteenth-century England. I personally thought *Adam Bede* and *Silas Marner* were also fairly good novels.

_____

43. Although I was qualified to practice medicine, I devoted my life to composing poetry. Leigh Hunt, a dear friend and editor of the *Examiner,* published my sonnet, "On First Looking into Chapman's Homer." *Endymion,* a poem of 4,000 lines, was not well received by the critics. Between 1818 and 1819 two of my greatest works "Ode on a Grecian Urn" and "To a Nightingale" were composed. One of the most famous British Romantic poets, I died in Rome in 1821.

_____

44. I am an American writer who wrote a major novel, *Other Voices, Other Rooms,* before I was twenty-five. Another of my works, *Breakfast at Tiffany's,* also features characters who are both eccentric and alienated. Many of you recall *In Cold Blood,* my account of the brutal slayings of the Kansas Clutter family. Last, I was featured in the Broadway play, *Tru.*

_____

45. Encouraged to write by novelist Ford Madox Ford, I wrote my first book in 1927. My most famous work, *Wide Sargasso Sea,* tells the story of Rochester's hidden and insane Creole wife whom you first met in Charlotte Brontë's *Jane Eyre.*

_____

46. I was a medical practitioner who loved to write. My short stories were such masterpieces that I decided to abandon my medical practice except to treat a few of my friends and neighbors when necessary. My plays include the problems of a changing Russia. Perhaps you have read *The Cherry Orchard, The Seagull,* or *Uncle Vanya?*

_____

47. A sixteenth-century British poet, often called the "poet's poet," I wrote long, descriptive allegories. I won favor with Queen Elizabeth with my work *The Shepherd's Calendar,* which depicted the beauty of the English countryside. I am best remembered for my great epic, *The Faerie Queene.*

_____

RIGHT FROM THE WRITER'S MOUTH (PART TWO) (continued)

48. Though I am remembered as an American novelist, I was raised in China and also taught school there. In addition to writing novels, I wrote plays, biographies, and children's books. In 1932 I accepted the Pulitzer Prize for my novel *The Good Earth*. Six years later I was awarded the Nobel Prize in Literature.

---

49. A leader of the Romantic movement in France, I wrote poems and novels. When I was forced into exile, I completed my great work, *Les Misérables*. Two decades earlier I had created the gypsy dancer, Esmeralda, and my famous deformed bellringer, Quasimodo. I died in 1885.

---

50. My father, unable to give proper financial support for our family, associated in the Concord, Massachusetts, area with Thoreau and Emerson. Because we needed the money, I wrote secretly under the pseudonym A. N. Barnard. Another portion of the title of my most widely read novel is *or Meg, Jo, Beth and Amy*.

ROUND-TABLE DISCUSSION

If each of the groups below had participated in a round-table discussion, which author could not have attended since he or she was of another era? Circle the name of the author who doesn't belong.

Group 1
T. S. Eliot
Eugene O'Neill
Katherine Mansfield
George Eliot

Group 2
William Dean Howells
Vladimir Nabokov
Bret Harte
Thomas Hardy

Group 3
William Butler Yeats
Ben Jonson
H. G. Wells
Luigi Pirandello

Group 4
Jonathan Edwards
Benjamin Franklin
Voltaire
Gerard Manley Hopkins

Group 5
Sir Thomas More
Hans Christian Andersen
Ralph Waldo Emerson
Nathaniel Hawthorne

Group 6
Colette
W. Somerset Maugham
James Fenimore Cooper
Robert Frost

Group 7
D. H. Lawrence
Emily Dickinson
Sinclair Lewis
Ezra Pound

Group 8
Louisa May Alcott
Lewis Carroll
Jules Verne
Rachel Carson

Group 9
John Cheever
O. Henry
Samuel Beckett
Richard Wright

Group 10
William Wordsworth
Sean O'Casey
Upton Sinclair
E. M. Forster

Group 11
Daniel Defoe
Jonathan Swift
Virginia Woolf
Joseph Addison

Group 12
Anton Chekhov
James Barrie
A. E. Housman
James Michener

Group 13
Willa Cather
Charles Dickens
W.E.B. Du Bois
Edith Wharton

Group 14
Joseph Pulitzer
Ernest Hemingway
Thomas Wolfe
F. Scott Fitzgerald

Group 15
Miguel de Cervantes
William Shakespeare
Plutarch
Sir Francis Bacon

AUTHORS' FUNNY NAMES

In this exercise you will see the scrambled-up **last names** of authors from the ancients to the contemporaries. The letters have been rearranged to make other words or names. Thus a name such as TOLSTOY easily becomes LOST TOY and HILLERMAN become ILL HERMAN.

See how many of these others you can identify. Good luck.

1. _____ SUMAC

2. _____ REWARN

3. _____ ILL ONE

4. _____ WILES

5. _____ EAR SLING

6. _____ WINE BURNS

7. _____ LES HOWL

8. _____ BALM

9. _____ RAY HACKET

10. _____ L.X. HUEY

11. _____ RON THAW

12. _____ MO ROE

13. _____ NO GNU VET

14. _____ WASH

15. _____ TESS CARED

16. _____ NO CHIP

17. _____ THOR

18. _____ JON SACK

19. _____ KID CEY

20. _____ NO SANDER

21. _____ HER CAT

22. _____ NEVER

23. _____ TINES

24. _____ LEE HININ

25. _____ STARER

26. _____ DACRON

27. _____ SICK NED

28. _____ SWORD THROW

29. _____ DON STAR

30. _____ N.Y. SONNET

31. _____ BINES

32. _____ BET RON

33. _____ SUN THOR

34. _____ RON B. WING

35. _____ RENE CLAW

36. _____ WAR SLING

37. _____ NOTES

38. _____ TOIL KEN

39. _____ QUEER ARM

40. _____ DEL RANCH

41. _____ LUKE FARN

42. _____ LIL NOSE

43. _____ NELL HAM

44. _____ LARGE

45. _____ PAT COE

46. _____ KING RON TAT

47. _____ SANER NED

48. _____ TAN ED

49. _____ DELL CLAW

50. _____ EL WISE

51. _____ PET ROT

52. _____ STEW

53. _____ LIAM WILS

54. _____ HOT LIN

55. _____ SKATE

56. _____ CY ERP

57. _____ GRAN DUBS

58. _____ MEL LITCH

59. _____ SUPER EDIE

60. _____ GIN BAR

61. _____ RANDI POLLE

62. _____ NO HINT

63. _____ BIG SON

64. _____ HIRE TWIT

65. _____ EEL

66. _____ DION C. SKIN

67. _____ MRS. LECLUC

68. _____ WET JET

69. _____ MA DU MAL

70. _____ DARN

71. _____ DAN'S HEIR

72. _____ LES WONK

73. _____ L.I. MEN

74. _____ BEN S. HARRY

75. _____ DON NOL

76. _____ LAB WIND

77. _____ LEW LOB

78. _____ ED GOD

79. _____ DON LIGG

80. _____ SWELL

81. _____ HEART

82. _____ C.Z. ZONES

83. _____ ED N. LARR

84. _____ DEAR MEAL

85. _____ CAL VERE

86. _____ VAL CELL

87. _____ MA TRESS

88. _____ LILI'S TOE

89. _____ WEST ART

90. _____ RED RISE

91. _____ WING ASHTON

92. _____ MAL ROWE

93. _____ TOTAL RISE

94. _____ THE BURR

95. _____ NED STAHL

96. _____ DIRE DOT

97. _____ LOU ANGE

98. _____ SAL WOGG

99. _____ NO CARS

100. _____ BLAMER

101. _____ MEL FING

102. _____ K.Z. TRAN

103. _____ KENT PARAS

104. _____ HAIR SOP

105. _____ LAST K.O.

106. _____ NO RAMS

107. _____ STEER NOTCH

108. _____ SAD DION

109. _____ MR. ALOU

SECTION 2

CHARACTERS—
LITERATURE'S LEGACIES

FAMOUS LITERARY CHARACTERS AND THEIR CREATORS

Here are thirty-six of literature's most famous characters. Your challenge is to match them up with their creators, their authors.

GROUP 1

Burroughs, Edgar Rice   Hemingway, Ernest   Shaw, George Bernard
Carroll, Lewis   Lewis, Sinclair   Steinbeck, John
Defoe, Daniel   Melville, Herman   Swift, Jonathan
Flaubert, Gustave   Salinger, John David   Voltaire

1. _____ Lemuel Gulliver

2. _____ Robinson Crusoe

3. _____ Alice in Wonderland

4. _____ Lennie Small

5. _____ Holden Caulfield

6. _____ Elmer Gantry

7. _____ Tarzan

8. _____ Captain Ahab

9. _____ Candide

10. _____ Eliza Doolittle

11. _____ Santiago

12. _____ Emma Bovary

FAMOUS LITERARY CHARACTERS AND THEIR CREATORS (continued)

GROUP 2

Brontë, Charlotte
Cervantes, Miguel
Christie, Agatha
Dickens, Charles

Fielding, Henry
Fitzgerald, F. Scott
Mitchell, Margaret
Pasternak, Boris

Rostand, Edmond
Shelley, Mary
Tolkien, J.R.R.
Wilde, Oscar

1. _____ Rhett Butler

2. _____ Jane Eyre

3. _____ Don Quixote

4. _____ Jay Gatsby

5. _____ Hercule Poirot

6. _____ Tom Jones

7. _____ Dorian Gray

8. _____ Dr. Yuri Zhivago

9. _____ David Copperfield

10. _____ Cyrano de Bergerac

11. _____ Frankenstein

12. _____ Bilbo Boggins

GROUP 3

Barrie, James M.
Doyle, Sir Arthur Conan
Kazantzakis, Nikos
Lee, Harper

Miller, Arthur
Milne, A. A.
Potter, Beatrix
Saint-Exupéry, Antoine de

Sheridan, Richard Brinsley
Stoker, Bram
Twain, Mark
Williams, Tennessee

1. _____ Willie Loman

2. _____ Dracula

3. _____ Tom Sawyer

4. _____ Peter Rabbit

5. _____ Peter Pan

6. _____ Stanley Kowalski

7. _____ Zorba the Greek

8. _____ The Little Prince

9. _____ Winnie-the-Pooh

10. _____ Mrs. Malaprop

11. _____ Sherlock Holmes

12. _____ Atticus Finch

FICTIONAL AMERICAN LITERATURE CHARACTERS

Here's an alphabetized list of famous fictional characters whose names are familiar to many readers. Fill the blanks in numbers 1–20 to see how you stack up in your knowledge of famous American literature fictional characters.

Nick Adams
Martin Arrowsmith
Bartleby
Holden Caulfield
Arthur Dimmesdale
Henry Fleming
Hiawatha

Ligeia
Jo March
Francie Nolan
Scarlett O'Hara
Hester Prynne
Jaffrey Pyncheon
Queequeg

Uncle Remus
Tom Sawyer
Ebenezer Scrooge
Lennie Small
Becky Thatcher
Yossarian

1. _____ She is the heroine of Margaret Mitchell's 1936 novel, *Gone with the Wind*. This southern belle is the wife of Rhett Butler.

2. _____ He is the teenage protagonist in J. D. Salinger's *Catcher in the Rye*. He dislikes the phonies he encounters while at Pencey Prep and elsewhere.

3. _____ He is Mark Twain's boy of the Mississippi River whose story has been enjoyed by many readers over the years.

4. _____ The hero of Henry Wadsworth Longfellow's poem, he eventually becomes the leader of his Indian tribe and teaches peace with the white man.

5. _____ He is the duplicitous judge in Nathaniel Hawthorne's *The House of the Seven Gables*. His acquisition of the house formerly owned by Matthew Maule brings nothing but trouble for his family.

6. _____ She is Tom Sawyer's sweetheart.

7. _____ He's the half-witted, powerful giant in Steinbeck's *Of Mice and Men*. His friend, George Milton, takes care of him and must shoot him so a gang will not kill him.

8. _____ He is the hero of Ernest Hemingway's stories in the collection entitled *In Our Time*. How autobiographically he has been sketched is interesting.

9. _____ Along with her sisters, Beth, Meg, and Amy, she is the tomboyish member of the family created by Louisa May Alcott in the novel, *Little Women*.

10. _____ He is Melville's character, a scrivener, who, upon numerous requests from his boss, responds, "I should prefer not to . . ."

11. _____ He's the main character in "A Christmas Carol" by Charles Dickens. This miser changes his attitude toward Christmas after visits from ghosts of Christmas Past, Christmas Present, and Christmas Future.

12. _____ He is a cotton plantation slave who tells folk tales based on fables of his race. Joel Chandler Harris created him.

FICTIONAL AMERICAN LITERATURE CHARACTERS (continued)

13. _____ She grows up in a city slum, the daughter of a drunken father and a determined, suffering mother.

14. _____ He is the titular character of Sinclair Lewis's novel about a research doctor who later fights diseases on an island in the West Indies.

15. _____ He is the hero of Stephen Crane's *The Red Badge of Courage*. He constantly battles fear in this novel, set during the Civil War.

16. _____ She is the woman forced to wear the scarlet letter "A" in the Puritan society depicted by Nathaniel Hawthorne in *The Scarlet Letter*.

17. _____ He is the antihero in Joseph Heller's *Catch-22*.

18. _____ You remember him as the harpooner and ship companion of Ishmael in Herman Melville's *Moby Dick*.

19. _____ She is the narrator's wife in Edgar Allen Poe's short story. She dies after an illness. Later the narrator thinks he sees her again.

20. _____ A minister in Hawthorne's *The Scarlet Letter*, he eventually admits to being the father of Pearl, the child born out of wedlock.

DO YOU KNOW WHO I AM?

Here are the names of twenty-five literary characters from books you have probably read. Even if you haven't read the book, perhaps the character's name rings a bell. Let's see if you are in the know when it comes to literary people. Fill the blanks in numbers 1–25 with the correct character's name from the list below.

Nick Adams	Fagin	Huw Morgan
Bartleby	Atticus Finch	Captain Nemo
Big Brother	Sondra Finchley	Scarlett O'Hara
Leopold Bloom	Elmer Gantry	Hercule Poirot
Billy Budd	Lemuel Gulliver	Hester Prynne
Holden Caulfield	Nora Helmer	Ebenezer Scrooge
Mr. Chips	Tom Joad	Rebecca Thatcher
Eliza Doolittle	Willy Loman	
Catherine Earnshaw	Ishmael	

1. _____ is a lawyer and the father of Jem and Scout in *To Kill a Mockingbird* by Harper Lee.

2. _____ is the handsome sailor who is eventually hanged after killing John Claggart.

3. _____, called "man mountain," this surgeon meets with the Brobdingnags and Lilliputians.

4. _____ is a former guttersnipe who has been transformed into a lady with the help of Henry Higgins and his speech lessons.

5. _____ is Agatha Christie's super sleuth.

6. _____ In Ireland June 16, 1904, is named after him since he spent that day wandering around Dublin.

7. _____ is the narrator of Herman Melville's *Moby Dick*.

8. _____ taught Oliver to pick a pocket or two.

9. _____ is a very well-liked and respected schoolteacher.

10. _____ is forever associated with the *Nautilus* and *20,000 Leagues Under the Sea*.

11. _____ is Clyde Griffiths' wealthy girlfriend in *An American Tragedy* by Theodore Dreiser.

12. _____ is the constant watcher in Oceania.

13. _____ is an Okie who led his family to the West.

14. _____ is a wealthy man who did a complete turn regarding his attitude toward Christmas and sharing.

15. _____ is the salesman who kills himself.

16. _____ is Heathcliff's beloved in Brontë's 1847 novel *Wuthering Heights.*

17. _____ is the character in many Ernest Hemingway's short stories.

18. _____ is Rhett Butler's belle in Margaret Mitchell's *Gone with the Wind.*

19. _____ is the heroine who bolts from her husband in Ibsen's *A Doll's House.*

20. _____ is the Salinger-created youth who despises the phoniness around him.

21. _____ didn't say much . . . why? He'd prefer not to.

22. _____ is Sinclair Lewis's titular evangelical preacher.

23. _____ is the lady who was forced to wear the scarlet letter in Salem, Massachusetts.

24. _____ is Tom Sawyer's love.

25. _____ is the son in the coal-mining region of Wales.

Name _____ Date _____ Period _____

PLEASE, MR. POSTMAN!

The following envelopes, all addressed to characters in British novels, are not complete. Fill in the missing information on the line below each envelope so that these characters can receive their mail. The authors have been used in the care of (c/o) slot to help you. Good luck!

1. Mr. C
Brookfield School
England
c/o James Hilton

_____

2. Mr. P. P., aka P.
The Gargery House
England
c/o Charles Dickens

_____

3. Dr. L. G.
Lilliput
c/o Jonathan Swift

_____

4. Mr. J. F.
Wessex, England
c/o Thomas Hardy

_____

5. Master J. M.
an island in the Pacific
c/o William Golding

_____

6. Mr. K, Inner Station Mgr.
Belgian Congo
c/o Joseph Conrad

_____

7. Master H. M.
Wales
c/o Richard Llewellyn

_____

8. Mr. H. W.
Howards End
c/o E. M. Forester

_____

9. Ms. F. P.
Mansfield Park
c/o Jane Austen

_____

10. Mayor M. H.
Casterbridge, Wessex
c/o Thomas Hardy

_____

11. Mrs. C. D.
London
c/o Virginia Woolf

_____

12. Mr. E. D.
Cloisterham, England
c/o Charles Dickens

_____

13. B. B.
Oceania
c/o George Orwell ☐

14. Mr. P. C.
Blackstable, near London
c/o W. Somerset Maugham ☐

15. Master O. T.
Workhouse north of London
c/o Charles Dickens ☐

16. Dr. A.
Marabar Caves
c/o E. M. Forster ☐

17. Mr. P. P.
Never Land
c/o J. M. Barrie ☐

18. Mr. D. G.
London
c/o Oscar Wilde ☐

19. Mr. C. Y.
Egdon Heath, England
c/o Thomas Hardy ☐

20. Mr. R. C. and his man, F.
S. American Coastal Island
c/o Daniel Defoe ☐

21. Mr. S. M., Weaver
Raveloe, England
c/o George Eliot ☐

22. Ms. A.
Wonderland
c/o Lewis Carroll ☐

23. Prince M.
Castle of Otranto, Italy
c/o Horace Walpole ☐

24. Master D. C.
Export Warehouse, England
c/o Charles Dickens ☐

25. Ms. E. W.
Hartfield Estate, Surrey
c/o Jane Austen ☐

ENVELOPE PLEASE!

The following envelopes, all addressed to characters found in American novels or tales, are not complete. Their authors' names have been used in the "care of" (c/o) slot to help you identify the characters' names. See how many of the following envelopes you can complete by filling in the missing information on the line below the envelopes. The first one is done for you.

1. Captain _____
   The Pequod
   c/o Herman Melville

   _____Ahab_____

2. Mr. G. F. and friend P.
   Devon School
   c/o John Knowles

   _____

3. Ms. S. O.
   Tara Plantation
   Georgia
   c/o Margaret Mitchell

   _____

4. Captain W. L.
   The Ghost
   c/o Jack London

   _____

5. Mr. A. F., Esq.
   Maycomb County
   Alabama
   c/o Harper Lee

   _____

6. Mr. T. S.
   Sutpen's Hundred
   Yoknapatawpha County
   Mississippi
   c/o William Faulkner

   _____

7. Brother _____
   San Luis Rey Bridge
   Peru
   c/o Thornton Wilder

   _____

8. Mr. C. G.
   Lycurgus, NY
   c/o Theodore Dreiser

   _____

9. Mr. B. B.
   The Indomitable
   c/o Herman Melville

   _____

10. Mr. G. B.
    Zenith City
    c/o Sinclair Lewis

    _____

11. Mr. N. A.
    NY, NY
    c/o Edith Wharton

    _____

12. Rev. E. G.
    Methodist Church
    c/o Sinclair Lewis

    _____

ENVELOPE PLEASE! (continued)

13. Mr. J. G.
West Egg, Long Island
c/o F. Scott Fitzgerald ☐

14. Mr. W. L.
Northern China
c/o Pearl S. Buck ☐

15. Mr. J. G.
Harlem, NY
c/o James Baldwin ☐

16. Mr. R. J. and the Loyalist Guerillas
Spain
c/o Ernest Hemingway ☐

17. Mr. E. F. and wife Z.
Starkfield, Massachusetts
c/o Edith Wharton ☐

18. Detective S. S.
San Francisco
c/o Dashiell Hammett ☐

19. Mr. T. J. and Family
Formerly of Oklahoma
c/o John Steinbeck ☐

20. Colonel P. and Family
The House of the Seven Gables
Salem, Massachusetts
c/o Nathaniel Hawthorne ☐

21. Captain and Mrs. F.
Sweet Water, Nebraska
c/o Willa Cather ☐

22. Mr. L. S.
Salinas Valley, California
c/o John Steinbeck ☐

23. Lieutenant W. B.
Captain of the H.M.S. *Bounty*
South Pacific and Tahiti
c/o Nordoff and Hall ☐

24. S. and companion M.
The Gulf Stream
c/o Ernest Hemingway ☐

25. Mr. P. N., Man without a Country
One ship or another
c/o Edward Everett Hale ☐

26. Mr. I. C.
Sleepy Hollow
c/o Washington Irving ☐

27. Ms. A. S.
Nebraska prairie
c/o Willa Cather ☐

28. Ms. C. M.
Chicago or New York
c/o Theodore Dreiser ☐

29. Ms. H. P. and daughter P.
Salem, Massachusetts
c/o Nathaniel Hawthorne ☐

30. Mr. H. F.
Mississippi River
c/o Mark Twain ☐

Name _____ **Date** _____ **Period** _____

LETTERS AROUND THE WORLD

Since all the following plays, novels, and epic poems were written by world authors (no American or British authors appear), the letters have destinations around the globe. They are addressed incompletely so it is up to you to finish the job. Insert the letter recipient's name in the space below the envelope. The care of (c/o) line is designed to expedite the process. Hint: You can send a letter to yourself!

1.
> Ms. A. K.
> Moscow
> c/o Leo Tolstoy

_____

2.
> Mr. D. K. and Brothers
> Skotoprigonyevski, Russia
> c/o Fyodor Dostoyevsky

_____

3.
> Mr. E. D.
> Chateau D'If
> c/o Alexandre Dumas

_____

4.
> Mr. R. R.
> St. Petersburg, Russia
> c/o Fyodor Dostoyevsky

_____

5.
> Poet C. de B.
> France
> c/o Edmond Rostånd

_____

6.
> Mr. D. Q.
> La Mancha, Spain
> c/o Miguel de Cervantes

_____

7.
> Tsar B. G.
> Russia
> c/o Alexander Pushkin

_____

8.
> Count D.
> Transylvania
> c/o Bram Stoker

_____

9.
> Madame R.
> The Cherry Orchard
> c/o Anton Chekhov

_____

10.
> Ms. N. H.
> Norway
> c/o Henrik Ibsen

_____

11. Dr. T. S.
Norwegian coastal town
c/o Henrik Ibsen
☐

_____

12. Mr. D. J.
Spain, Turkey, Russia, England
c/o Lord Byron
☐

_____

13. Mr. D. A.
Hell, Purgatory, Heaven
c/o Dante Alighieri
☐

_____

14. Ms. P., wife of O.
Island of Ithaca
c/o Homer
☐

_____

15. The wife of B.
Heading for St. Thomas
à Becket's shrine
c/o Geoffrey Chaucer
☐

_____

16. O., the Sphinx Slayer
Thebes or Colonus
c/o Sophocles
☐

_____

17. Charles and Emma B.
France
c/o Gustave Flaubert
☐

_____

18. Mr. Q.
Cathedral of Notre Dame
c/o Victor Hugo
☐

_____

19. King P.
Troy
c/o Homer
☐

_____

20. Mr. H. S., the Master Builder
Norway
c/o Henrik Ibsen
☐

_____

THEIR OTHER NAMES

Most people know the name Frankenstein. Yet, how many of us know his first name? The columns below list either the given name or the surname of famous literary characters. Be a true literary trivia expert by answering the bell in this name challenge. Write the letter in the blank after the number to complete the name in the first column. Then write the book in which that character appears in the middle column. The first one is done for you.

CHARACTER'S NAME	BOOK	CHARACTER'S OTHER NAME
1. __F__ Mr. Chips	_Goodbye, Mr. Chips_	a. Gulliver
2. _____ Jude	_____	b. Meeber
3. _____ Sister Carrie	_____	c. Mrs. Dalloway
4. _____ George	_____	d. Faustus
5. _____ Madame Bovary	_____	e. Brutus
6. _____ Frankenstein	_____	f. Arthur Chipping
7. _____ Clarissa	_____	g. Yury
8. _____ Antonia	_____	h. Shimerda
9. _____ Lemuel	_____	i. Fawley
10. _____ Jones	_____	j. Connie
11. _____ Jay	_____	k. Gatsby
12. _____ Lady Chatterley	_____	l. Victor
13. _____ John	_____	m. Emma
14. _____ Emma	_____	n. Babbitt
15. _____ Dr. Zhivago	_____	o. Wodehouse

CHARACTERS IN LITERATURE WRITTEN BEFORE THE YEAR 1600

Here is a test of your literary knowledge of characters in works that were written prior to the year 1600. Some of these are oldies but goodies! Write the literary work on the line provided. Since Shakespeare has his own section in this resource, his works will be included there.

1. _____ Inanna, Enkidu, Utnapishtim, Humbaba, Tammuz, Urshanabi

2. _____ Agamemnon, Paris, Helen, Athene, Hector, Ajax, Achilles

3. _____ Odysseus, Lotus-Eaters, Cyclops, Scylla and Charybdis, Circe

4. _____ Creon, Jocasta, Tiresias, Antigone

5. _____ Antigone, Ismene, Creon, Eurydice, Haemon, Tiresias

6. _____ Clytaemestra, Herald, Cassandra, Aegisthus, Chorus of Argive Elders

7. _____ Dionysius, Agave, Cadmus, Tiresius, Pentheus

8. _____ Dido, Anchises, Ascanius, Latinus, Turnus

9. _____ Grendel, Geats, Hygelac, Hrothgar, Unferth

10. _____ Charlemagne, Ogier the Dane, Ganelon, Bertha, Olivier

11. _____ Siegfried, Saxons, Gunther, Kriemhild, Burgundian kings, Brunhild, Hagen

12. _____ Vergil's spirit, Beatrice, God, Minos

13. _____ Harry Bailey, Merchant, Miller, Wife of Bath, Franklin, Pardoner

14. _____ a Florentine church, the year of the Black Death, the three Tedaldo sons, Alessandro, Tancred, the Prince of Salerno

15. _____ Bercilak, Morgan Le Fay, Bercilak's wife, King Arthur's knights

16. _____ Tower of Truth, Dungeon of Wrong, Holy Church, St. Truth, Conscience, Thought Wit, Study

17. _____ Coll, Gib, Daw, Mak, Gill, Angel, Mary

18. _____ King Arthur, Sir Mordred, Queen Guinevere, Sir Tristram, Sir Lancelot, Sir Bedivere

19. _____ Scheherazade, Sinbad the Sailor, Periebanou, Ali Baba, Aladdin

20. _____ Fellowship, Death, Five-Wits, Knowledge, Good Deeds, Confession, Beauty, Strength

21. _____ Angelica, Rinaldo, Ruggiero, Olimpia, Astolfo, Bradamante, Rodomonte

22. _____ Peter Giles, Master Raphael Hythloday, people of Nowhere, Pride, the Anemolians

23. _____ Mathew Merygreeke, Dame Christian Custance

24. _____ Ghost of Don Andrea, Balthazar, Lorenzo, Bel-Imperia, Horatio

25. _____ Wagner, Good Angel and Bad Angel, Lucifer, Mephistophilis, Belzebub, Pope Adrian

26. _____ Red Cross Knight, Una, Duessa, Britomart, Gloriana

Name _____ Date _____ Period _____

COUPLES, THEIR LITERARY TITLES, AND THEIR AUTHORS

    Match the couples below with their literary works and authors. Write the correct answers to Columns B and C in the space provided next to the numbers in Column A. The answers to question number one have been inserted for you. Enjoy!

COLUMN A

Work Author

1. ___h___ - ___pp___ Eliza Doolittle and Freddy Eynsford-Hill

2. _____ Paul Morel and Miriam Lievers

3. _____ Leopold and Molly Bloom

4. _____ Catherine and Heathcliff

5. _____ Carol Kennicott and Dr. Will Kennicott

6. _____ Daisy and Tom Buchanan

7. _____ Mr. and Mrs. George Tesman

8. _____ Mr. and Mrs. Tom Joad

9. _____ Frederic Henry and Catherine Barkley

10. _____ Wang Lung and O-lan

11. _____ Philip Carey and Emily Wilkinson

12. _____ Joe Christmas and Joanna Burden

13. _____ Mr. and Mrs. Jeeter Lester

14. _____ Mr. and Mrs. Clarence Day, Sr.

15. _____ Scarlett O'Hara and Rhett Butler

16. _____ Dr. and Mrs. Gibbs

17. _____ Mr. and Mrs. Maxim de Winter

18. _____ Mr. and Mrs. Ezra Mannon

19. _____ Newland Archer and May Welland

20. _____ Caroline Meeber and G. W. Hurstwood

COUPLES, THEIR LITERARY TITLES, AND THEIR AUTHORS (continued)

Column B	Column C
a. *The Age of Innocence*	aa. Pearl S. Buck
b. *Rebecca*	bb. Erskine Caldwell
c. *Ulysses*	cc. Theodore Dreiser
d. *Main Street*	dd. D. H. Lawrence
e. *A Farewell to Arms*	ee. Henrik Ibsen
f. *Sister Carrie*	ff. F. Scott Fitzgerald
g. *Mourning Becomes Electra*	gg. Margaret Mitchell
h. *Pygmalion*	hh. Sinclair Lewis
i. *The Grapes of Wrath*	ii. Eugene O'Neill
j. *Sons and Lovers*	jj. W. Somerset Maugham
k. *Hedda Gabler*	kk. Emily Brontë
l. *Light in August*	ll. Edith Wharton
m. *Life with Father*	mm. Ernest Hemingway
n. *Of Human Bondage*	nn. William Faulkner
o. *Gone with the Wind*	oo. John Steinbeck
p. *The Good Earth*	pp. George Bernard Shaw
q. *The Great Gatsby*	qq. James Joyce
r. *Wuthering Heights*	rr. Thornton Wilder
s. *Our Town*	ss. Daphne du Maurier
t. *Tobacco Road*	tt. Clarence Day, Jr.

Name _____ Date _____ Period _____

FAMOUS PAIRS AND THEIR LAST NAMES

This exercise is intended to test your knowledge and research abilities. Here are the first names of famous pairs in literature. You are asked to match them with their last names. Good luck!

1. _____ Henry and Edward

2. _____ Lennie and George

3. _____ Romeo and Juliet

4. _____ Scarlett and Rhett

5. _____ Edgar and Catherine

6. _____ Hester and Arthur

7. _____ Ma and Pa

8. _____ Nora and Torvald

9. _____ Anna and Aleksei

10. _____ Don and Sancho

11. _____ Leopold and Molly

12. _____ Finny and Gene

13. _____ Cyrano and Roxanne

14. _____ Stanley and Stella

15. _____ Jane and Edward

A. Montague and Capulet

B. Quixote and Panza

C. Joad

D. (no name given) and Forester

E. Linton and Earnshaw

F. Eyre and Rochester

G. Small and Milton

H. Karenina and Vronski

I. Helmer

J. Kowalski

K. Jekyll and Hyde

L. de Bergerac and Robin

M. Prynne and Dimmesdale

N. Bloom

O. O'Hara and Butler

WOMEN'S NAMES IN TITLES

Each of the following titles contains a female's first name. Identify the author of each work by writing his or her name next to the character's name.

	AUTHOR	**TITLE**
A.	_____	Anna Karenina
B.	_____	Barbara Frietchie
C.	_____	Cass Timberlane
D.	_____	Daisy Miller
E.	_____	Emma
F.	_____	Fanny
G.	_____	Georgina
H.	_____	Hedda Gabler
I.	_____	Iphigenia in Aulis
J.	_____	Jane Eyre
K.	_____	Kristen Lavransdatter
L.	_____	Lorna Doone
M.	_____	Moll Flanders
N.	_____	Nana
O.	_____	Olga Romanoff
P.	_____	Pamela
Q.	_____	The Queen of Spades
R.	_____	Rebecca
S.	_____	Sappho
T.	_____	Tess of the D'Urbervilles
U.	_____	Ursule Minouet
V.	_____	Vanessa
W.	_____	Winnie-the-Pooh
X.	_____	Xingu (Brazilian men and women)
Y.	_____	Yvette
Z.	_____	Zelda

MEN'S NAMES IN LITERARY TITLES

Name the authors of these works containing male names.

1. _____ *Ben Hur*

2. _____ *Don Quixote*

3. _____ *Cyrano de Bergerac*

4. _____ *My Name Is Asher Lev*

5. _____ *Abe Lincoln in Illinois*

6. _____ *Uncle Tom's Cabin*

7. _____ *The Confessions of Nat Turner*

8. _____ "The Secret Life of Walter Mitty"

9. _____ *The Adventures of Huckleberry Finn*

10. _____ *Deadeye Dick*

11. _____ *Ethan Frome*

12. _____ *The Bridge of San Luis Rey*

13. _____ *Peter Pan*

14. _____ *The Life of Samuel Johnson*

15. _____ *The Adventures of Tom Sawyer*

16. _____ *Childe Harold's Pilgrimage*

17. _____ *Don Juan*

18. _____ *Lord Jim*

19. _____ *Oliver Twist*

20. _____ *A Connecticut Yankee in King Arthur's Court*

21. _____ *David Copperfield*

22. _____ *Silas Marner*

23. _____ *Tom Jones*

24. _____ *Bartholomew Fair*

25. _____ *Tom Brown's School Days*

MEN'S NAMES IN LITERARY TITLES (continued)

26. _____ *Pincher Martin*

27. _____ *Joseph Andrews*

28. _____ *Jude the Obscure*

29. _____ *Tattered Tom Series*

30. _____ *Harvey*

31. _____ *Marty*

32. _____ *Hans Brinker*

33. _____ *Citizen Tom Paine*

34. _____ *The Autobiography of Malcolm X*

35. _____ *The Rise of Silas Lapham*

36. _____ *Elmer Gantry*

37. _____ *Glengarry Glen Ross*

38. _____ *Moby Dick*

39. _____ *Billy Budd*

40. _____ *Pal Joey*

41. _____ *Adam Bede*

42. _____ *Master Harold and the Boys*

LADIES OF LITERATURE

The author and part of the literary work's title containing a woman's name are given below. How many of these ladies can you identify?

1. _____ *of a Thousand Days* by Maxwell Anderson

2. _____ *Allen* by Gwendolyn Brooks

3. *My* _____ by Willa Cather

4. _____: *A Girl of the Streets* by Stephen Crane

5. *Sister* _____ by Theodore Dreiser

6. _____'s *Baby* by Ira Levin

7. _____ by Vladimir Nabokov

8. _____ *Christie* by Eugene O'Neill

9. _____'s *Choice* by William Styron

10. _____ *Adams* by Booth Tarkington

11. _____ by Jane Austen

12. _____ *Eyre* by Charlotte Brontë

13. _____'s *Adventures in Wonderland* by Lewis Carroll

14. _____ by Daphne Du Maurier

15. *Major* _____ by George Bernard Shaw

16. *Miss* _____ by August Strindberg

17. _____ *of the D'Urbervilles* by Thomas Hardy

18. *Saint* _____ by George Bernard Shaw

19. *The Prime of Miss* _____ *Brodie* by Muriel Spark

20. _____ *Karenina* by Leo Tolstoy

SECTION 3

TIMING
IS EVERYTHING

Name _____ Date _____ Period _____

THE START OF CIVILIZATION . . . 3500 B.C.–1 B.C.

Sixteen people who shaped this period have gathered to tell about their accomplishments. From the names below match the historical figures with their actions.

Aeschylus	Caesar	Homer	Socrates
Aesop	Cleopatra	Moses	Sophocles
Alexander the Great	Hammurabi	Pericles	Tutankhamen
Aristophanes	Hippocrates	Pindar	Vergil

1. _____ "I was the Ionian poet who wrote the *Iliad* and the *Odyssey.*"

2. _____ "I was put to death in 399 B.C. for teaching heresies to the Greek youths."

3. _____ "I was the Greek fablist who lived from 620 to 560 B.C."

4. _____ "My body was embalmed after my death at the age of nineteen in 1352 B.C. My tomb was explored in 1922. This gave modern man a great look at Egyptian life of my time."

5. _____ "My Babylonian code of laws guaranteed justice for all, especially the impoverished."

6. _____ "I was murdered by conspirators in 44 B.C."

7. _____ "I was the Greek physician considered the Father of Medicine. I died in 377 B.C."

8. _____ "I was the Greek statesman who was so popular and powerful in about 460 B.C. that an age of time was named in my honor."

9. _____ "I was the Egyptian queen who married Mark Antony."

10. _____ "My comedic genius was evident in my plays, such as *The Birds, Lysistrata,* and *The Frogs* written in the late fifth century B.C."

11. _____ "Considered the first great Greek tragedian, I wrote ninety plays, but only seven survived. *The Persians, Prometheus Bound,* and *The Eumenides* were composed in the fifth century B.C."

12. _____ "I, the Thebean poet, wrote popular odes to honor the victors in the Olympic Games. I died in 438 B.C."

13. _____ "I led the Israelites out of Egypt."

14. _____ "As a Greek tragedian who wrote in the middle of the fifth century B.C., I added a third actor and painted scenery to the tragedies. I also wrote what is considered the classic Greek tragedy, *Oedipus Rex.*"

15. _____ "Born in 356 B.C., I conquered the civilized world. I died at the age of thirty-three."

16. _____ "Along with Ovid and Horace, I was a Latin poet who lived in the first century B.C."

THE MISSING LINK . . . 1 A.D.–999

Chris the Cub Reporter of the newspaper, *Classic Chronicles,* has a problem. While rummaging through his newspaper's files, he has found accounts of historical events that occurred between the years 1 and 999. The problem is that since the newspapers are so old, ripped, and yellowed, there are no dates to go along with the events of so long ago. Help Chris by correctly writing the correct date next to its event.

5	c. 300	700
68	360	760
79	391	800
175	425	891
285	625	984

1. _____ Vesuvius erupts and destroys Pompeii.

2. _____ Jutes, Angles, and Saxons invade Britain.

3. _____ The Anglo-Saxon ballad, *Beowulf,* is written down.

4. _____ Eric the Red founds colonies in Greenland.

5. _____ Charlemagne is crowned as Roman emperor of the West.

6. _____ Ovid's *Metamorphosis* is written.

7. _____ Early religious plays are performed.

8. _____ King Alfred starts the *Anglo-Saxon Chronicle.*

9. _____ The Christians are persecuted in Rome.

10. _____ Nero commits suicide.

11. _____ The Huns invade Europe.

12. _____ Rome is partitioned into western and eastern empires.

13. _____ Mohammed begins to dictate the *Koran.*

14. _____ Christianity becomes Rome's state religion.

15. _____ The Irish *Book of Kells* is written.

Name _____ Date _____ Period _____

THE HEADLINES OF THE TIME . . . 1000–1400

Knowing that you have a nose for the news and a good memory, you can probably fill in the missing information from headlines that recount the events of the eleventh, twelfth, and thirteenth centuries. Write your answers in the spaces within the headlines.

1. Eric the Red's son, ____, explores North America in the beginning of the eleventh century.

2. _____ murders Duncan and becomes Scotland's king in 1040.

3. William's Normans defeat Harold's Saxons in the 1066 Battle of _____.

4. The _____ Book, England's tax assessment book, is completed in 1086.

5. The First _____ to wrest control of the Holy Land from the Muslims begins in 1096.

6. The French epic entitled _____ is written in 1100.

7. The Persian poet, _____, who wrote the *Rubáiyát,* dies in 1123.

8. Thomas à Becket is murdered in _____ Cathedral by four Norman knights in 1170.

9. Richard the _____, England's king, is killed in 1199.

10. The _____, the German epic poem, is completed around 1204.

11. _____ is the Mongol leader in 1206.

12. The _____, which proclaims the citizens' rights, is signed by King John.

13. _____ writes the "La Vita Nuova."

14. Seer predicts that the Hundred Years War, which begins in 1337, will end in the year ____.

15. A plague called the _____ invades Europe in 1347.

16. Petrarch, the poet who wrote sonnets to a woman named _____, dies in 1374.

17. *The Canterbury Tales'* author, _____, dies in the year 1400.

18. In 1348 Boccaccio writes his most famous work, _____.

FRAUDULENT FRED'S FACT OR FICTION? . . . 1400–1599

Over the years Fred has truly earned the name Fraudulent Fred since so much of what he says is not true. Yet there are those moments when he does speak the truth.

Below are twenty-five statements Fred has made concerning the fifteenth and sixteenth centuries. Some are factual; others are fictional. The dates in each statement are correct. If there is an error in Fred's statement, it has nothing to do with the date. In the blank next to each question, write the word **fact** or **fiction** to indicate the truth behind Fred's statement. Cross out the incorrect information and insert the correct information when appropriate. An example of an incorrect statement is done for you.

Since the period of tremendous exploration took place during this time, each correct answer counts as one country. The answer must be **entirely** correct in order to gain a country. See how many countries you can accumulate. Good luck.

                                          French
Example: _____Fiction_____ Joan of Arc, the ~~German~~ heroine, was burned at the stake.

1. _____ In 1450 Glass, famous for his invention of the printing press, printed the "Constance Mass Book."

2. _____ The Hundred Years War between England and Italy began in 1337 and ended in 1453.

3. _____ In 1467 a ballad about the Swiss national hero, William Tell, appeared.

4. _____ In 1492 Galileo drew a flying machine.

5. _____ On Christmas Day 1492, Magellan's ship, the *Santa Maria,* was wrecked near Haiti.

6. _____ Leonardo da Vinci painted *The Last Supper* in 1495.

7. _____ Raphael's *Mona Lisa* was painted in 1503.

8. _____ Michelangelo painted the Sistine Chapel located in Canterbury Cathedral.

9. _____ Henry VIII married Catherine of Aragon, his brother's widow, in 1509.

10. _____ In 1517 Martin Luther posted his forty-five theses.

11. _____ Magellan returned successfully after his circumnavigation of the earth in 1521.

12. _____ In 1533 Henry VIII married Alice Boleyn.

13. _____ In 1542 Mary, Queen of Scots, ascended the throne after her father, James V, died.

14. _____ French astrologer Nostradamus made predictions during the first part of the sixteenth century.

© 1994 by The Center for Applied Research in Education

15. _____ England and Rome began reconciliation after Mary I became Queen of England.

16. _____ When Mary, Queen of England, died in 1558, Elizabeth I became queen.

17. _____ William Shakespeare was born in Stratford-upon-Thames, England, in 1564.

18. _____ In 1568 Mary, Queen of Scots, was driven into exile and imprisoned by Henry VIII of England.

19. _____ Sir Francis Drake reached the Arctic Ocean in 1573.

20. _____ Richard Burton opened London's *The Theatre* in London in 1576.

21. _____ In 1588 the Spanish Armor was defeated by the English fleet.

22. _____ Edmund Spenser wrote the first three books of *The Faerie Queene* in 1590.

23. _____ London theaters closed in 1593 for about a year due to poor attendance.

24. _____ Christopher Marlowe, author of *Doctor Faustus* and a Shakespeare contemporary, died naturally in 1593.

25. _____ The Thames River Playhouse, the home of Shakespeare's performances, was built in 1599.

VOICES FROM LONG AGO . . . THE 1600s

The seventeenth century included much warfare, artistic endeavors, and important writings. This exercise features voices from those people who made the century what it was.

Identify the speaker from the list below and earn one of the priceless paintings of the artistic masters of the 1600s. Each point is worth one painting. Write the correct answer in the space next to the question and you're on your way to accumulating much artistic wealth. Good luck.

Francis Bacon
Giovanni Bernini
Miguel de Cervantes
Charles II
Oliver Cromwell
René Descartes
John Dryden
El Greco

William Harvey
James I of Scotland
Ben Jonson
Jean de La Fontaine
John Milton
Molière
Sir Isaac Newton

Peter the Great
Puritans
Sir Walter Raleigh
Harmensz van Rijn Rembrandt
Sir Anthony Van Dyck
Lope de Vega
Sir Christopher Wren

1. _____ "I succeeded Queen Elizabeth I of England."

2. _____ "A Spaniard, I wrote more than 400 plays."

3. _____ "I wrote *Don Quixote.*"

4. _____ "My father died before I was born. I killed a man in a duel. My son died when he was seven. Despite these tragic events, I persisted and wrote *Every Man in His Humour, Every Man out of His Humour,* and *Volpone.* In 1617 I was appointed poet laureate by James I."

5. _____ "I was the Cretan-Spanish painter who died in 1614. My real name was Domenikos Theotokopoulos. I painted the *Assumption* and *View of Toledo.*"

6. _____ "Known for my poem, 'The Nymph's Reply to the Shepherd,' I was tried and executed in 1618 because I had attacked a Spanish settlement."

7. _____ "I was the English statesman and philosopher who published *Novum Organum* and *The Advancement of Learning.*"

8. _____ "I was the Flemish painter who painted *The Betrayal of Christ, Elevation of the Cross,* and *Crucifixion.*"

9. _____ "In 1619 I announced my discovery of the circulation of blood."

10. _____ "I was a famous Dutch painter who painted *Night Watch* and *A Lady and Gentleman in Black.* I died in 1669."

11. _____ "A philosopher and mathematician who devised analytical geometry, I made famous the axiom, 'I think; therefore, I exist.'"

12. _____ "A great epic poet who lost his eyesight, I wrote *Paradise Lost, Paradise Regained, Lycidas,* and *Comus.* My death was in 1674."

VOICES FROM LONG AGO . . . THE 1600s (continued)

13. _____ "We are the group that closed the English theaters in 1660."

14. _____ "I designed much of Rome including the pope's palace and the square in front of St. Peter's. My *David* (1623) is quite famous."

15. _____ "I led the Puritans during the English Civil War and was also Lord Protector from 1653 to 1658."

16. _____ "Known better by my pen name than my real name (Jean Baptiste Poquelin), I was one of the greatest French dramatists. My plays include *The School for Wives, The Misanthrope, The Ridiculous Misses,* and *Tartuffe.*"

17. _____ "The 'Merrie Monarch,' I was crowned King of England in 1660 after my exile and later escape to France."

18. _____ "An architect known for rebuilding St. Paul's Cathedral in particular, I was in charge of rebuilding much of London after the Great Fire of 1666. I was knighted in 1673."

19. _____ "An English poet, playwright, and critic, I published the satirical *Absalom and Achitophel, All for Love,* and *Essay of Dramatic Poesie.*"

20. _____ "In 1689 I became the Czar of Russia."

21. _____ "Born in 1642, I made many scientific discoveries between 1665 and 1667. I taught at Cambridge for more than thirty years. My laws of physics are well known."

22. _____ "I was a French poet famous for my *Fables* in verse. My animal characters behave like human beings."

THE CONFUSED TOWN CRIER . . . THE 1700s

Poor Carrie, the Town Crier. She was the official disseminator of information that occurred in the eighteenth century. Carrie meant well, but somehow she always mixed up the information.

Help Carrie redeem herself by correcting the misinformation found in each of her statements below. On the line adjacent to the statement, write the information necessary to make the statement true. Any dates found in the following statements are correct. The other information is the wrong information. Score one point for each correctly amended statement. Good luck!

1. _____ Englishman Samuel Pepys was best known for writing melodrama.

2. _____ *The Spectator* was a series of essays published solely by Richard Steele.

3. _____ David Garrick was a popular English playwright of this time.

4. _____ In 1718 Voltaire, a French writer, was imprisoned in Newgate Prison in Paris.

5. _____ Daniel Defoe wrote both *Robinson Crusoe* and *Emma*.

6. _____ Catherine succeeded her husband, Frederick, as czar of Russia.

7. _____ Jonathan Burns wrote *Gulliver's Travels* in 1726.

8. _____ Roger Williams founded Savannah, Georgia.

9. _____ In 1732 Benjamin Franklin wrote the initial issue of *Poor Richard's Allegory*.

10. _____ Handel, Bach, Haydn, Beethoven, and Stravinsky were influential composers of this century.

11. _____ William Howard painted *The Rake's Progress* in 1735.

12. _____ John Peter Zenger won a "freedom of religion" trial in 1735.

13. _____ In 1738 a papal bull was released and never captured.

14. _____ Thomas Green wrote his famous poem, "Elegy Written in a Country Churchyard" in 1750.

15. _____ Thomas Bowdler, the editor, made his fame by writing lengthy essays against the morals of the thespians of his day.

16. _____ Kant, Montesquieu, Edwards, and Rousseau were playwrights of this time.

17. _____ The American Revolution and Jane Austen's death both occurred in 1775.

18. _____ In 1789 William Wordsworth wrote his "Songs of Experience."

19. _____ Marie Antoinette choked and died in 1793.

20. _____ Napolean married Geraldine de Beauharnais in 1796.

21. _____ Though Goethe wrote "Kubla Khan" in 1797, it was not published until 1816.

22. _____ In the last year of the eighteenth century, George Washington, known as the Father of Our Country, was born.

THE SPORTING LIFE . . . THE 1800s

The 1800s ushered in baseball, America's favorite pastime. In 1846 the New York Knicker-bockers played the New York Nine in an organized baseball game. Thirteen years later Amherst played Williams College in the first college baseball game.

The powerful lineup of nineteenth-century writers below should be fair game for you to score many runs in this doubleheader of an exercise. For each author correctly matched with his or her work, score one run. Here's your bat. Take a good swing . . .

GAME 1

AUTHOR	WRITING
1. _____ Washington Irving	a. "The Masque of the Red Death" (1841)
2. _____ Jane Austen	b. "Ode to a Nightingale" (1820)
3. _____ Lord Byron	c. "Morte d'Arthur" (1843)
4. _____ John Keats	d. *Wuthering Heights* (1847)
5. _____ Alexandr Pushkin	e. *The Three Musketeers* (1828)
6. _____ James Fenimore Cooper	f. *The Scarlet Letter* (1850)
7. _____ Alexander Dumas	g. *Sense and Sensibility* (1811)
8. _____ Charles Dickens	h. Moby Dick (1851)
9. _____ Edgar Allan Poe	i. *Leaves of Grass* (1855)
10. _____ William M. Thackeray	j. Adam Bede (1859)
11. _____ Alfred Tennyson	k. "Rip Van Winkle" (1809)
12. _____ Emily Brontë	l. *Madame Bovary* (1856)
13. _____ Charlotte Brontë	m. *Sonnets from the Portuguese* (1850)
14. _____ Elizabeth B. Browning	n. *Don Juan* (1818–1823)
15. _____ Herman Melville	o. *Barry Lyndon* (1844)
16. _____ Nathaniel Hawthorne	p. *The Last of the Mohicans* (1826)
17. _____ Henry David Thoreau	q. *Walden, or Life in the Woods* (1854)
18. _____ Walt Whitman	r. *Boris Gudunov* (1825)
19. _____ Gustave Flaubert	s. *Jane Eyre* (1847)
20. _____ George Eliot	t. *Oliver Twist* (1838)

Bonus Run Opportunity: Who wrote about 1775 poems but had few published during her life-time? When her sister Lavinia found the many others, she decided to find a publisher for them.

GAME 2

AUTHOR	WRITING
1. _____ Victor Hugo	a. *Treasure Island* (1882)
2. _____ Edward Everett Hale	b. *Little Women* (1868)
3. _____ Leo Tolstoy	c. *A Doll's House* (1879)
4. _____ Lewis Carroll	d. *The Brothers Karamazov* (1880)
5. _____ Louisa May Alcott	e. *Les Misérables* (1862)
6. _____ Wilkie Collins	f. *The Turn of the Screw* (1898)
7. _____ Jules Verne	g. *Twenty Thousand Leagues Under the Sea* (1870)
8. _____ Samuel Butler	h. *Ben Hur* (1880)
9. _____ Mark Twain	i. *The Time Machine* (1895)
10. _____ Henrik Ibsen	j. *Alice's Adventures in Wonderland* (1865)
11. _____ Fyodor Dostoyevsky	k. *The Adventures of Sherlock Holmes* (1891)
12. _____ Lew Wallace	l. *War and Peace* (1864)
13. _____ Emile Zola	m. *The Adventures of Tom Sawyer* (1875)
14. _____ R. L. Stevenson	n. *The Moonstone* (1868)
15. _____ Oscar Wilde	o. *Nana* (1880)
16. _____ Sir Arthur Conan Doyle	p. *Captains Courageous* (1897)
17. _____ H. G. Wells	q. *The Picture of Dorian Gray* (1890)
18. _____ Anton Chekhov	r. *The Man Without a Country* (1863)
19. _____ Rudyard Kipling	s. *The Sea Gull* (1896)
20. _____ Henry James	t. *Erewhon* (1872)

Bonus Run Opportunity: Born in 1865, this Irish poet won the Nobel Prize in 1923. *The Wild Swans at Coole* is one of his famous works.

_____

THE CENTURY OF COMMUNICATIONS . . . THE 1900s

The communications improvements of the 1900s have made the world a smaller place. Lands once thought to be distant can be reached within minutes. The telephone, television, satellites, and the fax machine are just a few of the ways people can communicate more effectively with one another.

For each question below, identify the famous twentieth-century figures, mostly writers, who are sending these messages. The year the message was sent follows the message itself. Write the answer in the space next to the question. Give yourself one free week of telephone use for each correct answer. You could save yourself some cash in the process. Good luck!

1. _____ "I have *Sister Carrie* ready for publication." (1900)

2. _____ "My *Uncle Vanya* is bound to fill the seats." (1900)

3. _____ "Study my Superman theory . . . I'm dying." (1900)

4. _____ "You'll be entranced by my publication, *The Interpretation of Dreams.*" (1900)

5. _____ "Do you think my quantum theory has merit?" (1901)

6. _____ "I have a story about a rabbit named Peter I'd like to publish." (1902)

7. _____ "Yes, we're in Kitty Hawk. Believe it or not, we got the thing off the ground." (1903)

8. _____ "It's about a mean captain I call Wolf and a couple who are eventually able to escape from him." (1904)

9. _____ "The New York police closed my play, *Mrs. Warren's Profession,* after one performance." (1905)

10. _____ "This Special Theory of Relativity of mine should shake 'em up a bit." (1905)

11. _____ "As its author, I kind of like *A Room with a View* myself." (1908)

12. _____ "They'll probably remember me as the world's most famous nurse." (1910)

13. _____ "I'll have this New England farmer and this younger woman get injured in a sledding accident. Then his wife will have to take care of both of them." (1911)

14. _____ "My medals and trophies from the Stockholm Olympic Games were taken away because I had played semiprofessional baseball." (1912)

15. _____ "Pierre, my wonderful husband, they are going to give me the Nobel Prize for chemistry. This is my second Nobel Prize in eight years. I'm very fortunate." (1911)

16. _____ "My cars will be produced more efficiently with the new assembly-line techniques." (1913)

17. _____ "My wife and I are going to Sarajevo this June. I can't wait to assume the Austrian throne." (1914)

18. _____ "That's right. It will be a bunch of dead people talking from their graves in Spoon River." (1915)

19. _____ "I punched Jess Willard silly and now I'm World Champ." (1919)

20. _____ "Two this year . . . *The Emperor Jones* and *Beyond the Horizon.* My father, the actor, would be pleased." (1920)

21. _____ "They burned five hundred copies in America and published it in Paris. Who can figure it out? Perhaps Molly Bloom herself." (1922)

22. _____ "I write many of my poems about New England. Have you read *North of Boston* yet?" (1923)

23. _____ "I did say, 'I never met a man I didn't like.'" (1924)

24. _____ "The setting is this rich place I'll call either West or East Egg. I'm not sure just yet. Nick Carroway will be my narrator. That's a certainty." (1924)

25. _____ "They're giving me the Pulitzer Prize since they like my 'wholesome' American midwestern novels, but I don't think I'll accept it. My novels aren't 'wholesome.'" (1925)

26. _____ "The creature's name is Winnie. I think the kids will love the book." (1926)

27. _____ "I hit number sixty today. Way out there. Let's go celebrate with the other players." (1927)

28. _____ "They think my novel about Connie Chatterley is a bit too foul. Do you agree?" (1928)

29. _____ "Hey, don't blame the Depression on me. And don't go naming those settlements after me . . . I'm only the President." (1929)

30. _____ "I told my Parliament about that darned German air attack. No "V" for victory sign yet." (1934)

31. _____ "Four gold medals . . . right in Berlin. Hitler was beside himself." (1936)

32. _____ "George is the friend of the big, slow-witted guy named Lenny. I think it'll sell." (1937)

33. _____ "When we did *War of the Worlds,* I thought it would be interesting. It was!" (1938)

34. _____ "Fifty-six games with a hit in a row. Baseball has been good to me." (1941)

35. _____ "I'm going up to my retreat. I'll probably kill myself. There is little more to do in this war." (1945)

36. _____ "Blanche and Stanley and Stella . . . You'll never forget them." (1947)

37. _____ "Did I need college to beat Thomas Dewey? I just 'gave 'em hell.' " (1948)

38. _____ "I named him Holden. He's a loner. The book will catch on with the kids." (1951)

39. _____ "The Pulitzer Prize is mine. Santiago went almost three months without a fish, but I caught the biggest prize with this Pulitzer." (1952)

40. _____ "Maybe if I get to be President of the United States, my *Profiles in Courage* will be famous." (1956)

41. _____ "Atticus Finch is an Alabama lawyer whose client will be accused of a heinous crime." (1959)

42. _____ "A history professor who is married to the college president's daughter. Another couple spends the evening with this George and Martha and then . . ." (1962)

43. _____ "I hope somebody will be able to spell Yoknapatawpha when I'm gone." (1962)

44. _____ "I have a dream. Join hands, brothers, and help brotherhood overcome racism and bigotry." (1963)

45. _____ "I am pretty. I float like a butterfly and sting like a bee." (1965)

46. _____ "Felix Unger and Oscar Madison live in a New York City apartment. One is a clean freak and the other is a slob." (1965)

47. _____ "We'll entitle it *All the President's Men*. This book will make history." (1973)

48. _____ "I worked twelve years just researching *Roots.*" (1977)

49. _____ *"Beloved, Song of Solomon,* and *Sula* were my novels." (1988)

50. _____ "When do you plan on reading my book, *The Firm?*" (1993)

ENGLISH LITERATURE TIME PERIODS
(PART ONE)

Match the person or literary event with the correct English literature time period. Write your answer next to the question's number.

A. The Middle Ages   (to 1485)
B. The Sixteenth Century   1485–1603
C. The Seventeenth Century   1603–1660
D. The Restoration and the Eighteenth Century   1660–1798
E. The Romantic Age   1798–1832
F. The Victorian Age   1832–1901
G. The Twentieth Century   1890–present

Note: The following literature time periods are based on the time periods designated by the editors of *The Norton Anthology of English Literature*. [1]

1. _____ Oscar Wilde's *The Picture of Dorian Gray* is published.

2. _____ John Dryden

3. _____ *Childe Harold's Pilgrimage*

4. _____ Alexander Pope's *An Essay on Criticism*

5. _____ "The Charge of the Light Brigade," a poem recounting the Crimean War exploits of the six hundred who rode into the valley of Death, is written by Alfred Lord Tennyson.

6. _____ The life story of Dr. Samuel Johnson is written by diarist James Boswell.

7. _____ Robert Browning's "My Last Duchess"

8. _____ "Ode on a Grecian Urn," "Ode on Melancholy," and "Ode to Psyche"

9. _____ Addison, Steele, *The Tatler,* and *The Spectator*

10. _____ *The Canterbury Tales*

11. _____ Sir Thomas More writes *Utopia*.

12. _____ "Dover Beach"

13. _____ *Murder in the Cathedral*

14. _____ John Donne tells his readers to "Go and catch a falling star."

15. _____ *The Pilgrim's Progress*

16. _____ George Bernard Shaw's *Pygmalion*

[1]*Norton Anthology of English Literature Revised,* M. H. Abrams, General Editor, Vols. 1 & 2, 1968, W. W. Norton & Co., Inc., New York, N.Y.

17. _____ Rudyard Kipling, A. E. Housman, and Wilfred Owen

18. _____ *Sir Gawain and the Green Knight*

19. _____ Sir Walter Raleigh's "The Nymph's Reply to the Shepherd"

20. _____ Sir Thomas Malory's *Le Morte d'Arthur*

21. _____ Graham Greene's novel, *A Burnt-Out Case,* is written.

22. _____ *A Portrait of the Artist as a Young Man*

23. _____ "Musée des Beaux Arts"

24. _____ "Lycidas," "Il Penseroso," and *Paradise Lost*

25. _____ John Henry Cardinal Newman writes *Apologia pro vita sua,* the story of his religious development and conversion to Catholicism.

Alfred, Lord Tennyson

ENGLISH LITERATURE TIME PERIODS
PART TWO

Match the person or literary event with the correct English literature time period. Write your answer next to the question's number.

A. The Middle Ages   (to 1485)   E. The Romantic Age   1798–1832
B. The Sixteenth Century   1485–1603   F. The Victorian Age   1832–1901
C. The Seventeenth Century 1603–1660   G. The Twentieth Century   1890–present
D. The Restoration and the
   Eighteenth Century   1660–1798

Note: The following literature time periods are based on the time periods designated by the editors of *The Norton Anthology of English Literature.*

1. _____ Edward Fitzgerald translates the *Rubáiyát of Omar Khayyám.*

2. _____ Francis Bacon's *The Advancement of Learning*

3. _____ Robert Herrick, Ben Jonson, Richard Crawshaw, and George Herbert

4. _____ "Jabberwocky"

5. _____ Samuel Coleridge and Percy Bysshe Shelley

6. _____ Edmund Spenser's *The Faerie Queene*

7. _____ *Piers Plowman* or *The Vision of William Concerning Piers Plowman*

8. _____ "Barbara Allan," "Lord Randall," and "Sir Patrick Spens"

9. _____ "The Tiger" and "The Lamb"

10. _____ Christopher Marlowe

11. _____ Dante Gabriel Rossetti and Christina Rossetti

12. _____ Joseph Conrad's *Heart of Darkness*

13. _____ A. E. Housman's "To an Athlete Dying Young"

14. _____ The Jacobean Era

15. _____ Jonathan Swift's *Gulliver's Travels*

16. _____ *The Way of the World*

17. _____ *The Jungle Book*

18. _____ *The Origin of Species*

19. _____ *Peter Pan*

20. _____ Charles Dickens

21. _____ Shakespeare's Sonnets

22. _____ *Waiting for Godot*

23. _____ *Idylls of the King*

24. _____ *Vanity Fair*

25. _____ The Venerable Bede

Charlotte Brontë

ENGLISH LITERATURE TIME PERIODS
PART THREE

Match the person or literary event with the correct English literature time period. Write your answer next to the question's number.

A. The Middle Ages   (to 1485)   E. The Romantic Age   1798–1832
B. The Sixteenth Century   1485–1603   F. The Victorian Age   1832–1901
C. The Seventeenth Century   1603–1660   G. The Twentieth Century 1890–present
D. The Restoration and the
   Eighteenth Century   1660–1798

Note: The following literature periods are based on the time periods designated by the editors of *The Norton Anthology of English Literature.*

1. _____ *Lyrical Ballads*

2. _____ *Brideshead Revisited*

3. _____ *Jane Eyre*

4. _____ *Beowulf*

5. _____ *Domesday Book*

6. _____ *Macbeth*

7. _____ Lady Godiva

8. _____ *Adam Bede*

9. _____ *Bleak House*

10. _____ *A Passage to India*

11. _____ Synge's *The Playboy of the Western World*

12. _____ *Portrait of the Artist as a Young Dog*

13. _____ Jane Austen's *Mansfield Park*

14. _____ *Joseph Andrews* is released.

15. _____ *The School for Scandal* and *She Stoops to Conquer*

16. _____ *Hero and Leander*

17. _____ *Women in Love*

18. _____ Samuel Pepys writes his famous *Diary,* which includes an account of the Great Fire of London.

19. _____ *The Time Machine*

20. _____ Horatio Hornblower comes to life.

21. _____ *The Hobbit*

22. _____ "Ode: Intimations of Immortality from Recollections of Early Childhood"

23. _____ *Ivanhoe,* a tale of medieval chivalry, is published.

24. _____ *King Lear* is presented by William Shakespeare.

25. _____ O'Casey's *Juno and the Paycock* is first presented.

ENGLISH LITERATURE TIME PERIODS
PART FOUR

Match the person or literary event with the correct English literature time period. Write your answer next to the question's number.

A. The Middle Ages   (to 1485)   E. The Romantic Age   1798–1832
B. The Sixteenth Century   1485–1603   F. The Victorian Age   1832–1901
C. The Seventeenth Century 1603–1660   G. The Twentieth Century 1890–present
D. The Restoration and the
    Eighteenth Century   1660–1798

Note: The following time periods are based on the time periods designated by the editors of *The Norton Anthology of English Literature.*

1. _____ Stevenson recounts the adventures of David Balfour in *Kidnapped.*

2. _____ The ban on *Lady Chatterley's Lover* is lifted in the United States.

3. _____ Thomas Hobbes publishes *Leviathan,* a political treatise.

4. _____ Alan Sillitoe's short story about a reform school runner, "The Loneliness of the Long Distance Runner," is released.

5. _____ The Metaphysical Poets

6. _____ Jonathan Swift's essay, *A Modest Proposal,* offers a solution to Ireland's poverty. Children of Ireland's poor should be cooked and served as dinner for the wealthy class.

7. _____ Shakespeare's *Much Ado About Nothing* is first performed.

8. _____ The prophetic *Nineteen Eighty-Four* is published.

9. _____ Maugham's fine work, *Of Human Bondage,* is first enjoyed by its readers.

10. _____ John Stuart Mill's essay, *On Liberty,* addresses the ills of modern democracies.

11. _____ Robert Browning enchants his readers with the narrative poem "The Pied Piper of Hamelin."

12. _____ The first poet laureateship is bestowed.

13. _____ Thomas Hardy writes his sixth novel, *The Return of the Native.*

14. _____ Robinson Crusoe and his Man Friday come to life.

15. _____ The story of a lonely weaver, Silas Marner, is told by George Eliot.

16. _____ "Through the Tunnel," a short story written by Doris Lessing, is published.

17. _____ Stratford-upon-Avon's most famous native son is born.

ENGLISH LITERATURE TIME PERIODS (PART FOUR) (continued)

18. _____ The story of Charles Darney, Lucy Manette, and Sydney Carton is brought to the public.

19. _____ Alexandre Dumas père completes *The Three Musketeers.*

20. _____ The novel whose full title is *The History of Tom Jones, a Foundling* portrays London and country life of this era.

21. _____ *Under Milk Wood,* a radio play written by Dylan Thomas, is heard by the people of Wales.

22. _____ While laissez-faire, economics, and utilitarianism became popular during this age, this time period's literature featured leisurely, middle-class novels written by authors such as Thackeray, Eliot, and Hardy.

23. _____ The children's classic, *The Wind in the Willows,* is written by Kenneth Grahame.

24. _____ *Ralph Roister Doister*

25. _____ Yeats writes his poem, "Sailing to Byzantium."

Name _____ Date _____ Period _____

AMERICAN LITERATURE
TIME PERIODS . . . COLONIALUTIONARY PERIOD

You will not find the word "Colonialutionary" in your dictionary. It is a made-up blend of two words, Colonial and Revolutionary, that will help you to remember the two American literature periods that preceded the year 1800. Thus, the time periods that make up this American literature period are generally referred to as Colonial literature and Revolutionary literature. The years are from the early seventeenth century to the adoption of the United States Constitution in 1787.

Match the influential Colonialutionary authors with their works by writing the correct letter next to the number. Good luck.

AUTHORS	WRITINGS
1. _____ William Bradford	A. *Poor Richard's Almanack* (1732)
2. _____ Anne Bradstreet	B. *The Tenth Muse Lately Sprung Up in America* (1650)
3. _____ Mary Rowlandson	C. *Poems on Various Subjects, Religious and Moral* (1773)
4. _____ Cotton Mather	D. *Freedom of the Will* (1754)
5. _____ Jonathan Edwards	E. *The Federalist* (1777–1778)
6. _____ Benjamin Franklin	F. Declaration of Independence (1776)
7. _____ Thomas Paine	G. *History of Plimouth Plantation* (pub. 1856)
8. _____ Phillis Wheatley	H. *Captivity and Restauration* (1682)
9. _____ Thomas Jefferson	I. *Common Sense* (1776)
10. _____ Hamilton, Jay, and Madison	J. *Ecclesiastical History of New England from its First Planting in the New Year 1620, unto the Year of our Lord 1698* (1702)

AMERICAN LITERATURE
TIME PERIODS . . . THE NINETEENTH CENTURY

THE AUTHORS SPEAK FOR THEMSELVES!

Nineteenth-century American literature included several important literary movements. The first of these movements was nationalism as America sought its cultural independence following the Revolutionary War. This need for nationalism and independence was true as well in the field of literature where American writers began to express the values of their new nation.

Another prominent movement of the nineteenth century was the New England Renaissance. Known also as the American romantic movement, this period also included the Transcendentalists, who believed in the power of intuition transcending pure reason when it came to understanding God, the soul, existence, and more.

Still another movement of nineteenth-century American literature was influenced strongly by the Civil War. With a nation divided and trying to rebuild from the Civil War, regional or "local color" became an important type of American literature. Additionally, Mark Twain was influential in establishing realism or "telling it as it really is." Last, the final decade of the nineteenth century saw a movement toward naturalism, an extreme form of realism. All in all, it was a century filled with different types of writings.

Match the important nineteenth-century writer with his or her description below. Write the author's or group's initials in the space next to the description. Good luck.

Ambrose Bierce	Ralph Waldo Emerson	Herman Melville
William Cullen Bryant	Fireside Poets	Frank Norris
Cambridge Scholars	Bret Harte	Edgar Allan Poe
Kate Chopin	Nathaniel Hawthorne	Harriet Beecher Stowe
James Fenimore Cooper	Oliver Wendell Holmes	Henry David Thoreau
Concord Group	William Dean Howells	Mark Twain
Stephen Crane	Washington Irving	Noah Webster
Emily Dickinson	Henry James	Edith Wharton
Frederick Douglass	Sarah Orne Jewett	Walt Whitman
Theodore Dreiser	Henry Wadsworth Longfellow	James Greenleaf Whittier

1. _____ I am the author recognized as America's first man of letters.

2. _____ I am the poet who was influenced by the English Graveyard Poets and who wrote the poem "Thanatopsis."

3. _____ I wrote *An American Dictionary of the English Language.*

4. _____ I am the essayist known as the "Sage of Concord" and the author of numerous essays and stirring addresses.

5. _____ I'm the creator of Natty Bumpo and the Leatherstocking Tales including *The Deerslayer.*

6. _____ As writers, Emerson, Hawthorne, Thoreau, and Bronson Alcott were members of this group.

7. _____ Longfellow, Whittier, and Holmes were members of this group.

8. _____ I am the author of *Evangeline, Hiawatha,* and *The Courtship of Miles Standish.*

AMERICAN LITERATURE . . . THE NINETEENTH CENTURY (continued)

9. _____ I am the creator of the poems, "Barbara Frietchie" and "The Barefoot Boy."

10. _____ I wrote "Old Ironsides."

11. _____ Longfellow, Holmes, and James Russell Lowell belonged to a group of writers by this name.

12. _____ I am the gloomy romantic and master of gothic horror writer who wrote "A Tell-Tale Heart" and "The Raven."

13. _____ A Transcendentalist, I wrote *Walden, or Life in the Woods*.

14. _____ I dedicated my first edition of *Leaves of Grass* to Ralph Waldo Emerson.

15. _____ Only about seven of my poems were published during my lifetime. My sister found another 1,750-plus after I died.

16. _____ My stories about the Puritans and early American history as seen in my symbolic romance entitled *The Scarlet Letter* are famous.

17. _____ My novels about the sea and adventure were not really appreciated by the readers of my day. "Call me Ishmael" was finally recognized as the first line of a masterful novel well after I died.

18. _____ Though Lincoln said I may have been somewhat responsible for starting the Civil War, my novel featuring Little Eva was a best seller.

19. _____ My realistic depictions of both manners and American speech were unsurpassed in my day. Just ask Tom or Huck.

20. _____ I opposed provincialism in literature. I also wrote about a farmer who loses his wealth after moving to Boston in a famous novel entitled *The Rise of Silas Lapham*.

21. _____ I wrote about expatriate Americans in *Daisy Miller* and also wrote novels having psychological realism, as in *The Portrait of a Lady*.

22. _____ I wrote *The Awakening*.

23. _____ My two most famous novels are *Ethan Frome* and *The Age of Innocence*.

24. _____ Dubbed a regionalist, I wrote two famous short stories, "The Outcasts of Poker Flat" and "The Luck of Roaring Camp."

25. _____ I wrote the short story, "The Occurrence at Owl Creek Bridge," and *The Devil's Dictionary*.

26. _____ A regionalist, I wrote about Maine in the novel, *The Country of the Pointed Firs*.

27. _____ I authored *The Narrative of the Live of an American Slave*.

28. _____ A naturalist, I created both *Maggie: A Girl of the Streets* and the classic *The Red Badge of Courage*.

29. _____ *McTeague* and *The Octopus* exhibited my naturalistic style.

30. _____ Probably the most naturalistic writer of the late 1890s, I wrote *Sister Carrie* and later penned *An American Tragedy* in 1925.

Name _____ **Date** _____ **Period** _____

AMERICAN LITERATURE TIME PERIODS . . . 1900–1950

THE WRIGHT WAR DEPRESSION WAR

Don't be concerned by the unusual title. The four-word title is simply a convenient way to remember the half century from 1900 to 1950. The Wright Brothers in Kitty Hawk, North Carolina, flew their airplane for the first time in 1903. The First World War was fought between 1914 and 1918. The stock market crashed in 1929 and started a world depression. The Second World War was fought from 1939 until 1945.

The American literature of those years reflected those events and others that occurred in the first half of the twentieth century. Complete these sentences by filling in the correct name of the author, title, or literary movement of this time period.

1. The literary movement called _____ is closely aligned with realism in that it depicted life objectively and truthfully. Theodore Dreiser's *An American Tragedy* is an example of such a movement or technique.

2. Another writer who looked at America realistically and truthfully was Frank Norris. In his

   1901 novel, _____, Norris shows how the railroad tried to strangle the wheat growers in California.

3. The author known for his portrayals of the bitter, brutal north is _____. His books such as *The Call of the Wild, The Sea Wolf,* and *White Fang* are classics. He died at the age of forty.

4. In 1902 a famous American author was born and a famous French author died. The latter,

   Emile Zola, wrote *Nana* and *The Experimental Novel.* The former, _____, went on to write *The Grapes of Wrath* and *Of Mice and Men.*

5. Edith Wharton was famous for her novels of manners in which she examined the behavior of

   people and classes. Her 1920 novel of manners, _____, portrayed the New York wealthy society of the 1870s.

6. The famous short-story writer, William Sydney Porter, known better for his pen name

   _____, wrote stories with ironic endings including "The Ransom of Red Chief," "The Gift of the Magi," and "After Twenty Years."

7. The American poet, critic, and editor _____, friends with Ernest Hemingway and Gertrude Stein, was arrested in 1945 for broadcasting Fascist propaganda. Tried for his broadcasts, he was judged insane and confined in an institution for twelve years.

8. An author associated with the Western pioneers and Nebraska especially is _____. Her novels include *O Pioneers!, A Lost Lady,* and *My Ántonia.*

9. *A Boy's Will* and *North of Boston* are two volumes of verse by poet _____, forever associated with images of rural New England life. His poems "Mending Wall," "Home Burial," and "Stopping by Woods on a Snowy Evening" are memorable.

10. Another poet associated with a region was _____, whose *Chicago Poems* (1916) and *Corn Huskers* solidified his reputation as a poet.

11. A leading novelist who graphically depicted the faults of America through his portrayals of small-town life was _____. His novels *Babbitt, Elmer Gantry, Main Street,* and *Arrowsmith* earned him the 1930 Nobel Prize for Literature. He declined acceptance of the Pulitzer Prize on philosophical grounds.

12. The Ohio-born novelist and short-story writer who left a profitable business career to write *Windy McPherson's Son* and *Winesburg, Ohio* was _____. His writings influenced the likes of Faulkner and Hemingway.

13. The expatriate who was friends with Fitzgerald, Hemingway, Alice B. Toklas, and Picasso was _____. Her writings included *Three Lives, Tender Buttons,* and *The Autobiography of Alice B. Toklas.*

14. Known primarily for his lowercase letters in his poems, _____ also wrote an autobiographical novel, *The Enormous Room,* concerning his imprisonment for treason in a French concentration camp.

15. The recipient of a Pulitzer Prize for her novel *So Big* was _____. She also wrote *Stage Door* and *Cimarron.*

16. The Harvard graduate famous for his writings, *The Manhattan Transfer, U.S.A.,* and *The 42nd Parallel,* was _____. He served in the war with e. e. cummings and Hemingway.

17. In 1925 poet _____, famous for her poems "Patterns" and "Lilacs," died.

18. F. Scott Fitzgerald published his most famous novel in 1925. Set on Long Island, New York, _____ is narrated by Nick Carraway, who lives next door to the titular character.

19. Eugene Gant is the character modeled after author _____ in his novel, *Look Homeward, Angel.* This writer's name is often confused with the author of the novels, *The Right Stuff* and *The Bonfire of the Vanities.*

20. *The Day of the Locust* examines Hollywood and *Miss Lonelyhearts* looks at modern-day loneliness. Both novels were written by _____, who died in 1940. His reputation as a quality writer came at least a decade after his death.

21. If F. Scott Fitzgerald is one of the most prominent American writers of this period, the other is _____. His writings include *The Old Man and the Sea, A Farewell to Arms,* and *The Sun Also Rises.*

22. Awarded the Nobel Prize for Literature in 1949, _____ made the fictitious county of Yoknapatawpha famous. His novels, written in the stream of consciousness, include *The Sound and the Fury* and *As I Lay Dying.*

23. An author who died in 1916, this writer, whose brother William, the philosopher and psychologist, coined the phrase "stream of consciousness," is _____. His writings, which influenced other writers, include *Daisy Miller, The Portrait of a Lady, The Europeans,* and *The Turn of the Screw.*

24. The winner of the 1932 Pulitzer Prize for her novel *The Good Earth* was _____. Her early life in China influenced this novel's writing.

25. The faults and frailties of the fictitious Tyrone family of *Long Day's Journey into Night* were brought to America's attention by the playwright _____. He also wrote *Desire Under the Elms, The Hairy Ape, The Emperor Jones,* and *Mourning Becomes Electra.*

AMERICAN LITERATURE TIME PERIODS . . . 1900–1950 (continued)

26. In 1944 *The Glass Menagerie* written by _____ was produced. Three years later his play *A Streetcar Named Desire* was presented.

27. Known for her portrayals of Southern people and towns, _____ wrote *The Heart Is a Lonely Hunter* and *The Member of the Wedding.*

28. The novel, *The Bridge of San Luis Rey,* won a Pulitzer Prize. So did the play, *Our Town.* So did *The Skin of Our Teeth,* another play. The playwright who created these three award-winning plays was _____.

29. Two schoolteachers are accused of homosexuality by one of their students in the play *The Children's Hour.* Two other dramas written by _____ were *The Little Foxes* and *Watch on the Rhine.*

30. Though he is known for his novel about political life, *All the King's Men,* _____ also won two Pulitzer Prizes for his poetry.

31. A Renaissance man, who in addition to his artistic talent wrote plays, essays, short stories, and humorous pieces was _____. Besides being a frequent contributor to *The New Yorker,* he also created the short story, "The Secret Life of Walter Mitty."

AMERICAN LITERATURE TIME PERIODS . . . 1951–PRESENT

THE FAX OF MODERN AMERICAN LITERATURE

This exercise pays homage to the century of communications. To celebrate the achievements of the American writers of the latter half of the twentieth century and to forever record their great writings, "fax back" the author's name of each literary work below. Score one point for each "fax fact" answered correctly.

Here is the list of possible fax responses.

Edward Albee	Archibald MacLeish	Dr. Seuss
Samuel Beckett	Norman Mailer	Anne Sexton
Saul Bellow	Bernard Malamud	Neil Simon
Truman Capote	James Michener	William Styron
John Cheever	Marianne Moore	John Updike
Ralph Ellison	Toni Morrison	Kurt Vonnegut
Lorraine Hansberry	Dorothy Parker	Alice Walker
Joseph Heller	Sylvia Plath	Richard Wilbur
Langston Hughes	Chaim Potok	William Carlos Williams
MacKinlay Kantor	Ayn Rand	August Wilson
John F. Kennedy	Theodore Roethke	Tom Wolfe
Jack Kerouac	Philip Roth	Richard Wright
Harper Lee	J. D. Salinger	

1. _____ My 1951 novel, *Lie Down in Darkness,* was published before my more famous novels, *The Confessions of Nat Turner* and *Sophie's Choice.*

2. _____ A friend of James Joyce, I was an advocate of the Theatre of the Absurd with plays such as *Waiting for Godot* and *Endgame.* I also won the Nobel Prize for Literature in 1969.

3. _____ Emblematic of the skill that earned me the Pulitzer Prize for *Collected Poems* in 1952, I wrote verses such as "Poetry" and "Silence." I was a big fan of the Brooklyn Dodgers.

4. _____ A graduate of Harvard Law School, I was strongly influenced by Ezra Pound and T. S. Eliot. My 1959 Pulitzer Prize-winning play, *J.B.,* and my Pulitzer Prize-winning poetry, *Collected Poems,* brought me acclaim.

5. _____ My anti-heroes in the Jewish literary tradition are involved in existential turmoils. *The Adventures of Augie March, Seize the Day,* and *Henderson the Rain King* are my novels.

6. _____ My most famous poem is "My Papa's Waltz."

7. _____ I am most widely recognized as the man who wrote *Andersonville,* The Pulitzer Prize winner about the Confederate prison.

8. _____ A future U.S. President, I penned *Profiles in Courage* in 1956.

9. _____ Strongly influenced by the works of the Metaphysical Poets, I also translated works by Molière and Racine. In 1987 I succeeded Robert Penn Warren as U.S. poet laureate.

10. _____ You probably know me better by my pen name instead of my real name, Theodor Geisel. My writings include *Green Eggs and Ham, The Cat in the Hat,* and *How the Grinch Stole Christmas.*

11. _____ Though as a poet and novelist I was closely associated with the Beat Generation, I am most well known for the novel, *On the Road.*

12. _____ A Russian-born exponent of objective philosophy, I wrote *Atlas Shrugged, The Fountainhead,* and *We the Living.*

13. _____ My World War II novel, *The Naked and the Dead,* brought me fame. I also won a Pulitzer Prize for *The Armies of the Night.*

14. _____ My play, *A Raisin in the Sun,* made me (at the age of twenty-nine) the first black playwright and the youngest American to win the Best Play Award from the New York Drama Critics' Circle. Published posthumously was my other famous work, *To Be Young, Gifted and Black.*

15. _____ *Goodbye, Columbus; Portnoy's Complaint;* and *The Anatomy Lesson* were my creations.

16. _____ My only novel, *To Kill a Mockingbird,* won the 1961 Pulitzer Prize and was made into a movie starring Gregory Peck.

17. _____ My novel, *The Catcher in the Rye,* was a big hit. *Franny and Zooey* did okay too.

18. _____ By naming my novel *Catch-22,* I unknowingly was adding a new term to the English language. My antihero, Yossarian, is a blast.

19. _____ I wrote in the Theatre of the Absurd mode with one-act plays such as *The Zoo Story* and *The Sandbox. Tiny Alice, A Delicate Balance,* and *Who's Afraid of Virginia Woolf?* are my other famous plays. My stage adaptation of Carson McCullers' *The Ballad of the Sad Café* was praised.

20. _____ My first novel, *The Natural,* was made into a movie starring Robert Redford. *The Assistant, The Fixer* (Pulitzer Prize winner), and *The Tenants* are my novels that have Jewish characters in them.

21. _____ A pediatrician from New Jersey, I wrote about commonplace (local) subjects and objects such as a red wheelbarrow and plums in everyday (local) language.

22. _____ A colorful character, I wrote the well-known *Breakfast at Tiffany's* and the account of the Kansas Clutter family's murders in *In Cold Blood.*

23. _____ I published my first novel, the popular Pulitzer Prize-winning *Tales of the South Pacific* when I was forty years old. Many of my semidocumentary novels focus on specific places such as Hawaii, Chesapeake, Texas, and Poland.

24. _____ A leader of the Harlem Renaissance, I wrote the famous poems, "Cross" and "Dream Deferred."

25. _____ My novel depicting the struggles of fourteen-year-old Celie, *The Color Purple,* won a Pulitzer Prize.

26. _____ My writings focus on black women and their experiences. Novels such as *Sula, Beloved, The Bluest Eye,* and *Tar Baby* are examples of this. *Song of Solomon* tells of a man's search for his past. I won the 1993 Nobel Prize for literature.

27. _____ I wrote *Bonfire of the Vanities* and *The Right Stuff.*

28. _____ My plays such as *Fences* and *The Piano Lesson* focus on the black experience.

29. _____ My plays are comedies such as *The Odd Couple, Brighton Beach Memoirs,* and *Lost in Yonkers.*

30. _____ My writings, many of which appeared in *The New Yorker,* target the suburban rich. The best seller *The Wapshot Chronicle* was followed by *The Wapshot Scandal.*

31. _____ I'm best known for my *Rabbit* novels.

32. _____ A Confessional Poet, I wrote harsh poems about my father, mental illness, and other dark subjects. My *The Bell Jar* was written under the pseudonym, Victoria Lucas. I took my life when I was only thirty-one years old.

33. _____ I, too, was a Confessional Poet. My writings include *Live or Die* and *To Bedlam and Part Way Back.* Mentally ill, I took my own life when I was forty-six years old.

34. _____ Probably known better for my sarcastic wit and sharp retorts, I was also a short-story writer, a drama critic, and a book reviewer for *The New Yorker.* You could easily spot me amongst the intelligent people gathered at the Algonquin Hotel in New York City.

35. _____ My novels include *The Chosen* and *The Promise.*

36. _____ A prolific writer, I created the novels *Slaughterhouse Five, The Sirens of Titan,* and *Cat's Cradle.*

37. _____ My writings generally portrayed the black man's condition in society. *Native Son* is an example of this portrayal. My autobiography is entitled *Black Boy.*

38. _____ My first novel, *Invisible Man,* won the 1953 National Book Award.

© 1994 by The Center for Applied Research in Education

THROUGH THE YEARS

This is not a test for the weak of heart. Below you will find a group of people who were born in the same decade. Some of the people are writers and some have gained fame in other areas. See if you can correctly match the decade with the group. Write your answer next to the group number. Good luck!

1620–1629	1780–1789	1820–1829	1850–1859	1890–1899
1720–1729	1810–1819	1840–1849	1870–1879	1910–1919

GROUP 1 _____

John Steinbeck—author of *Of Mice and Men*
Erskine Caldwell—author of *Tobacco Road*
Charles Lindbergh—American aviator
Louis Leakey—archaeologist
Marian Anderson—American contralto
Richard Rogers—American composer

GROUP 2 _____

Daniel Webster—American statesman
Martin Van Buren—U.S. President
John C. Calhoun—American statesman
Washington Irving—author of "The Legend of Sleepy Hollow"
Stendhal (Marie Henri Boyle)—French novelist

GROUP 3 _____

Molière (Jean Baptiste Poquelin)—author of *Tartuffe*
Andrew Marvell—English poet
Blaise Pascal—French philosopher and scientist
Jean de la Fontaine—fablist

GROUP 4 _____

Carl Sandburg—American poet
Albert Einstein—physicist
E. M. Forster—author of *A Passage to India*
Will Rogers—American humorist
Joseph Stalin—Russian revolutionist

GROUP 5 _____

Immanuel Kant—German philosopher
Samuel Adams—American political leader
Tobias Smollett—author of *The Expedition of Humphrey Clinker*
Adam Smith—Scottish economist
Catherine the Great—Empress of Russia

GROUP 6 _____

Susan B. Anthony—American reformer
Florence Nightingale—English nurse
Louis Pasteur—chemist and microbiologist
Wilkie Collins—English novelist
Henrik Ibsen—author of *A Doll's House*

GROUP 7 _____

Oscar Wilde—author of *The Picture of Dorian Gray*
John Philip Sousa—American bandmaster
Vincent Van Gogh—Dutch painter
Robert Louis Stevenson—author of *Treasure Island*
Sigmund Freud—Austrian neurologist and psychoanalyst

GROUP 8 _____

William McKinley—twenty-fifth American president
Henry James—author of *Daisy Miller* and *Washington Square*
Gerard Manley Hopkins—English poet
Friedrich Nietzsche—German philosopher
Thomas Alva Edison—American inventor

GROUP 9 _____

Harriet Beecher Stowe—author of *Uncle Tom's Cabin*
Robert Browning—English poet
Karl Marx—German socialist and political theorist
Ivan Turgenev—Russian novelist
George Eliot (Mary Ann Evans)—author of *Silas Marner*
James Russell Lowell—American poet and diplomat
Herman Melville—author of *Moby Dick*

GROUP 10 _____

Charles de Gaulle—French soldier and
    statesman
Dwight Eisenhower—thirty-fourth American
    president
Ho Chi Minh—Vietnamese Communist
    leader
Francisco Franco—Spanish soldier and
    dictator
Tito (Josip Broz)—Yugoslav Communist
    leader
Mao Tse-tung—Chinese Communist leader
Edward VIII of Great Britain—king of Great
    Britain
Nikita Khrushchev—Russian Communist
    leader
Boris Pasternak—author of *Doctor Zhivago*
Edna St. Vincent Millay—American poet
e.e. cummings—American poet
Aldous Huxley—author of *Brave New World*
F. Scott Fitzgerald—author of *The Great
    Gatsby*
William Faulkner—author of *The Sound and
    the Fury*
Thornton Wilder—author of *The Skin of Our
    Teeth*
Bertolt Brecht—German playwright and
    poet
Ernest Hemingway—author of *The Sun Also
    Rises*
Vladimir Nabakov—Russian-American
    novelist

THE EVENTS OF THE YEARS

Below are eleven specific years ranging from 1791 to 1988. On the following pages are the events (literary, world, and other types of happenings) that occurred during those years. Your goal is to correctly match the events with their correct years. The year 1959 is already done for you. Write your answers on both the answer key provided at the end of the exercise and on the space next to each letter below.

1791	1870	1907	1941	1977
1815	1890	1922	1959	1988
1850				

GROUP 1 . . . LITERARY EVENTS

Year   **Events**

_____ A. James Joyce, Sherwood Anderson, and Virginia Woolf die.

_____ B. This famous line appears in the *Hartford Courant:* "Everybody talks about the weather, but nobody does anything about it." (supposedly Twain's quote)

Hedda Gabler by Ibsen appears.

Poems by Emily Dickinson is published on Emily's sister's (Lavinia) insistence.

_____ C. *David Copperfield* (Dickens), *The Scarlet Letter* (Hawthorne), and *Sonnets from the Portuguese* (Elizabeth Barrett Browning) are published.

_____ D. Both T. S. Eliot and Eugene O'Neill would have been one hundred years old this year.

_____ E. *Annie* is awarded year's best musical.

_____ F. Thomas Paine's *The Rights of Man* and James Boswell's *The Life of Samuel Johnson* are published.

_____ G. James Michener's *Hawaii* and William Gibson's *The Miracle Worker* are favorites.

_____ H. Shaw's *Don Juan in Hell,* Synge's *The Playboy of the Western World,* and Conrad's *The Secret Agent* are hits.

_____ I. *Fairy Tales* by the Brothers Grimm and Sir Walter Scott's *The Antiquary* are published.

_____ J. Emerson's *Civilization, The Mystery of Edwin Drood,* written by the recently deceased Charles Dickens, and Jules Verne's *Twenty Thousand Leagues Under the Sea* all appear this year.

_____ K. Eugene O'Neill's *Anna Christie* and *The Hairy Ape*

T.S. Eliot's *The Waste Land*

GROUP 2 . . . POLITICAL AND HISTORICAL EVENTS

_____ AA. Battle of Waterloo, Battle of New Orleans, and Napoleon's "trip" to St. Helena's occur.

_____ BB. Hawaii becomes the fiftieth state.

_____ CC. Battle of Wounded Knee is fought, Cecil Rhodes becomes prime minister of Africa's Cape Colony, and Idaho and Wyoming are admitted as states.

_____ DD. Bill of Rights becomes U.S. law; Louis XVI is returned to Paris.

THE EVENTS OF THE YEARS (continued)

_____ EE. Fifteenth Amendment (forbidding denial of right to vote) is ratified.

_____ FF. Margaret Thatcher makes her last official visit to President Ronald Reagan in Washington, D.C.

_____ GG. President Carter signs the Panama Canal Treaty.

_____ HH. Former Idaho governor Frank Steunenberg dies because of an assassin's bomb; The Great White Fleet prepares for a cruise around the world.

_____ II. The United States and Britain declare war on Japan.

_____ JJ. California is admitted as the thirty-first state; First national women's rights convention is held in Worcester, Massachusetts.

_____ KK. Mussolini marches on Rome; Irish Free State is officially proclaimed.

GROUP 3 . . . OTHER EVENTS

_____ AAA. New York City's population is 700,000 and the world's population is at least 1 billion; _The New York Times_ begins publication.

_____ BBB. Mozart's _Magic Flute_ is first performed; Samuel Morse of electric telegraph fame is born; Buratti designs Venice's San Giorgio's bell tower.

_____ CCC. Louis Leakey finds Nutcracker Man's skull in Tanganyika; First seven U.S. astronauts are selected.

_____ DDD. New York State Legislature agrees to finance the building of the Erie Canal.

_____ EEE. Lincoln Memorial in Washington, D.C. is dedicated; Insulin is first administered to diabetic patients.

_____ FFF. Passenger service on the _Concorde_ SST between New York and Paris and London begins.

_____ GGG. Mendeleev publishes his _The Principles of Chemistry_ featuring the periodic table of sixty-three known elements; _Harper's Weekly_ prints donkey as symbol of the Democratic Party.

_____ HHH. Edward Hopper's _Nighthawks_ and Orson Welles' _Citizen Kane_ are popular.

_____ III. Nelly Bly continues her attempt to circle the world in fewer than eighty days; Louis Sullivan's first skyscraper, the Wainwright Building in Chicago, is completed.

_____ JJJ. "Stars and Stripes" wins the America's Cup; Cher, Michael Douglas, and _The Last Emperor_ are Oscar winners.

_____ KKK. The _Lusitania_ makes her maiden voyage; Tinkers-to-Evers-to-Chance combination propels the Chicago Cubs to a victorious World Series.

THE EVENTS OF THE YEARS

Year	Literary Events	Historical and Political Events	Other Events
1791	_____	_____	_____
1815	_____	_____	_____
1850	_____	_____	_____
1870	_____	_____	_____
1890	_____	_____	_____
1907	_____	_____	_____
1922	_____	_____	_____
1941	_____	_____	_____
1959	G	BB	CCC
1977	_____	_____	_____
1988	_____	_____	_____

LITERATURE WRITTEN DURING THE 1600s AND THE 1700s

The following characters are found in works that were written between 1600 and 1799. Show your knowledge of these two important literary centuries by identifying as many of these works as you can.

TITLE   **CHARACTERS**

1. _____ a knight-errant, Sancho Panza, Dulcinea de Toboso, Alonzo Quixano

2. _____ Giovanna, Antonio, Ferdinand, The Cardinal

3. _____ The Lady, Sabrina, The elder Brother, The second Brother, Sweet Echo

4. _____ Arnolphie, Agnes, Horace, Chrysalde, Enrique, Oronte

5. _____ Orgon, Madame Pernelle, Elmire, Damis, Mariane, Cleante

6. _____ Alceste, Celimene, Eliante, Philinte, Oronte

7. _____ God the Father, Christ the Son, Satan, Adam, Eve

8. _____ Samson, Manoa, Dalila, Harapha, Chorus of Danites

9. _____ Theseus, Hippolyte, Oenone, Neptune, Aricie, wife of the king of Athens

10. _____ Christian, Evangelist, Mr. Wordly-Wiseman, Despair, Hypocrisy, Faithful

11. _____ Jebusites, David, Amnon, Saul, and other biblical figures who represent the feuding Tories and Whigs of 1678 England

12. _____ Fainall Mirabell, Petulant, Sir Wilfull Witwoud, Lady Wishfort, Mrs. Millamant, Mrs. Marwood

13. _____ Belinda, Lord Petre, Thalestris, Ariel, Umbriel

14. _____ the son of a middle-class English family who is presently a castaway, his man and servant, Friday

15. _____ a female rogue; Robin, her husband; a sea captain; Jemmy E

16. _____ H. F., the narrator, who is a London saddler in the year 1665

17. _____ a surgeon named Lemuel, Lilliputians, Brobdingnags

18. _____ a servant girl named Andrews; Mr. B, her master; Mrs. Jervis; Mrs. Jewkes; Lady Davers

LITERATURE WRITTEN DURING THE 1600s AND THE 1700s (continued)

19. _____ a footman to Lady Booby, Pamela Andrews. Lady Booby, Fanny, Mrs. Slipslop, Parson Adams

20. _____ a foundling, Squire Allworthy, Allworthy's sister, Bridget, Master Bliful, Mr. Partridge, Sophia Western

21. _____ Captain Booth, Elizabeth Harris, Sergeant Atkinson, Dr. Harrison, Colonel James, Miss Matthews

22. _____ Cunégonde, Cacambo, Baron Thunder-Ten-Tronckh, Pangloss

23. _____ Mr. Walter Shandy, Uncle Toby, Corporal Trim, Mr. Yorick, Dr. Slop

24. _____ Manfred, Matilda, Conrad, Isabella, Alfonso, Theodore

25. _____ Dr. Primrose, George, Deborah, Olivia, Sophia, Squire Thornhill

26. _____ Mr. Hardcastle, Mrs. Hardcastle, Tony Lumpkin, Sir Charles, Hastings

27. _____ Matthew Bramble, Tabitha Bramble, Lydia Melford, Winifred Jenkins, Lieutenant Obadiah Lismahago

28. _____ Mrs. Malaprop, Captain Jack Absolute, Sir Anthony Absolute, Bob Acres, Julia Melville

29. _____ Lady Sneerwell, Charles Surface, Lady Teazle, Sir Peter

30. _____ an old seaman, a wedding guest, an albatross, Death, Life-in-Death

SECTION 4

NOVELS—
TALES TO REMEMBER

JUST FOR STARTERS
PART ONE

Here are the first lines from thirty-five popular novels. They are listed alphabetically according to the authors' last names. An author may have more than one work cited. List the title and the author on the line next to the novel's first line.

Life has its good and bad moments and so does this exercise. Since the novels' beginnings have been copied exactly, some are very difficult and some are dead giveaways. Keep in mind that the excerpts are listed according to the authors' last names. The first one is done for you. Good luck.

1. _____Little Women-Alcott_____ "Christmas won't be Christmas without any presents," grumbled Jo, lying on the rug.

2. _____ It is a truth universally acknowledged, that a single man in possession of a good fortune must be in want of a wife.

3. _____ Everyone had always said that John would be a preacher when he grew up, just like his father.

4. _____ All children, except one, grow up.

5. _____ It was a pleasure to burn.

6. _____ There was no possibility of taking a walk that day.

7. _____ 1801—I have just returned from a visit to my landlord— the solitary neighbour that I shall be troubled with.

8. _____ It was Wang Lung's marriage day.

9. _____ "Ho, Diomed, well met! Do you sup with Glaucus tonight?" said a young man with small stature, who wore his tunic in those loose and effeminate folds which proved him to be a gentleman and a coxcomb.

10. _____ Lov Bensey trudged homeward through the deep white sand of the gully-washed tobacco road with a sack of winter turnips on his back.

11. _____ Maman died today.

12. _____ Alice was beginning to get very tired of sitting by her sister on the bank, and of having nothing to do.

13. _____ I first heard of Antonia on what seemed to me an interminable journey across the great midland plain of North America.

14. _____ At a village of La Mancha, whose name I do not wish to remember, there lived a little while ago one of those gentlemen who are wont to keep a lance in the rack, an old buckler, a lean horse and a swift greyhound.

15. _____ A green and yellow parrot, which hung in a cage outside the door, kept repeating over and over: "Allez vous-en! Allez vous-en! Sapristi! That's all right!"

16. _____ The *Nellie,* a cruising yawl, swung to her anchor without a flutter of the sails, and was at rest.

17. _____ The cold passed reluctantly from the earth and the retiring fogs revealed an army stretched out on the hills, resting.

18. _____ I was born in the year 1632, in the city of York, of a good family, though not of that country, my father being a foreigner of Bremen who settled first at Hull.

19. _____ Marley was dead, to begin with.

20. _____ Whether I shall turn out to be the hero of my own life, or whether that station will be held by anybody else, these pages must show.

21. _____ My father's name being Pirrip, and my Christian name Philip, my infant tongue could make of both names nothing longer or more explicit than Pip.

22. _____ Among other public buildings in a certain town, which for many reasons it will be prudent to refrain from mentioning, and to which I will assign no fictitious name, there is one anciently common to most towns great or small: to wit, a workhouse; and in this workhouse was born—on a day and date which I need not trouble myself to repeat, inasmuch as it can be of no possible consequence to the reader, in this stage the business at all events—the item of mortality whose name is prefixed to the head of this chapter.

23. _____ It was the best of times, it was the worst of times, it was the age of wisdom, it was the age of foolishness, it was the epoch of belief, it was the epic of incredulity, it was the season of Light, it was the season of Darkness, it was the spring of hope, it was the winter of despair . . .

24. _____ Alexey Fyodorovitch Karamazov was the third son of Fyodor Pavlovitch Karamazov, a landowner well known in our district in his own day, and still remembered among us owing to his gloomy and tragic death, which happened thirteen years ago, and which I shall describe in its proper place.

25. _____ On an exceptionally hot evening early in July a young man came out of the garret in which he lodged in S. Place and walked slowly, as though in hesitation, towards K, bridge.

26. _____ Dusk—of a summer night.

27. _____ On February 24, 1815, the watchtower at Marseilles signaled the arrival of the three-master *Pharaon,* coming from Smyrna, Trieste and Naples.

28. _____ Last night I dreamt I went to Manderley again.

29. _____ In the days when the spinning wheels hummed busily in the farmhouses—and even great ladies, clothed in silk and thread lace, had their toy spinning wheels of polished oak—there might be seen, in districts far away among the lanes, or deep in the bosom of the hills, certain pallid undersized men who, by the side of the brawny countryfolk, looked like the remnants of a disinherited race.

30. _____ I am an invisible man.

31. _____ Through the fence, between the curling flower spaces, I could see them hitting.

32. _____ Jewel and I come up from the field, following the path in single file.

33. _____ An author ought to consider himself, not as a gentleman who gives a private or eleemosynary treat, but rather as one who keeps a public ordinary, at which all persons are welcome for their money.

34. _____ In my younger and more vulnerable years my father gave me some advice that I've been turning over in my mind ever since.

35. _____ On the pleasant shore of the French Riviera, about halfway between Marseilles and the Italian border, stands a large, proud, rose-colored hotel.

Name _____ **Date** _____ **Period** _____

JUST FOR STARTERS
PART TWO

Here are the first lines from thirty-five popular novels. They are listed alphabetically according to the authors' last names. An author may have more than one work cited. List the title and the author next to the novel's first line.

Since these excerpts have been copied exactly, some are very difficult and some are easy. Keep in mind that the excerpts are listed according to the authors' last names. The first one is done for you. Good luck!

1. _____A Passage to India-Forster_____ Except for the Marabar Caves—and they are twenty miles off—the city of Chandrapore presents nothing extraordinary.

2. _____ The boy with the fair hair lowered himself down the last few feet of rock and began to pick his way toward the lagoon.

3. _____ Hade knew they meant to murder him before he had been in Brighton three hours with his inky fingers and his bitten nails, his manner cynical and nervous, anybody could tell he didn't belong to the early summer sun, the cool Whitsun wind off the sea, the holiday crowd.

4. _____ Samuel Spade's jaw was long and bony, his chin a jutting v under the more flexible v of his mouth.

5. _____ The schoolmaster was leaving the village, and everybody seemed sorry.

6. _____ Halfway down a bystreet of one of our New England towns stands a rusty wooden house, with seven acutely peaked gables, facing towards various points of the compass, and a huge, clustered chimney in the midst.

7. _____ A throng of bearded men, in sad-colored garments and gray, steeple-crowned hats, intermixed with women, some wearing hoods, and others bareheaded was assembled in front of a wooden edifice, the door of which was heavily timbered with oak and studded with iron spikes.

8. _____ It was love at first sight. The first time Yossarian saw the chaplain he fell madly in love with him.

9. _____ He lay flat on the brown, pine-needled floor of the forest, his chin on his folded arms and high overhead the wind blew in the tops of the pine trees.

10. _____ He was an old man who fished alone in a skiff in the Gulf stream and he had gone eighty-four days now without taking a fish.

11. _____ Robert Cohn was once middleweight champion of Princeton. Do not think that I am very impressed by that as a boxing title, but it meant a lot to Cohn.

12. _____ Invasion had come to the town of Adano.

13. _____ In the shade of the house, in the sunshine on the river bank by the boats, in the shade of the sallow wood and the fig tree, Siddhartha, the handsome Brahmin's son, grew up with his friend Govinda.

14. _____ On January 6, 1482, the people of Paris were awakened by the tumultuous clanging of all the bells in the city.

15. _____ An hour before sunset, on the evening of a day in the beginning of October, 1815, a man traveling afoot entered the little town of D_____.

16. _____ A squat grey building of only thirty-four stories. Over the main entrance the words CENTRAL LONDON HATCHERY AND CONDITIONING CENTRE, and, in a shield, the world State's motto, COMMUNITY, IDENTITY, STABILITY.

17. _____ Once upon a time and a very good time it was there was a moocow coming down along the road and this moocow that was coming down along the road met a nicens little boy named baby tuckoo . . .

18. _____ Stately, plump Buck Mulligan came from the stairhead, bearing a bowl of lather on which a mirror and a razor lay crossed.

19. _____ I went back to the Devon School not long ago, and found it looking oddly newer than when I was a student there fifteen years before.

20. _____ "The Bottoms" succeeded to "Hell Row." Hell Row was a block of thatched, bulging cottages that stood by the brookside on Greenhill Lane.

21. _____ When he was thirteen, my brother Jem got his arm badly broken at the elbow.

22. _____ The towers of Zenith aspired above the morning mist; austere towers of steel and cement and limestone, sturdy as cliffs and delicate as silver rods.

23. _____ This is America—a town of a few thousand, in a region of wheat and corn and little groves. The town is, in our tale, called "Gopher Prairie, Minnesota." (from the preface)

24. _____ Buck did not read the newspapers, or he would have known that trouble was brewing not alone for himself, but for every tide-water dog, strong of muscle and with warm, long hair, from Puget Sound to San Diego.

25. _____ I scarcely know where to begin, though I sometimes facetiously place the cause of it all to Charley Furuseth's credit.

26. _____ The early November street was dark though night had ended, but the wind, to the grocer's surprise, already clawed . . . Morris Bober dragged the heavy boxes to the door, panting.

27. _____ The day broke grey and dull. The clouds hung heavily, and there was a rawness in the air that suggested snow.

28. _____ In the time before steamships, or then more frequently than now, a stroller along the docks of any considerable seaport would occasionally have his attention arrested by a group of bronzed mariners, man-of-war's men or merchant-sailors in holiday attire ashore on liberty.

29. _____ Call me Ishmael.

30. _____ Scarlett O'Hara was not beautiful, but men seldom realized it when caught by her charm as the Tarleton twins were.

31. _____ Full of baby's venom. The women in the house knew it and so did the children. For years each put up with the spite in his own way, but by 1873 Sethe and her daughter Denver were its only victims.

32. _____ The North Carolina Mutual Life Insurance agent promised to fly from Mercy to the other side of Lake Superior at three o'clock. Two days before the event was to take place he tacked a note on the door of his yellow House:

33. _____ Mr. Jones, of the Manor Farm, had locked the hen-houses for the night, but was too drunk to remember to shut the popholes.

34. _____ It was a bright cold day in April, and the clocks were striking thirteen. Winston Smith, his chin nuzzled into his breast in an effort to escape the vile wind, slipped quickly through the glass doors of Victory Mansions . . .

35. _____ There is a lovely road that runs from Ixopo into the hills. These hills are grass-covered and rolling, and they are lovely beyond any singing of it.

JUST FOR STARTERS
PART THREE

Here are the first lines of thirty-four popular novels. They are listed alphabetically according to the authors' last names. An author may have more than one work cited. List the title and the author next to the novel's first line.

Since these excerpts have been copied exactly, some are very difficult and some are easy. Keep in mind that the excerpts are listed according to the authors' last names. The first one is done for you. Good luck!

1. _____The Bell Jar-Plath_____ It was a queer, sultry summer, the summer they electrocuted the Rosenbergs, and I didn't know what I was doing in New York.

2. _____ A column of smoke rose thin and straight from the cabin chimney. The smoke was blue where it left the red of the clay. It trailed into the blue of the April sky and was no longer blue but gray.

3. _____ We are at rest five miles behind the front. Yesterday we were relieved, and now our bellies are full of beef and haricot.

4. _____ If you really want to hear about it, the first thing you'll probably want to know is where I was born and what my lousy childhood was like, and how my parents were occupied and all before they had me, and all that David Copperfield kind of crap, but I don't feel like going into it, if you want to know the truth.

5. _____ You will rejoice to hear that no disaster has accompanied the commencement of an enterprise which you have regarded with such evil forebodings. I arrived here yesterday, and my first task is to assure my dear sister of my welfare and increasing confidence in the success of my undertaking.

6. _____ Lieutenant Commander Peter Holmes of the Royal Australian Navy woke soon after dawn.

7. _____ It was four o'clock when the ceremony was over and the carriages began to arrive. There had been a crowd following all the way, owing to the exuberance of Marija Berczynskas.

8. _____ Reveille was sounded, as always, at 5 A.M.—a hammer pounding on a rail outside camp HQ. The ringing noise came faintly on and off through the windowpanes covered with ice more than an inch thick, and died fast away.

9. _____ To the red country and part of the gray country of Oklahoma, the last rains came gently, and they did not cut the scarred earth.

10. _____ A few miles south of Soledad, the Salinas River drops in close to the hillside bank and runs deep and green. The water is warm, too, for it has slipped twinkling over the yellow sands in the sunlight before reaching the narrow pool.

11. _____ Kino awakened in the near dark. The stars still shone and the day had drawn only a pale wash of light in the lower sky to the east.

12. _____ 3 May, Bistritz.—Left Munich at 8:35 P.M., on 1st May, arriving at Vienna early next morning; should have arrived at 6:46, but train was an hour late. Buda-Pesth seems a wonderful place . . .

JUST FOR STARTERS (PART THREE) (continued)

13. _____ Late in the afternoon of a chilly day in February, two gentlemen were sitting alone over their wine, in a well-furnished dining parlor, in the town of P_____, in Kentucky. There were no servants present, and the gentlemen, with chairs closely approaching, seemed to be discussing some subject with great earnestness.

14. _____ My father had a small estate in Nottinghamshire; I was the third of five sons. He sent me to Emmanuel College in Cambridge at fourteen years old, where I resided three years, and applied my self to my studies;

15. _____ All happy families are like one another; each unhappy family is unhappy in its own way . . . Everything was in confusion in the Oblonsky household.

16. _____ You don't know about me without you have read a book by the name of *The Adventures of Tom Sawyer;* but that ain't no matter.

17. _____ "Tom!" No answer. "Tom!" No answer.

18. _____ "Well, Piotr not in sight yet?" was the question asked on May the 20th, 1859, by a gentleman of a little over forty, in a dusty coat and checked trousers, who came out without his hat on to the low steps of the posting station at S_____. He was addressing his servant, a chubby young fellow, with whitish down on his chin, and little, lack-lustre eyes.

19. _____ When Pearl was dying, a funny thought occurred to her. It twitched her lips and rustled her breath, and she felt her son lean forward from where he kept watch by her bed. "Get . . ." she told him. "You should have got . . ."

20. _____ Boys are playing basketball around a telephone pole with a backboard bolted to it. Legs, shouts. The scrape and snap of Keds on loose alley pebbles seems to catapult their voices high into the moist March air blue above the wires. Rabbit Angstrom, coming up the alley in a business suit, stops and watches, though he's twenty-two and six three.

21. _____ The year 1866 was marked by a strange event, an unexplainable occurrence which is undoubtedly still fresh in everyone's memory. Those living in coastal towns or in the interior of continents were aroused by all sorts or rumors; but it was the seafaring people who were particularly excited.

22. _____ All this happened, more or less. The war parts, anyway, are pretty much true. One guy I knew really was shot in Dresden for taking a teapot that wasn't his. Another guy I knew really did threaten to have his personal enemies killed by hired gunmen after the war. And so on. I've changed all the names.

23. _____ Dear God, I am fourteen years old. I have always been a good girl.

24. _____ Mason City. To get there you follow Highway 58, going northeast out of the city, and it is a good highway and new. Or was new, that day we went up it.

25. _____ When I reached C Company lines, which were at the top of the hill, I paused and looked back at the camp, just coming into full view below me through the grey mist of the early morning. We were leaving that day. When we marched in, three months before, the place was under snow; now the first leaves of spring were unfolding.

26. _____ The Time Traveller (for so it will be convenient to speak of him) was expounding a recondite matter to us.

JUST FOR STARTERS (PART THREE) (continued)

27. _____ The nickname of the train was the Yellow Dog. Its real name was Yazoo-Delta. It was a mixed train. The day was the 10th of September, 1923—afternoon.

28. _____ On a January evening of the early seventies, Christine Nilsson was singing in Faust at the Academy of Music in New York.

29. _____ I had the story, bit by bit, from various people, and, as generally happens in such cases, each time it was a different story. . . . If you know Starkfield, Massachusetts, you know the post-office.

30. _____ (from the preface) The artist is the creator of beautiful things. To reveal art and conceal the artist is art's aim.

31. _____ (from the prologue) "And then say what? Say, 'Forget you're hungry, forget you got shot inna back by some racist cop—Chuck was here? Chuck come up to Harlem—'"

32. _____ Mrs. Dalloway said she would buy the flowers herself.

33. _____ "Yes, of course, if it's fine tomorrow," said Mrs. Ramsay. "But you'll have to be up with the lark," she added.

34. _____ Brrrrrrriiiiiiiiiiiiiiiiiinng! An alarm clock clanged in the dark and silent room. A bedspring creaked. A woman's voice sang out impatiently: "Bigger, shut that thing off!"

Name _____ Date _____ Period _____

A NOVEL FITNESS TEST
PART ONE

This exercise will challenge even the most sophisticated and prolific readers. The twenty-five novels quoted below and listed in alphabetical order according to their titles can be answered in an individual, group, or class setting. The goal is to have fun while you are learning.

The novel's date of publication and the author's nationality are listed in brackets after the novel's excerpt. Identify the novel and the novel's author by writing the title and author on the blank lines following each question. The first one is already done for you.

1. "So there is. Run Lisbeth, run to meet Aunt Poyser. Come in Adam, and rest; it has been a hard day for thee." [1859; English]

   Adam Bede _____   George Eliot _____

2. "Doan' you 'member de house dat was float'n down de river, en dey wuz a man in dah, kivered up, en I went in en unkivered him and didn't let you come in? Well, den, you kin git yo' money when you wants it, kase dat wuz him." [1884; American]

   _____   _____

3. "Ben, I'd like to, honest injun; but Aunt Polly—well Jim wanted to do it, but she wouldn't let him; Sid wanted to do it, and she wouldn't let Sid. Now don't you see how I'm fixed?" [1876; American]

   _____   _____

4. "We must do it as quickly as we can. A consul can marry people. That officer in there spoke about a consul. As soon as we get to the coast . . ." [1935; English]

   _____   _____

5. "We were eighteen and had begun to love life and the world; and we had to shoot it to pieces. The first bomb, the first explosion, burst in our hearts . . . we believe in war." [1929; German]

   _____   _____

6. "I thought I'd name him for Tom. I thought that for quite a while. Then it came to it. I would name him for Willie. His name is Willie Stark." [1946; American]

   _____   _____

7. "And a hundred and forty pound man is afraid to go near a weak, sick, hundred-pound little girl who is drowning, for fear she will cling to him and drag him under." [1925; American]

   _____   _____

8. "When the sea goes down, there will come from the mainland boats and men. And they will find ten dead bodies and an unsolved problem on Indian Island." [1939–1940; English]

   _____   _____

9. "But things are now under control. We have the organism, and can continue to study it. We've already begun to characterize a variety of mutant forms." [1969; American]

   _____   _____

10. "All the habits of Man are evil. And, above all, no animal must ever tyrannise over his own kind. Weak or strong, clever or simple, we are all brothers. No animal must ever kill any other animal. All animals are equal." [1945–1946; English]

_____   _____

11. "Yes, I'm very much worried, and that's what reason was given me for, to escape; so then one must escape. Why not put out the light when there's nothing more to look at, when it's sickening to look at it at all? But how? Why did the conductor run along the footboard, why are they shrieking, those young men in that train? Why are they talking, why are they laughing? It's all falsehood, all lying, all humbug, all evil! . . ." [1875–1877; Russian]

_____   _____

12. "A true Englishman doesn't joke when he is talking about so serious a thing as a wager. I will bet twenty thousand pounds against anyone who wishes, that I will make the tour of the world . . . in nineteen hundred and twenty hours, or a hundred and fifteen thousand two hundred minutes. Do you accept?" [1873; French]

_____   _____

13. "Oh, Professor Gottlieb, my name is _____. I'm a medic freshman, Winnemac B.A. I'd like to take bacteriology this fall instead of next year." [1925; American]

_____   _____

14. "Jewel, do you know that Addie Bundren is going to die? Addie Bundren is going to die?" [1930; American]

_____   _____

15. "We both know that if Taggart Transcontinental runs trains in Colorado the way it did five years ago, it will ruin me. I know that that is what you people intend to do. You expect to feed off me while you can and to find another carcass to pick dry after you have finished mine. This is the policy of mankind today. So here is my ultimatum: it is now in your power to destroy me; I may have to go; but if I go, I'll make sure that I will take all the rest of you along with me." [1957; Russian-born American]

_____   _____

16. "Well, those folks in there will try to bully you, and tame you down. Tell 'em to go to the devil! I'll back you. Take your factory job, if you want to. Don't be scared of the family. No, nor all of Zenith. Nor of yourself, the way I've been. Go ahead, old man! The world is yours!" [1922; American]

_____   _____

17. "It was a queer, sultry summer, the summer they electrocuted the Rosenbergs, and I didn't know what I was doing in New York. It had nothing to do with me, but I couldn't help wondering what it would be like, being burned alive all along your nerves." [1963; American]

_____   _____

18. "When good people take you in and treat you good, you ought to try to be good back. You don't . . . Sethe loves you. Much as her own daughter. You know that." [1987; American]

_____   _____

19. "In wartime at sea a man-of-war's man strikes his superior in grade, and the blow kills. Apart from its effect the blow itself is, according to the Articles of War, a capital crime . . ." [written in 1891, published in 1924; American]

_____   _____

20. "Honoured, indeed by another visit from the wards is Jarndyce." [1852 or 1853; English]

    _____   _____

21. "This case is fulla ifs, Reverend Bacon. If we find a car and an owner, and if the owner says, 'Yeah, I hit this young man the other night, and I didn't stop, and I didn't report it,' then we got a case. Otherwise, we got a lot of problems." [1987; American]

    _____   _____

22. "We-want-the-whip! We-want-the-whip!" [1932; English]

    _____   _____

23. "But soon we shall die and all memory of those five will have left the earth, and we ourselves shall be loved for a while and forgotten . . . There is a land of the living and a land of meaning." [1927; American]

    _____   _____

24. "I don't know, Pinkie. I got confused. I thought I'd go to confession." [1938; English]

    _____   _____

25. "I plead guilty to drunkenness and dissipation to idleness and debauchery. . . . But I am not guilty of the death of that old man, my enemy and my father. No, no, I am not guilty of robbing him." [1880; Russian]

    _____   _____

A NOVEL FITNESS TEST
PART TWO

The twenty-five novels quoted below and listed in alphabetical order according to their titles can be answered in an individual, group, or class setting. The goal is to have fun while you are learning.

The novel's date of publication and the author's nationality are listed in brackets after the novel's excerpt. Identify the novel and its author by writing the title and the author on the blank lines following the question. The first one is done for you.

1. "Get up there, Buck! Get up there! Mush on!" [1903; American]

   _____ *The Call of the Wild* _____   _____ Jack London _____

2. "I'm dying, Joey. There's Sean, Joey, and the little Colleen. You'll take care of them, Joey, for himself. You'll mind them?" [1972; English-born American]

   _____   _____

3. ". . . And regulations do say that you have to obey every order. That's the catch. Even if the colonel was disobeying a Twenty-seventh Air Force order by making you fly more missions, you'd still have to fly them, or you'd be guilty of disobeying an order of his . . . " [1961; American]

   _____   _____

4. "That's all I'm going to tell about. I could probably tell you what I did after I went home, and how I got sick and all, and what school I'm supposed to go to next fall, after I get out of here, but I don't feel like it. I really don't." [1951; American]

   _____   _____

5. "Call me, Jonah. My parents did, or nearly did. They called me John." [1963; American]

   _____   _____

6. "About three or four such Hasidic sects populated the area in which Danny and I grew up, each with its own rabbi, its own little synagogue, its own fierce loyalties . . ." [1967; American]

   _____   _____

7. "That's right, Manson. Andrew Manson is the name." [1937; Scottish]

   _____   _____

8. "Dear God,

   I am fourteen years old. I have always been a good girl. Maybe you can give a sign letting me know what is happening to me." [1982; American]

   _____   _____

9. "So the Lord told you: *Confess that all nations may know.* I don't think you realize what divine justice lies in that phrase. For near onto about ten weeks now, there's been a mighty clamor to *know* not only in the Virginia but all over America . . ." [1967; American]

   _____   _____

10. "Now, my friend, you know as much about it as I do. If we should escape together, half the treasure is yours; if I die here and you escape alone, it all belongs to you." [1844; French]

_____   _____

11. "Svidrigailov shot himself!" [1866; Russian]

_____   _____

12. "This is a terrible loss for South Africa. For this Arthur Jarvis was a courageous young man, and a great fighter for justice . . ." [1948; South African]

_____   _____

13. "Whether I shall turn out to be the hero of my own life or whether that station will be held by anybody else, these pages must show. To begin my life with the beginning of my life, I record that I was born (as I have been informed and believe) on a Friday, at twelve o'clock at night. It was remarked that the clock began to strike, and I began to cry, simultaneously." [1849–1850; English]

_____   _____

14. "But he also masqueraded as a Dane, an American, and a Frenchman, under two stolen passports and one set of forged French papers. As far as we are concerned, our enquiries established that the assassin was travelling in France under a false passport . . ." [1971; English]

_____   _____

15. "Mr. Keating? Sir? O Captain! My Captain?" [1989; American]

_____   _____

16. "Then what do you want now? To live? Live how? Live as you lived in the law courts when the usher proclaimed 'The judge is coming! The judge is coming, the judge!'" [1884; Russian]

_____   _____

17. "Madame, will you permit an entire stranger to serve you with a word of advice and warning which self-interest prevents others from uttering? Go away. Leave here at once, without delay, with Tadzio and your daughters. Venice is in the grip of pestilence." [1911; German]

_____   _____

18. ". . . . the very first fire that we kindle, after our return, shall be lighted with the brocade dress, and fed by every article that you may think unfit for the woman you wish to live with!" [1841; American]

_____   _____

19. "You'll have to listen within yourself, then you will notice that I am with you. Do you understand? And something else. Frau Eva said that if you ever were in a bad way I was to give you a kiss from her that she sends by me . . . Close your eyes, Sinclair!" [1919; German]

_____   _____

20. "What have I done? What have I done? I've given her up, renounced her, given her away. I must run after them. Lara! Lara!" [1957; Russian]

_____   _____

21. "I shall not be such a fool as to turn knight-errant, for I plainly see that it is not the fashion of the day to do as they used to in the times when these famous knights are said to have wandered about the world." [1605, 1615; Spanish]

    _____   _____

22. "I saw the Count lying within the box upon the earth, some of which the rude falling from the cart had scattered over him. He was deathly pale, just like a waxen image, and the red eyes glared with a horrible vindictive look which I knew too well." [1897; Irish]

    _____   _____

23. "Yes, he went home. And when I was only a week in the convent he died and he was buried in Oughterard where his people came from. O, the day I heard that, he was dead!" [1914; Irish]

    _____   _____

24. "Let me count this day, Lord, as the beginning of a new and more vigorous life, as the beginning of a crusade for complete morality and the domination of the Christian church through all the land. Dear Lord, thy work is but begun! We shall yet make these United States a moral nation!" [1927; American]

    _____   _____

25. "It is. We're book burners, too. We read books and burnt them, afraid they'd be found." [1953; American]

    _____   _____

A NOVEL FITNESS TEST
PART THREE

The twenty-five novels quoted below and listed in alphabetical order according to their titles can be answered in an individual, group, or class setting. The goal is to have fun while you are learning.

The novel's date of publication and the author's nationality are listed in brackets after the novel's excerpt. Identify the novel and its author by writing the title and the author on the blank lines following the question. The first one is done for you.

1. "A few years ago I was a lawyer in Paris and, indeed, a rather well known lawyer. Of course, I didn't tell you my real name. I had a speciality: noble cases." [1956; Algerian-born French]

   The Fall _____   Albert Camus _____

2. "Now, Bathsheba, was anybody so provoking? You know it was purely that I, as an unmarried man, carrying on a business for you as a very taking young woman . . ." [1874; English]

   _____   _____

3. ". . . they glimpsed the fixer, were openly weeping, wringing their hands. One thinly bearded man clawed his face. One or two waved at Yakov." [1966; American]

   _____   _____

4. "Robert Jordan lay behind the tree, holding onto himself very carefully and delicately to keep his hands steady." [1940; American]

   _____   _____

5. "If you consider the behavior of the world at present and the disaster toward which it is moving you might find the undertaking preposterous. The age of the skyscraper is gone. This is the age of the housing project. Which is always a prelude to the age of the cave. . . . This will be the last skyscraper ever built in New York. It is proper that it should be so. The last achievement of man on earth before mankind destroys itself." [1943; Russian-born American]

   _____   _____

6. "He came through, didn't he, Deacon Grimes? The Lord done laid him out, and turned him around and wrote his name in glory. Bless our God!" [1953; American]

   _____   _____

7. "After all, tomorrow is another day." [1936; American]

   _____   _____

8. "It is the end of a family—when they begin to sell the land. Out of the land we came and into it we must go—and if you will hold your land you can live—no one can rob you of land." [1931; American]

   _____   _____

9. "It may be possibly seem to you, Robertson—at this particular moment in the world's history—umph—that the affairs of Caesar in Gaul some two thousand years ago—are—umph—of somewhat secondary importance and that—umph—the irregular conjugation of the verb *tollo* is—umph—even less important still." [1935; English]

_____   _____

10. "Lay down, Rosasharn. Lay down an' res'. I'll try to figger some way to dry you off." [1939; American]

_____   _____

11. "My father's family name being Pirrup, and my Christian name Philip, my infant tongue could make of both names nothing more explicit than Pip." [1861; English]

_____   _____

12. "Well, first Daisy turned away from the woman toward the other car, and then she lost her nerve and turned back. The second my hand reached the wheel I felt the shock—it must have killed her instantly." [1925; American]

_____   _____

13. "Bull Meecham was a lover of flight, a pilot who took joy in the immense pleasure, the supreme and indescribable pleasure in flying an F-8 faster than the speed of sound." [1976; American]

_____   _____

14. "And is there less probability in my account of the Houyhnhnms or Yahoos . . ." [1726; English]

_____   _____

15. "His card read:

    I am a deaf-mute, but I read the lips and understand what is said to me. Please do not shout." [1943; American]

_____   _____

16. "The horror! The horror!" [1902; Polish-born English]

_____   _____

17. "He was writing in it when he died—oh, nothing interesting, just the temperatures. He always kept the temperatures. He wasn't romantic. God knows what he saw in him to make it worthwhile." [1948; English]

_____   _____

18. "I find that before the terrible event occurred several people had seen a creature upon the moor . . . and which could not possibly be any animal known to science." [1902; English]

_____   _____

19. ". . . Old Maid Pyncheon has been in trade just about as long, and rides off in her carriage with a couple of hundred thousand—reckoning her share, and Clifford and Phoebe's—and some say twice as much!" [1851; American]

_____   _____

20. "Dai is going to give you lessons in the art of boxing, Huw." [1940; Welsh]

_____   _____

21. "He can talk when he wants to. He became deaf from ringing the bells, but he's not dumb." [1830; French]

_____   _____

22. "No, I am not a spook like those who haunted Edgar Allan Poe; nor am I one of your Hollywood-movie ectoplasms. I am a man of substance, of flesh and bone, fiber and liquids—and I might even be said to possess a mind . . ." [1952; American]

_____   _____

23. "Mary, I have been married to Mr. Rochester this morning." [1847; English]

_____   _____

24. "You're breaking my heart. You got a fish needs killing. I'll try to kill it for you. No guarantees, but I'll do my best. And my best is worth four hundred dollars a day." [1974; American]

_____   _____

25. "Also, after the hams had been smoked, there would be found some that had gone to the bad. Formerly these had been sold as 'Number Three Grade,' but later on some ingenious person had hit upon a new device, and now they would extract the bone, about which the bad part generally lay, and insert in the hole a white hot iron . . ." [1906; American]

_____   _____

A NOVEL FITNESS TEST
PART FOUR

The twenty-five novels quoted below and listed in alphabetical order according to their titles can be answered in an individual, group, or class setting. The goal is to have fun while you are learning.

The novel's date of publication and the author's nationality are listed in brackets after the novel's excerpt. Identify the novel and its author by writing the title and the author on the blank lines following the question. The first one is done for you.

1. "My dear Francis, you seem to wish to administer my diocese." [1941; Scottish]

   _____ *The Keys of the Kingdom* _____   _____ A. J. Cronin _____

2. "For example, would you even consider supporting Skeffington in an election?" [1956; American]

   _____   _____

3. "The palefaces are masters of the earth, and the time of the red men has not come yet again. My day has been too long." [1826; American]

   _____   _____

4. "I tell you that there is no Monsieur Madeline, and that there is no Monsieur the Mayor. There is a robber, there is a brigand, there is a convict called Jean Valjean, and I have got him." [1862; French]

   _____   _____

5. "Mother Superior tells me that you are going to build her a chapel." [1962; American]

   _____   _____

6. "I reckon they won't do no harm out there. And it ain't none of my house to tell her to get out of it. And like Byron told her, Burch or Brown or whatever his name is, is going to be right for a while longer yet." [1932; American]

   _____   _____

7. "You are dead, Ben. You must be dead. I saw you die, Ben . . . Don't you remember, Ben? Co-her, Helen, Bessie Gant who nursed you, Mrs. Pert? The oxygen tent? . . ." [1929; American]

   _____   _____

8. "The crowd, which had fallen apart behind Jim as soon as Doraman had raised his hand, rushed tumultuously forward after the shot. They say that the white man sent right and left at all those faces a proud and unflinching glance. Then with his hand over his lips he fell forward dead." [1900; English]

   _____   _____

9. "Kill the beast! Cut his throat! Spill his blood!" [1954; English]

   _____   _____

10. "You may give it another title and call it with justice *A History of the Adulteries of a Provincial Wife.*" [1857; French]

    _____   _____

11. "I do not admit that Gopher Prairie is greater or more generous than Europe! I do not admit that dish-washing is enough to satisfy all women! I may not have fought the good fight, but I have kept the faith." [1920; American]

    _____   _____

© 1994 by The Center for Applied Research in Education

A NOVEL FITNESS TEST (PART FOUR) (continued)

12. "But, what Foolish? Your brother come home with the girl he means to marry and took dinner with you and your Daddy. They intend to marry at her home in Winter Hill this coming Sunday. You and your Daddy are going to the wedding. And that is the A and the Z of the matter. So what ails you?" [1946; American]

   _____   _____

13. "It's a white whale, I say, a white whale. Skin your eyes for him, men;" [1851; American]

   _____   _____

14. "The first time I ever met Scott Fitzgerald a very strange thing happened. Many strange things happened with Scott but this one I was never able to forget." [1964; American]

   _____   _____

15. "Two natures clashed on the stage of that drama of long ago, two men as strong and enigmatical as any I have known—Fletcher Christian and William Bligh." [1932; American]

   _____   _____

16. "I was ten years old then; I had lost both my father and mother within a year, and my Virginia relatives were sending me out to my grandparents, who lived in Nebraska. I travelled in the care of a mountain boy, Jake Marpole . . ." [1919; American]

   _____   _____

17. "Then the time has come for you to take the last step. You must love Big Brother." [1949; English]

   _____   _____

18. "Name of the state of California. Cut off from your train." [1901; American]

   _____   _____

19. "Yes, he's got a club foot. It was such a grief to his mother." [1915; English]

   _____   _____

20. "I was jus' playin' with him . . . an' he made like he's gonna bite me . . . an' I made like I was gonna smack him . . . an' I done it. An' then he was dead." [1937; American]

   _____   _____

21. "I had a dream before I went to Lincoln—But I will tell you about that afterward, after we are married . . . I think we shall be very happy. I haven't any fears. I think when friends marry, they are safe." [1913; American]

   _____   _____

22. "Fish. Fish, you are going to have to die anyway. Do you have to kill me too?" [1952; American]

   _____   _____

23. "We can't take a chance, Son. It would be you or me or Lisbeth next. I'll shoot him if you can't, but either way, we've got to do it. We just can't take the chance!" [1956; American]

   _____   _____

24. "Please, sir, I want some more." [1837–1839; English]

   _____   _____

25. "I've heard that the Chief, years ago, received more than two hundred shock treatments when they were really the vogue. Imagine what this could do to a mind that is already slipping. Look at him: a giant janitor." [1962; American]

   _____   _____

A NOVEL FITNESS TEST
PART FIVE

The twenty-five novels quoted below and listed in alphabetical order according to their titles can be answered in an individual, group, or class setting. The goal is to have fun while you are learning.

The novel's date of publication and the author's nationality are listed in brackets after the novel's excerpt. Identify the novel and its author by writing the title and the author on the blank lines following the question. The first one is done for you.

1. "I had everything, justice, pity, even the backing—and I knew it—and I let those three men hang because I was afraid." [1940; American]

   _____*The Ox-Bow Incident*_____   _____Walter Van Tilburg Clark_____

2. "Then he followed her into the cave and made insulting advances. She hit at him with her field-glasses; he pulled at them and the strap broke, and that is how she got away. When we searched him just now, they were in his pocket." [1924; English]

   _____   _____

3. "Even if I hadn't gotten the acid in my eyes—on my face (by accident: Rose had meant for Harry, who was, as I said, unexpected). Even if I hadn't got the acid I'd never have seen my father again." [1961; Australian]

   _____   _____

4. "Let us destroy it before it destroys us. Let us crush it between two stones. Let us—let us throw it back in the sea where it belongs. Kino, it is evil, it is evil." [1945; American]

   _____   _____

5. "O, Peter, don't waste the fairy dust on me." [1902; Scottish]

   _____   _____

6. "It was his skeleton. I did not recognize it by the ugliness of the head, for all men are ugly when they have been dead as long as that, but by the plain gold ring which he wore and which Christine Daaé had certainly slipped on his finger." [1910; French]

   _____   _____

7. "You have changed, of course, but not in appearance. I wish you would tell me your secret. To get back my youth I would do anything in the world, except take exercise, get up early, or be respectable." [1891; Anglo-Irish]

   _____   _____

8. "Out here, Dedalus. Lazy little schemer. I see schemer in your face. Where did you break your glasses?" [1916; Irish]

   _____   _____

9. "They led him out into the prison yard. No need to bind those hands now busy with his beads. In that short walk to the wall of execution, did young Juan look back on those few, those happy years he had so bravely spent? Did he remember his days in the seminary?" [1940; English]

   _____   _____

10. "You are joking, Lizzie. This cannot be!—engaged to Mr. Darcy. No, no, you shall not deceive me. I know it to be impossible." [1813; English]

    _____   _____

11. "In Savannah's apartment, I began to look for clues that might give me some insight into the secret life she had been leading before she slit her wrists." [1986; American]

_____

12. "Last night I dreamt I went to Manderlay again." [1938; English]

_____

13. "I've thought it might get too hot for Jim Conklin in some of them scrimmages, and if a whole lot of boys started and run why, I s'pose I'd start and run." [1895; American]

_____

14. "Wellingborough, as you are going to sea, suppose you take this shooting-jacket of mine along; it's just the thing—take it, it will save the expense of another." [1849; American]

_____

15. "Clym's alive!" [1878; English]

_____

16. "When I took leave of this island I carried on board for relics the goatskin cap I had made, my umbrella, and one of my parrots." [1719; English]

_____

17. "I want to see the Arno. The rooms the Signora promised us in her letter would have looked over the Arno." [1908; English]

_____

18. "A wise sentence! Thus she will be a living sermon against sin, until the ignominious letter be engraved upon her tombstone." [1850; American]

_____

19. "But, man! You advance the fact that it is your ship as though it were a moral right. You have never considered morals in dealing with others." [1904; American]

_____

20. "We'll jump together to cement our partnership. We'll form a suicide society, and the membership requirements is one jump out of this tree." [1960; American]

_____

21. "O Illustrious One, in one thing above all have I admired your teachings. Everything is completely clear and proved. You show the world as a complete, unbroken chain, an eternal chain, linked together by cause and effect." [1922; German-born Swiss]

_____

22. "God will clear me: I know nothing about the knife being there, or the money being gone. Search me and my dwelling: you will find nothing but three pound five of my own savings, which William Dane knows I have had these six months." [1861; English]

_____

23. "If what Billy Pilgrim learned from the Tralfamadorians is true, that we all live forever, no matter how dead we may sometimes seem to be, I am not overjoyed. Still—if I am going to spend eternity visiting this moment and that, I'm grateful that so many of these moments are nice." [1969; American]

_____

24. "But to be quite honest, Stingo, like I told you . . . The Russians were coming and the SS wanted the children destroyed. Most of them were Polish; the Jewish children were already dead." [1979; American]

_____

25. "Walter Morel's wanted, number 42, Hard. Summat's amiss; there's his lad here." [1913; English]

_____

A NOVEL FITNESS TEST
PART SIX

The twenty-two novels quoted below and listed in alphabetical order according to their titles can be answered in an individual, group, or class setting. The goal is to have fun while you are learning.

The novel's date of publication and the author's nationality are listed in brackets after the novel's excerpt. Identify the novel and its author by writing the title and the author on the blank lines following the question. The first one is done for you.

1. "You old crazy loon. I'm going to tell Dilsey about the way you let him follow everywhere I go. I'm going to make her whip you good." [1929; American]

    _____ *The Sound and the Fury* _____   _____ William Faulkner _____

2. "Gentlemen there stands before you Harry Haller, accused and found guilty of the willful misuse of our Magic Theater." [1927; German]

    _____   _____

3. "Yes, I preferred the elderly and discontented doctor, surrounded by friends and cherishing honest hopes; and bade a resolute farewell to the liberty, the comparative youth, the light step, leaping impulses and secret pleasures . . ." [1886; Scottish]

    _____   _____

4. "Maman died today. Or yesterday maybe, I don't know. I got a telegram from the home: 'Mother deceased. Funeral tomorrow. Faithfully yours.'" [1942; Algerian-born French]

    _____   _____

5. "Begin Stereoplay. Rough draft. Working title: 'A Martian Named Smith.'" [1961; American]

    _____   _____

6. "Oh, Jake, we could have had such a damned good time together." [1926; American]

    _____   _____

7. "It was the best of times, it was the worst of times." [1859; English]

    _____   _____

8. "There isn't any beginning, at least there isn't any insanity in the family that I know of, on either side. Nicole's mother died when she was eleven and I've sort of been father and mother to her . . ." [1934; American]

    _____   _____

9. "Some ten days ago I was arrested, in a manner that seems ridiculous even to myself, though that is immaterial at the moment. I was seized in bed before I could get up—perhaps—it is not unlikely, considering the Examining Magistrate's statement—perhaps they had orders to arrest some house painter . . ." [1925; Austro-Czech]

    _____   _____

10. "Bob Ewell's lyin' on the ground under that tree down yonder with a kitchen knife stuck up under his ribs. He's dead. Mr. Finch." [1960; American]

    _____   _____

11. "I take up my pen in the year of grace 17—, and go back to the time when my father kept the "Admiral Benbow" inn, and the brown old seaman, with the sabre cut, first took up his lodging under our roof . . ." [1883; Scottish]

   _____   _____

12. "But you were also named Mary after my mother. Your real name is Mary Frances Nolan." [1943; American]

   _____   _____

13. "Introibo ad altare Dei." [1922; Irish]

   _____   _____

14. "My child! this boy! he'd sold him! There is his Mas'r. Oh, Mr. Symmes, you've got a little boy!" [1852; American]

   _____   _____

15. "This is room 304. My name is on the board: Miss Barrett. I'll have you for homeroom all term, and I hope to meet some of you in my English class." [1965; American]

   _____   _____

16. "I should think I might. I disappoint every one—father and Aunt Penniman." [1881; American]

   _____   _____

17. "Out of your mouths be it. Just as I contended right along. No mere dog could have done what he did. He's a wolf." [1906; American]

   _____   _____

18. ". . . You're Tom Willard's son and you'll wake up. I'm not afraid. What you say clears things up. If being a newspaper man had put the notion of becoming a writer into your mind that's all right." [1919; American]

   _____   _____

19. "An epilogue is more than a body count. An epilogue, in the disguise of wrapping up the past, is really a way of warning us about the future." [1978; American]

   _____   _____

20. "Oh, he's dead, Heathcliff! He's dead!" [1847; English]

   _____   _____

21. "Ory, I got one thing to say, and I'm sayin' it now, and then I'll have no more talk of it. The leethe fawn's as welcome in this house as Jody. It's hissen. We'll raise it without grudgment o' milk or meal." [1938; American]

   _____   _____

22. "I first met him in Piraeus. I wanted to take the boat for Crete and had gone down to the port." [1946; Greek]

   _____   _____

Name _____ Date _____ Period _____

NOVELS IN OTHER WORDS

Here is a test of your ability to see novels (or at least their titles) in a whole new way. The words within the title have been translated into their dictionary definitions.

Example: The Wife of the King from the Dark Continent is another way of saying *The African Queen* by E. M. Forster.

How many of these American, English, or world novel titles can you identify from their new dictionary format? Score *two points* if you can identify the title without the help of the author's name and *one point* if you need the author's name. The author's names are listed on the page following these questions as an extra hint.

Notes: (1) In most cases the letters of the words in the revised title are in lower case unless the situation demands otherwise.

(2) The novels in this section were written by authors whose last names fall between the letters A through H inclusive.

(3) An author may have more than one novel in a section.

1. A story of a couple of centers of population larger or more important than a town or village

_____

2. Small females _____

3. The foreigner _____

4. Exaggerated self-esteem and bigotry _____

5. Very strong, virile, and agile man of the Gibbons _____

6. The two bones that hold the teeth and frame the mouth _____

7. Not talking season of the year _____

8. Killing upon the Eastern Railway characterized by speed _____

9. Within very chilly red fluid, consisting of plasma and red and white blood cells _____

_____

10. Half a score of Native Americans _____

11. Out of sight Homo Sapien _____

12. A fortress on a commanding height for defense of a city _____

13. Derivative of Adelaide's encountering of danger within imaginary land replete with marvels

_____

14. Rigor mortis arrives for one of the chief members of the church's hierarchy _____

15. The Reviving _____

16. Difficult periods between events _____

17. A very sad event of a United States citizen _____

18. Fragile is the day's opposite _____

19. A triad of soldiers armed with smoothbore, long-barreled firearm used by infantry soldiers

before the invention of the rifle _____

NOVELS IN OTHER WORDS (continued)

20. A movement from one place to the country whose capital is New Delhi _____

21. A setting free _____

22. Misdemeanor and penalty imposed upon offender _____

23. The unknown partaker _____

24. Gloomy abode _____

25. The female sibling whose name is the diminutive of Caroline _____

26. The man in the Garden of Eden whose surname is that of the venerable English historian and theologian whose feast day is May 27 _____

27. Biblical David's favorite son, biblical David's favorite son! _____

28. Large to an unspecified degree _____

29. A chamber possessing a range of vision _____

30. *Carpe diem* _____

31. A person of great size _____

32. Illumination during the eighth month _____

33. The very foolish person _____

34. The unidentifiable noise and the violent anger _____

35. The color that varies in hue from that of blood to pale rose or pink distinctive emblem of bravery _____

36. Wind or coil, you male, whose name means a host or army _____

37. Absence of light that possesses the hollow, muscular organ (in a vertebrate animal) that receives blood from the veins _____

38. The clearly explained hominid _____

39. Fermented use of grapes from a common weed with jagged leaves often used as greens _____

_____

40. The highway of a genus Nicotiana _____

41. Leave to reveal the object on the natural raised part of the earth's surface _____

42. This surface of the Garden of Eden _____

43. Courageous recently current earth _____

44. Unripe stately residences _____

45. Beclouded apostle whose feast day is October 28 _____

46. Missing line where the sky seems to meet the earth _____

47. The alphabet character that is very bright red with a slightly orange tinge _____

48. The aged adult male human being plus the large body of salt water wholly or partly enclosed by land _____

49. The coming back of the original inhabitant of the region _____

50. Master of the dipterous insect _____

THE AUTHORS OF NOVELS IN OTHER WORDS

1. Charles Dickens
2. Louisa May Alcott
3. Albert Camus
4. Jane Austen
5. Edgar Rice Burroughs
6. Peter Benchley
7. Rachel Carson
8. Agatha Christie
9. Truman Capote
10. Agatha Christie
11. Ralph Ellison
12. A. J. Cronin
13. Lewis Carroll
14. Willa Cather
15. Kate Chopin
16. Charles Dickens
17. Theodore Dreiser
18. F. Scott Fitzgerald
19. Alexander Dumas
20. E. M. Forster
21. James Dickey
22. Fyodor Dostoyevsky
23. Joseph Conrad
24. Charles Dickens
25. Theodore Dreiser
26. George Eliot
27. William Faulkner
28. Edna Ferber
29. E. M. Forster
30. Saul Bellow
31. Edna Ferber
32. William Faulkner
33. Fyodor Dostoyevsky
34. William Faulkner
35. Stephen Crane
36. Charles Dickens
37. Joseph Conrad
38. Ray Bradbury
39. Ray Bradbury
40. Erskine Caldwell
41. James Baldwin
42. F. Scott Fitzgerald
43. Aldous Huxley
44. W. H. Hudson
45. Thomas Hardy
46. James Hilton
47. Nathaniel Hawthorne
48. Ernest Hemingway
49. Thomas Hardy
50. William Golding

MORE NOVELS IN OTHER WORDS

Complete instructions can be found in the previous activity. The authors whose works are used in this section all have last names that begin with the letters J through P inclusive.

Remember you earn *two points* if you know the answer without the help of the author's name and *one point* if you need the author's name to correctly identify the novel's title. The list of authors is found after the last question.

1. The rotation of the mechanical device for fastening things _____

2. Those who live in Ireland's capital city _____

3. Out of this place to continuance without end _____

4. Sea vessel of persons with little sense _____

5. Brave chiefs _____

6. Upon the highway _____

7. Something traveled through the air above the snug retreat of the bird _____

8. The city of the Massachusetts witch trials' decision or choice _____

9. Male offspring and sweethearts _____

10. A town's most important public road _____

11. The hollow, muscular organ that receives blood from the veins and pumps it through the

    arteries is a isolated pursuer _____

12. The color containing all the visible rays of the spectrum canine tooth _____

13. Slavery typical of man _____

14. Departed in the company of the air in motion _____

15. Weep, the dearly loved land of one's birth _____

16. The bell-shaped container or cover made of glass used to keep gases, air, moisture, etc., in

    or out _____

17. 992 + 992 _____

18. Intelligent red fluid consisting of plasma, red and white blood cells, etc. _____

    _____

19. Forcible resistance to constituted authority upon the reward for killing certain harmful

    animals _____

MORE NOVELS IN OTHER WORDS (continued)

20. The sea animal possessing a soft, saclike body, a reduced coelum, an internal vestigal shell, and eight sucker-bearing arms around the mouth _____

21. The distinctive cry of the untamed _____

22. To put the passerine bird noted for its song to death _____

23. A severed absence of war _____

24. The permanent ending of life in the Italian city noted for its canals _____

25. The helper _____

26. The diminutive of William partly opened flower _____

27. The formal examination of the facts of a case by a court of law to decide the validity of a charge or claim _____

28. A verbal description of the person skilled in the fine arts when he was a youthful hominid

    _____

29. A common plant of the composite family bearing flowers with white rays around a yellow disk plus a person who operates a mill _____

30. The mender _____

THE AUTHORS OF MORE NOVELS IN OTHER WORDS

1. Henry James
2. James Joyce
3. James Jones
4. Katherine Anne Porter
5. Rudyard Kipling
6. Jack Kerouac
7. Ken Kesey
8. Stephen King
9. D. H. Lawrence
10. Sinclair Lewis
11. Carson McCullers
12. Jack London
13. W. Somerset Maugham
14. Margaret Mitchell
15. Alan Paton
16. Sylvia Plath (under the pseudonym Victoria Lewis)
17. George Orwell
18. Flannery O'Connor
19. Charles Nordoff and James Norman Hall
20. Frank Norris
21. Jack London
22. Harper Lee
23. John Knowles
24. Thomas Mann
25. Bernard Malamud
26. Herman Melville
27. Franz Kafka
28. James Joyce
29. Henry James
30. Bernard Malamud

THE NOVEL TOWN CRIER
PART ONE

In this exercise the Town Crier will tell you what happens in forty novels from around the world. His novel summaries contain clues related to the plot of that specific novel. The novel's author is given. Write the correct novel title on the line beneath each clue. The first one is done for you.

1. Judge plans to kill ten on Indian Island.
   _____*And Then There Were None*_____ Agatha Christie

2. Religious family's son goes to the electric chair in New York for drowning female companion.
   _____ Theodore Dreiser

3. German youths head for the front lines in WWI.
   _____ Erich Maria Remarque

4. Runaway slave boy spotted along Mississippi riverbank.
   _____ Mark Twain

5. Three country boys, alive and well, hear their own eulogies.
   _____ Mark Twain

6. Navy man will hang for killing shipmate; speech impediment cited as possible cause of murder.
   _____ Herman Melville

7. Social misfit takes sister, Phoebe, for carousel ride in Central Park.
   _____ J. D. Salinger

8. Judge Miller's dog kidnapped from sunny California and brought to the Yukon.
   _____ Jack London

9. Softball accident brings on friendship between two New York City Jewish boys.
   _____ Chaim Potok

10. Shark puts fear into Amity, Long Island, residents.
    _____ Peter Benchley

11. Pawnbroker's killer, thinking himself a superman, headed for Siberia.
    _____ Fyodor Dostoyevsky

12. Okies head out for California to survive.
    _____ John Steinbeck

13. Mystery of canine on moors solved by master sleuth of Baker Street.
    _____ Sir Arthur Conan Doyle

14. Kurtz witnesses the horror, the horror.
    _____ Joseph Conrad

15. Welsh boy finds father dead in mines.
    _____ Richard Llewellyn

16. Evacuated English boys rescued by navy man on island after companions are murdered.
    _____ William Golding

17. Keating, English teacher at boys' school, fired by conservative administration; students protest.
    _____ N. H. Kleinbaum

18. Winston Smith is tortured in Room 101.
    _____ George Orwell

THE NOVEL TOWN CRIER (PART ONE) (continued)

19. Man goes fishing eighty-four days straight without a catch.

   _____ Ernest Hemingway

20. Airborne protagonist who visits the Darlings refuses to mature.

   _____ J. M. Barrie

21. Hindu, friend of Govinda, finds fulfillment on river.

   _____ Herman Hesse

22. Look-alike man goes to guillotine for his friend.

   _____ Charles Dickens

23. New England minister admits guilt from scaffold.

   _____ Nathaniel Hawthorne

24. Maycomb County, Alabama, lawyer's children attacked in woods.

   _____ Harper Lee

25. Oedipal Complex stymies Welshman Morel's development.

   _____ D. H. Lawrence

26. New England's Devon School to hold Winter Carnival.

   _____ John Knowles

27. Collapsed Peruvian bridge accident forces minister to probe deaths of five people.

   _____ Thornton Wilder

28. Young newspaper reporter is disenchanted with midwestern small-town narrowmindedness.

   _____ Sherwood Anderson

29. Can Dad and Mom marry off their five daughters?

   _____ Jane Austen

30. Harlem youth surrounded by visions of demons during conversion.

   _____ James Baldwin

31. Before burning them, fireman memorizes books for preservation purposes.

   _____ Ray Bradbury

32. English governess to wed man with insane wife.

   _____ Charlotte Brontë

33. Starving Chinese woman kills her newborn.

   _____ Pearl S. Buck

34. Armagh family meets up with many misfortunes.

   _____ Taylor Caldwell

35. Mersault kills Arab beneath hot Algerian sun.

   _____ Albert Camus

36. New York lawyer tells all about memorable Nebraskan farm woman.

   _____ Willa Cather

37. Earth-mother tries to keep plains family together.

   _____ Willa Cather

38. Knight-errant attacks windmill.

   _____ Miguel de Cervantes

39. Illegal posse lynches cattle rustlers.

   _____ Walter Van Tilburg Clark

40. Feminist poet's attempted suicide brings her brother to New York City.

   _____ Pat Conroy

THE NOVEL TOWN CRIER
PART TWO

In this exercise the Town Crier will tell you what happens in forty novels from around the world. His novel summaries contain clues related to the plot of that specific novel. The novel's author is given. Write the correct novel title on the line beneath each clue. The first one is done for you.

1. Chancellorsville causes young Union soldier to flee.

   _____*The Red Badge of Courage*_____ Stephen Crane

2. Space satellite lands in Arizona; only two people are alive.

   _____ Michael Crichton

3. Former child bottle labeler marries Dora Spenlow.

   _____ Charles Dickens

4. Boy's prospective patron arrested; money confiscated.

   _____ Charles Dickens

5. Boy trained as pickpocket by Fagin.

   _____ Charles Dickens

6. Mother dies of adder bite; daughter-in-law drowns herself.

   _____ Thomas Hardy

7. Scentshop owner tries to protect brother from their malevolent cousin, a judge.

   _____ Nathaniel Hawthorne

8. Horse falls and crushes soldier's leg in Spanish Civil War.

   _____ Ernest Hemingway

9. Dmitry arrested in buffoon's murder.

   _____ Fyodor Dostoyevsky

10. Stage star abandons bar owner Hurstwood, who then commits suicide.

    _____ Theodore Dreiser

11. At Manderley, widower's new wife haunted by memories of first wife.

    _____ Daphne DuMaurier

12. Sacked, imprisoned sailor thrown into sea.

    _____ Alexander Dumas

13. Handloom weaver's name cleared sixteen years later.

    _____ George Eliot

14. Unembalmed Yoknapatawpha County person's body attracts vultures.

    _____ William Faulkner

15. Benjy, Quentin, and Jason tell of their decaying aristocratic Mississippi family.

    _____ William Faulkner

16. Physician accused of sexual assault in Marabar Caves.

    _____ E. M. Forster

17. Prospective baseball player, on way to major-league tryout, is shot by woman.

    _____ Bernard Malamud

18. Dog sold for a bottle of liquor.

    _____ Jack London

19. Wartime American ambulance driver and nurse-lover escape to Switzerland.

_____ Ernest Hemingway

20. DeGaulle is the target of mercenary.

_____ Frederick Forsyth

21. Nurse Ratched wants McMurphy lobotomized.

_____ Ken Kesey

22. Diamond smuggler, involved in blackmail and adultery, commits suicide.

_____ Graham Greene

23. "Zip and zowie" real-estate broker vacations in Maine with tar roofer.

_____ Sinclair Lewis

24. 16 June 1904—A Dublin day to remember!

_____ James Joyce

25. Doctor invalidates bubonic plague antitoxin testing.

_____ Sinclair Lewis

26. Humphrey and Maud escape Wolf and _The Ghost_.

_____ Jack London

27. Divorced psychiatrist abandons his Swiss clinic.

_____ F. Scott Fitzgerald

28. Calvin Coolidge High School welcomes first-year teacher Sylvia Barrett.

_____ Bel Kaufman

29. Bok accused of ritual murder of Christian boy in czarist Russia.

_____ Bernard Malamud

30. Gardener impresses U.S. President with advice.

_____ Jerzy Kosinski

31. Carol Milford and son leave Gopher Prairie, Minnesota, to join in war effort.

_____ Sinclair Lewis

32. Pubkeeper rues over Phoenix Park incident.

_____ James Joyce

33. Emasculated American newsman drinks heavily in Pampalona with tennis friend.

_____ Ernest Hemingway

34. Sutpen's Hundred burns down.

_____ William Faulkner

35. Samsa becomes monstrous vermin.

_____ Franz Kafka

36. Florence hotel room situation displeases couple.

_____ E. M. Forster

37. Irish schoolboy is guilt-ridden over sexual transgression.

_____ James Joyce

38. Mineworkers' boss is both raconteur and rake.

_____ Nikos Kazantzakis

39. Troy, thought drowned, reappears before wife after she becomes engaged to former suitor.

_____ Thomas Hardy

40. Lower-class English bank clerk killed by Charles Wilcox.

_____ E. M. Forster

THE NOVEL TOWN CRIER
PART THREE

In this exercise the Town Crier will tell you what happens in twenty-five novels from around the world. His novel summaries contain clues related to the plot of that specific novel. The novel's author is given. Write the correct novel title on the line beneath each clue. The first one is done for you.

1. Pansy is daughter of Madame Merle's extramarital affair.

   _____ *The Portrait of a Lady* _____ Henry James

2. Adulterous, debt-ridden doctor's wife takes her life.

   _____ Gustave Flaubert

3. Mindbender bombs his own base.

   _____ Joseph Heller

4. Thirty-two-year-old man, desiring to become smart, is outwitted by mouse.

   _____ Daniel Keyes

5. Sherman destroys Atlanta and Tara, the family estate.

   _____ Margaret Mitchell

6. Successful author dies of cholera in Italy.

   _____ Thomas Mann

7. Southern deaf-mute commits suicide after his best friend, another deaf-mute, dies.

   _____ Carson McCullers

8. Cook and six-year-old help adolescent girl cope with her brother's upcoming wedding.

   _____ Carson McCullers

9. Ahab, leg bitten off by whale, violently pursues him.

   _____ Herman Melville

10. Denver is in Cincinnati.

    _____ Toni Morrison

11. Legend says a dead man can fly.

    _____ Toni Morrison

12. Farmers take on the Pacific and Southern Railroad.

    _____ Frank Norris

13. Grotesques attracted to Church of Christ without Christ.

    _____ Flannery O'Connor

14. Pigs help to establish the Seven Commandments.

    _____ George Orwell

15. Yuri, a Russian doctor and Lara's lover, dies.

    _____ Boris Pasternak

16. Zulu clergyman's son faces execution on murder charge.

    _____ Alan Paton

© 1994 by The Center for Applied Research in Education

17. Women's magazine writer counseled by psychiatrist.

    _____ Sylvia Plath

18. Objectivist architect, quite independent, refuses to accept mediocrity.

    _____ Ayn Rand

19. Railroad executive, Dagny Taggart, ruing the loss of creative men in society, seeks to destroy the Destroyer.

    _____ Ayn Rand

20. Teenagers Hermie, Oscy, and Benji spend the wartime summer off the coast of Maine.

    _____ Herman Raucher

21. Father, bitten by rattlesnake, must kill doe; her fawn becomes son's playmate.

    _____ Marjorie Kinnan Rawlings

22. Creole heiress is mad Mrs. Rochester of Thornfield Hall.

    _____ Jean Rhys

23. Glass says that the fat lady in the audience is Christ.

    _____ J. D. Salinger

24. Gunfighter, escaping his past, settles in with the Wyoming Starretts.

    _____ Jack Schaefer

25. Monster is product of natural philosophy student's work with inanimate matter.

    _____ Mary Shelley

THE NOVEL TOWN CRIER
PART FOUR

In this exercise the Town Crier will tell you what happens in twenty-five novels from around the world. His novel summaries contain clues related to the plot of that specific novel. The novel's author is given. Write the correct novel title on the line beneath each clue. The first one is done for you.

1. Australians await death as atomic war repercussions drift southward.

   _____ *On the Beach* _____ Neville Shute

2. Packingtown poor man's son drowns in sewage.

   _____ Upton Sinclair

3. Migrant ranch hand kills retarded friend out of mercy.

   _____ John Steinbeck

4. Kino's find spells possible disaster for family.

   _____ John Steinbeck

5. Doctor discovers drug to create separate personality for himself.

   _____ Robert Louis Stevenson

6. Transylvania resident to move to England.

   _____ Bram Stoker

7. Mr. Legree mistreats former Kentuckian.

   _____ Harriet Beecher Stowe

8. Polish-Catholic woman makes decision on her child's life.

   _____ William Styron

9. Slave rebellion leader awaits execution for killing Whitehead.

   _____ William Styron

10. Adulterous woman leaps under a train.

    _____ Leo Tolstoy

11. Gollum briefs Bilbo on sinister ring.

    _____ J.R.R. Tolkien

12. Middle-earthians head for Mordor to destroy object in the fires.

    _____ J.R.R. Tolkien

13. Male rabbits travel across English downs in search of new home and women.

    _____ Richard Adams

14. Fogg and Passepartout win circumnavigation wager.

    _____ Jules Verne

15. During time-trip, shell-shocked soldier visits distant planet to learn about time and free will.

    _____ Kurt Vonnegut, Jr.

© 1994 by The Center for Applied Research in Education

16. Incestuous father sells Celie's two children.

   _____ Alice Walker

17. Journalist's investigations lead to suicide of Southern judge, his real father.

   _____ Robert Penn Warren

18. Traveler and machine disappear after discovery of Morlocks and a dying sun.

   _____ H. G. Wells

19. Newspaper advice columnist suffers emotional breakdown before being shot by crippled, re-
   vengeful husband.

   _____ Nathanael West

20. Yale graduate's "The Burning of Los Angeles" mural becomes reality.

   _____ Nathanael West

21. Two crippled in New England sledding accident.

   _____ Edith Wharton

22. Man with knife in heart found next to painting.

   _____ Oscar Wilde

23. Altamont, North Carolina, twenty-year-old leaves home to become a writer.

   _____ Thomas Wolfe

24. Investment banker and his Mercedes find difficulties in the South Bronx.

   _____ Tom Wolfe

25. Well-traveled, famous author, realizing happy days are gone, finds solace and inspiration in
   ordinary people around him.

   _____ Thomas Wolfe

A NOVEL WORLD WITHOUT VOWELS

Suppose for a while that the English language consists only of consonants. Vowels are nonexistent. How many titles of the world's greatest novels would you recognize?

Here is your opportunity to be an expert who can readily identify literary titles without the help of vowels. It is important to remember that if a title has more than one word, the examples don't show you where the words begin and end. If the first letter that appears in the clue is a capital letter, that letter is the initial letter in the work's title. The examples have no apostrophes, commas, periods, and other marks of punctuation found in the titles.

If you would like a little help, use Column B for assistance. If not, simply block it out. Example: Grtxpcttns is really Great Expectations.

NOVELS

Column A		Column B
1. lcsdvntrsnwndrlnd	_____	Lewis Carroll
2. Thrdbdgfcrge	_____	Stephen Crane
3. Thgrtgtsby	_____	F. Scott Fitzgerald
4. nvsblmn	_____	Ralph Ellison
5. Crmndpnshmnt	_____	Fyodor Dostoyevsky
6. Dnqxt	_____	Miguel de Cervantes
7. Jnyr	_____	Charlotte Brontë
8. Rbnsncrs	_____	Daniel Defoe
9. Thdvntrsfhcklbrryfnn	_____	Mark Twain
10. Gllvrstrvls	_____	Jonathan Swift
11. nmlfrm	_____	George Orwell
12. Frnknstn	_____	Mary Shelley
13. Thgrpsfwrth	_____	John Steinbeck
14. Thclrprpl	_____	Alice Walker
15. Ntvsn	_____	Richard Wright
16. Prdndprjdc	_____	Jane Austen
17. Gtlltnthmntn	_____	James Baldwin
18. Tmjns	_____	Henry Fielding
19. Snsndlvrs	_____	D. H. Lawrence
20. prtrtfthrtstsyngmn	_____	James Joyce

A NOVEL WORLD WITHOUT VOWELS (continued)

21. Thscrltlttr _____ Nathaniel Hawthorne

22. frwlltrms _____ Ernest Hemingway

23. Bbbtt _____ Sinclair Lewis

24. Dthnvnc _____ Thomas Mann

25. Brvnwwrld _____ Aldous Huxley

26. Thryswrwtchnggd _____ Zora Neale Hurston

27. Thctchrnthry _____ J. D. Salinger

28. Ivnh _____ Sir Walter Scott

29. Vntyfr _____ William M. Thackeray

30. Fthrsndsns _____ Ivan Turgenev

31. Thprtrtfldy _____ Henry James

32. Mbydck _____ Herman Melville

33. Wthrnghghts _____ Emily Brontë

34. dmbd _____ George Eliot

35. Jsphndrws _____ Henry Fielding

36. Dvdcpprfld _____ Charles Dickens

37. tlftwcts _____ Charles Dickens

38. Wnsbrgh _____ Sherwood Anderson

39. mdmbvry _____ Gustave Flaubert

40. nnkrnn _____ Leo Tolstoy

41. ncltmscbn _____ Harriet B. Stowe

42. omcndmn _____ John Steinbeck

43. Thblljr _____ Sylvia Plath

44. Thstrngr _____ Albert Camus

45. Nrthngrbby _____ Jane Austen

46. Crythblvdcntry _____ Alan Paton

47. Thbrthrskrmzv _____ Fyodor Dostoyevsky

48. llthkngsmn _____ Robert Penn Warren

49. Mrsdllwy _____ Virginia Woolf

50. Hrtfdrknss _____ Joseph Conrad

PULITZER PRIZE WINNERS' GRID

The names of twenty-one Pulitzer prize-winning novels are found in the forty-eight-square grid below. Simply cross out each word as you remember each novel's titles. When you are finished all the words in the grid should have been used. The names of the winning authors and the year they won the prize are listed on the next page. Fill in the name of the novel on the blank line.

The words *a, an, and, of,* and *the* are not in the grid though they are found in the titles of some of these winning novels. Use these words when needed.

The first one, *The Age of Innocence,* is done for you.

Grapes	Caine	in	Killer	All	Gone
Daughter	Old	So	South	Age	Death
Repose	Turner	Wind	with	Bell	Tales
Sea	for	Angels	Wrath	Men	Innocence
House	Mockingbird	Good	Yearling	Man	Big
Earth	Optimist's	To	Angle	House	Adano
King's	Nat	Pacific	Confessions	Kill	Made
Reivers	Dawn	Fixer	Family	Keepers	Mutiny

PULITZER PRIZE WINNERS' GRID (continued)

YEAR	AUTHOR	NOVEL
1921	Edith Wharton	_____
1925	Edna Ferber	_____
1932	Pearl S. Buck	_____
1937	Margaret Mitchell	_____
1939	Marjorie Kinnan Rawlings	_____
1940	John Steinbeck	_____
1945	John Hersey	_____
1947	Robert Penn Warren	_____
1948	James Michener	_____
1952	Herman Wouk	_____
1953	Ernest Hemingway	_____
1958	James Agee	_____
1961	Harper Lee	_____
1963	William Faulkner	_____
1965	Shirley Ann Grau	_____
1967	Bernard Malamud	_____
1968	William Styron	_____
1969	N. Scott Momaday	_____
1972	Wallace Stegner	_____
1973	Eudora Welty	_____
1975	Michael Shaara	_____

PULITZER PRIZE ANNOUNCEMENTS

Pretend that you have been in the banquet hall each year that the Pulitzer Prize for Fiction Winners have been acknowledged. Here are the announcements for those literary works that have won the Pulitzer Prize for Fiction over the years. See how many blanks you can fill with the correct author, work, or year.

1. "Is it merely coincidental that Joe DiMaggio's former team, The New York Yankees, won this year's World Series since this year's award-winning novel contains DiMaggio's name? We

   congratulate Ernest Hemingway for _____."

2. "In this year that the science field celebrates Alexander Fleming's discovery of penicillin, we in the literary world also recognize and congratulate Thornton Wilder for his Pulitzer Prize-

   winning novel _____."

3. "In this year that *Gone with the Wind* has captured the Oscar for Best Picture, the Pulitzer

   Prize winner for fiction in the year _____ is *The Yearling* by Marjorie Kinnan Rawlings."

4. "The 1982 winner for fiction is *Rabbit, Run.* Will _____ please come up to receive his award?"

5. "Though there was no Pulitzer Prize for Drama this year, let us not diminish the accom-

   plishment of Robert Penn Warren for his novel, _____."

6. "In this year that Ronald Reagan was elected President, we have selected _____

   _____'s *The Executioner's Song* for this prestigious award."

7. "This year, with the conviction of Sacco and Vanzetti, the question of innocence has been on everyone's mind. This year's Pulitzer Prize winner contains the word *innocence* in its title.

   Let's hear it for _____ and her book _____."

8. "This was certainly a sad year considering the assassination of John F. Kennedy and the death of our beloved Pope John XXIII. We have decided to award this year's prize posthu-

   mously to _____ for his work entitled *The Reivers.*"

9. "Gorbachev has been elected Soviet President and the Republicans have nominated George Bush for the presidency. Alfred Uhry's *Driving Miss Daisy* has won the Pulitzer Drama

   Award. Our Fiction winner this year is Toni Morrison for _____."

10. "We applauded Kaufman and Hart for their winning efforts with *You Can't Take It With You.* But we want the author of *Gone with the Wind* to take this Fiction prize home with her.

    _____, please come forward to receive your award."

11. "All of us certainly enjoyed her earlier novel, *Dinner at the Homesick Restaurant.* The 1989

    Pulitzer winner for Fiction is _____ for her novel *Breathing Lessons.*"

12. "This author's *Andersonville* is the story of the famous Confederate prison. We congratulate

    this year's recipient _____."

13. "The Berlin Wall was erected this year to stop the flood of refugees. But Harper Lee in her book _____ did a fine job in trying to break down the barriers of racial hatred."

14. "In this year's drama voting, I'm sure William Saroyan will begin to enjoy his award for _The Time of Your Life_. Yet the Joads did not have the time of their lives as they headed for California in _____'s book _____."

15. "In a year beset with the problems of war and, fortunately, the establishment of the United Nations, perhaps it is fitting that _____'s _A Bell for Adano,_ which recounts the American occupation of Italy, is the prize-winning book."

16. "We sadly announce that this year's winner, _____, has refused to accept his award for his novel, _Arrowsmith_. He believes that since the prize is not given for literary merit but for the best presentation of the wholesome atmosphere of American life, he will not accept his award."

17. "In the Pulitzer field this year, 1967, Anne Sexton has captured the Poetry Award for her _Live or Die;_ Edward Albee's _A Delicate Balance_ is the Drama winner and _____'s _The Fixer_ is the Fiction champion."

18. "In 1968 we honor William Styron for his novel, _____, which focuses on the 1831 slave rebellion in Virginia."

19. "Tennessee Williams has won the Drama Pulitzer for his play, _A Streetcar Named Desire_. We honor the Fiction winner _____ for his wonderful book, _Tales of the South Pacific._"

20. "Today with the world beset with problems of famine in the USSR, Japanese aggression toward Manchuria, and Charles Lindbergh's baby's kidnaping, the title of the prize-winning book, _The Good Earth,_ might sound as though we are being facetious. We acknowledge the author of this book, _____."

21. "You might remember this author for her novel _Delta Wedding_ and her novellas, _The Robber Bridegroom_ and _The Ponder Heart_. Today with her novel, _The Optimist's Daughter,_ _____ now joins the ranks of other Pulitzer Prize winners."

22. "This year Russell Baker's _Growing Up_ is our winner in the category of Biography or Autobiography. Continuing Baker's theme, this novelist's winning book, _The Color Purple_, takes in thirty years of the book's Southern protagonist, Celie. Will _____ please come up to the podium to receive her award?"

23. "This author's offering, which features his own name in its title, is our Pulitzer Prize winner for 1979. Let us congratulate _____ for _____."

24. "I'm sure you remember his 1906 account of the Chicago stockyards and the meat-packing industry. Will the author of this year's winning book, _Dragon's Teeth,_ _____, please come forward to accept his award?"

25. "This year there is no winner in the category of Pulitzer Prize for Fiction. Name the nine years that this was announced." _____

© 1994 by The Center for Applied Research in Education

ENGLISH AND IRISH NOVELISTS' EARLIEST WRITINGS

Below are the early writings of famous English and Irish authors. Sometimes the quality of these writings palls in comparison to the novelist's more renowned later work. In other instances the first writing was the most famous one. Identify the authors who are listed below in alphabetical order.

	NOVELIST	EARLIER WRITING	MORE FAMOUS WRITING
1.	_____	*Sense and Sensibility*	*Pride and Prejudice*
2.	_____	*Falkland*	*The Last Days of Pompeii*
3.	_____	*The Mysterious Affair at Styles*	*And Then There Were None*
4.	_____	*Antonia; or, The Fall of Rome*	*The Moonstone*
5.	_____	*Almayer's Folly*	*Heart of Darkness*
6.	_____	*The Consolidator*	*Robinson Crusoe*
7.	_____	*Sketches by Boz*	*David Copperfield*
8.	_____	*Scenes of Clerical Life* (stories)	*Silas Marner*
9.	_____	*An Apology for the Life of Mrs. Shamela Andrews*	*Tom Jones*
10.	_____	*The Shifting of the Fire*	*The Good Soldier*
11.	_____	*Napoleon and His Court*	*The African Queen*
12.	_____	*Where Angels Fear to Tread*	*A Passage to India*
13.	_____	*Jocelyn*	*The Forsythe Sage*
14.	_____	*The Man Within*	*The Power and the Glory*
15.	_____	*Dawn*	*King Solomon's Mine*
16.	_____	*Desperate Remedies*	*The Return of the Native*
17.	_____	*The Purple Land That England Lost*	*Green Mansions*
18.	_____	*Crome Yellow*	*Brave New World*
19.	_____	*Alton Locke, Tailor and Poet*	*Westward Ho!*
20.	_____	*The White Peacock*	*Sons and Lovers*
21.	_____	*The Pilgrim's Regress*	*The Lion, The Witch, and The Wardrobe*
22.	_____	*Lisa of Lambeth*	*Of Human Bondage*
23.	_____	*Once on a Time*	*Winnie-the-Pooh*
24.	_____	*The Left Bank and Other Stories*	*Wide Sargasso Sea*
25.	_____	*Catherine*	*Vanity Fair*
26.	_____	*Decline and Fall*	*Brideshead Revisited*
27.	_____	*The Voyage Out*	*To the Lighthouse*

The following authors hit the mark on their initial published novel:

NOVELIST	NOVEL
28. _____	*Jane Eyre*
29. _____	*Wuthering Heights*
30. _____	*Erewhon; or, Over the Range*
31. _____	*Alice's Adventures in Wonderland*
32. _____	*A Study in Scarlet*
33. _____	*Lord of the Flies*
34. _____	*Pamela*
35. _____	*Frankenstein*
36. _____	*Tristram Shandy*
37. _____	*Dracula*
38. _____	*The Time Machine*
39. _____	*The Picture of Dorian Gray*

IMPORTANT AMERICAN NOVELS

Below are the titles of fifty American novels that students will encounter in their study of the American novel or American literature in general. These literary works are commonly the most often read books in many high school literature programs.

Identify the author of each of these American novels.

TITLE	AUTHOR
1. *The Great Gatsby*	_____
2. *The Old Man and the Sea*	_____
3. *The Adventures of Huck Finn*	_____
4. *Invisible Man*	_____
5. *The Scarlet Letter*	_____
6. *As I Lay Dying*	_____
7. *Of Mice and Men*	_____
8. *To Kill a Mockingbird*	_____
9. *The Grapes of Wrath*	_____
10. *Moby Dick*	_____
11. *A Farewell to Arms*	_____
12. *Go Tell It on the Mountain*	_____
13. *Native Son*	_____
14. *The Awakening*	_____
15. *The Red Badge of Courage*	_____
16. *The Sound and the Fury*	_____
17. *Their Eyes Were Watching God*	_____
18. *The House of the Seven Gables*	_____
19. *The Catcher in the Rye*	_____
20. *Main Street*	_____

IMPORTANT AMERICAN NOVELS (continued)

21. *Billy Budd* _____

22. *Beloved* _____

23. *The Adventures of Tom Sawyer* _____

24. *The Age of Innocence* _____

25. *The Color Purple* _____

26. *A Separate Peace* _____

27. *Fahrenheit 451* _____

28. *The Good Earth* _____

29. *Song of Solomon* _____

30. *Uncle Tom's Cabin* _____

31. *O Pioneers!* _____

32. *An American Tragedy* _____

33. *The Sea Wolf* _____

34. *The Sun Also Rises* _____

35. *The Portrait of a Lady* _____

36. *On the Road* _____

37. *The Bridge of San Luis Rey* _____

38. *Arrowsmith* _____

39. *Ethan Frome* _____

40. *Rabbit, Run* _____

41. *Seventeen* _____

42. *Absalom, Absalom!* _____

43. *A Tree Grows in Brooklyn* _____

44. *The Jungle* _____

45. *The Human Comedy* _____

46. *Catch-22* _____

47. *The Yearling* _____

48. *Gone with the Wind* _____

49. *The Fixer* _____

50. *The Call of the Wild* _____

IMPORTANT ENGLISH NOVELS

Here are fifty British novels that are often studied in either the high school or the college literature class. This section gives you the initials of the book's author. Works by Irish authors are also included in this section. See how proficient you are when it comes to "Brit. Lit."

TITLE	AUTHOR'S INITIALS	AUTHOR'S NAME
1. *Wuthering Heights*	E. B.	_____
2. *Heart of Darkness*	J. C.	_____
3. *Pride and Prejudice*	J. A.	_____
4. *Ulysses*	J. J.	_____
5. *A Passage to India*	E.M.F.	_____
6. *Brave New World*	A. H.	_____
7. *Lord of the Flies*	W. G.	_____
8. *Silas Marner*	G. E.	_____
9. *David Copperfield*	C. D.	_____
10. *Frankenstein*	M. S.	_____
11. *To the Lighthouse*	V. W.	_____
12. *Gulliver's Travels*	J. S.	_____
13. *Robinson Crusoe*	D. D.	_____
14. *The Return of the Native*	T. H.	_____
15. *Animal Farm*	G. O.	_____
16. *A Portrait of the Artist as a Young Man*	J. J.	_____
17. *The Secret Sharer*	J. C.	_____
18. *Jane Eyre*	C. B.	_____
19. *Great Expectations*	C. D.	_____
20. *Howards End*	E.M.F.	_____
21. *Lord Jim*	J. C.	_____
22. *Tom Jones*	H. F.	_____

IMPORTANT ENGLISH NOVELS (continued)

23. *Sons and Lovers*   D.H.L.   _____

24. *The Hound of the Baskervilles*   A.C.D.   _____

25. *How Green Was My Valley*   R. L.   _____

26. *A Tale of Two Cities*   C. D.   _____

27. *1984*   G. O.   _____

28. *Alice's Adventures in Wonderland*   L.C.   _____

29. *Tess of the D'Urbervilles*   T. H.   _____

30. *Of Human Bondage*   W.S.M.   _____

31. *Ivanhoe*   W. S.   _____

32. *Emma*   J. A.   _____

33. *Joseph Andrews*   H. F.   _____

34. *The Good Soldier*   F.M.F.   _____

35. *Dubliners*   J. J.   _____

36. *The Picture of Dorian Gray*   O. W.   _____

37. *Jude the Obscure*   T. H.   _____

38. *Oliver Twist*   C. D.   _____

39. *The Forsyte Saga*   J. G.   _____

40. *Tristram Shandy*   L. S.   _____

41. *Sense and Sensibility*   J. A.   _____

42. *Hard Times*   C. D.   _____

43. *Women in Love*   D.H.L.   _____

44. *Joseph Andrews*   H. F.   _____

45. *The Spy Who Came in from the Cold*   J. L.   _____

46. *A Clockwork Orange*   A. B.   _____

47. *The Rainbow*   D.H.L.   _____

48. *Nostromo*   J. C.   _____

49. *The Mayor of Casterbridge*   T. H.   _____

50. *A Room with a View*   E.M.F.   _____

SECTION 5

SHORT STORIES— MASTERS AND MASTERPIECES

SHORT-STORY TERMS

Match each of the short-story terms with its correct definition.

antagonist	dialect	*in medias res*	rising action	symbol
character	exposition	incident	satire	theme
climax	flashback	locale	style	tone
denouement	framework story	protagonist	suspense	verbal irony

1. _____ the main character or hero of the story

2. _____ a word or phrase that is used for an idea

3. _____ the outcome or unraveling of the plot

4. _____ an author's attitude or point of view

5. _____ the central or dominant idea of the story

6. _____ a story contained within another story

7. _____ ridicule, sarcasm, or irony used to expose man's follies; in the exaggeration of the situation, the author intends the reader to laugh and think about the situation

8. _____ the author's form of expression as determined by his or her syntax and diction

9. _____ the hero's adversary

10. _____ that part of the story that leads up to the climax

11. _____ the author plunges into the middle of story and fills in the necessary details later

12. _____ mental uncertainty leading up to the climax

13. _____ the decisive point of the story; the point of highest interest

14. _____ that part of the story that provides the background of the characters or situation

15. _____ the writer says one thing and means another

16. _____ the scene or setting

17. _____ an event or occurrence in the story

18. _____ language of a particular region

19. _____ a person in the story

20. _____ a scene representing an earlier event

SCRAMBLED SHORT-STORY WRITERS

Unscramble the names of these thirty short-story writers.

1. HACELIME _____

2. RCEBIE _____

3. OEP _____

4. PDIUKE _____

5. AKFKA _____

6. RNCONOO _____

7. TWLYE _____

8. NODOLN _____

9. GGOOL _____

10. EALGSINR _____

11. LEALWLCD _____

12. RHATWNO _____

13. REOPRT _____

14. NAMN _____

15. UMAGAMH _____

16. OOFWL _____

17. OKHCEHV _____

18. NADLRER _____

19. ELITSILO _____

20. DYLOE _____

21. RNOUYN _____

22. JMSAE _____

23. VUNETERG _____

24. RDESEIR _____

25. ASAEUDMPASNT _____

26. OUNMR _____

27. LIKPING _____

28. ISNAMFELD _____

29. EHYAWGMIN _____

30. NERHAOTHW _____

ROLL CALL OF SHORT-STORY WRITERS
PART ONE

In the blank write the name of the author who wrote each set of short stories.

O. Henry   Jack London   Herman Melville   J. D. Salinger
Sarah Orne Jewett   Bernard Malamud   Flannery O'Connor   Isaac B. Singer
James Joyce   Thomas Mann   Tillie Olsen   James Thurber
Franz Kafka   Katherine Mansfield   Edgar Allan Poe   Leo Tolstoy
D. H. Lawrence   Guy de Maupassant   Katherine A. Porter   Mark Twain

1. _____ "The Celebrated Jumping Frog of Calaveras," "The Man That Corrupted Hadleyburg"

2. _____ "The Death of Ivan Ilyich," "How Much Land Does a Man Need?," "Three Deaths"

3. _____ "The Catbird Seat," "The Secret Life of Walter Mitty"

4. _____ "Gimpel the Fool." "Spinoza of Market Street," "Yentl the Yeshiva Boy"

5. _____ "A Perfect Day for Bananafish," "Uncle Wiggily in Connecticut"

6. _____ "The Black Cat," "The Gold-Bug," "The Tell-Tale Heart"

7. _____ "Flowering Judas," "Pale Horse, Pale Rider"

8. _____ "I Stand Here Ironing," "Tell Me a Riddle"

9. _____ "The Enduring Chill," "Everything That Rises Must Converge," "A Good Man Is Hard to Find"

10. _____ "The Necklace," "The Piece of String"

11. _____ "Bartleby the Scrivener," "Benito Cereno"

12. _____ "Death in Venice," "Disorder and Early Sorrow"

13. _____ "Bliss," "The Fly," "Her First Ball," "Miss Brill"

14. _____ "Idiots First," "The Magic Barrel," "Rembrandt's Hat"

15. _____ "A Piece of Steak," "To Build a Fire"

16. _____ "Odour of Chrysanthemums," "The Rocking-Horse Winner," "The Woman Who Rode Away"

17. _____ "A Hungry Artist," "In the Penal Colony," "The Metamorphosis"

18. _____ "Eveline," "Araby," "The Dead"

19. _____ "A White Heron," "A Native of Winby"

20. _____ "The Gift of the Magi," "The Ransom of Red Chief"

ROLL CALL FOR SHORT-STORY WRITERS
PART TWO

Identify the short-story writers who wrote each set of short stories.

Conrad Aiken	Ray Bradbury	Sir A. C. Doyle	Nathaniel Hawthorne
Sherwood Anderson	John Cheever	William Faulkner	Ernest Hemingway
James Baldwin	Anton Chekhov	F. Scott Fitzgerald	Washington Irving
Ann Beattie	Joseph Conrad	Nikolai Gogol	Shirley Jackson
Ambrose Bierce	Stephen Crane	Nadine Gordimer	Henry James

1. _____ "The Legend of Sleepy Hollow," "Rip Van Winkle"

2. _____ "Charles," "The Lottery"

3. _____ "A Clean, Well-Lighted Place," "The Killers," "The Short Happy Life of Francis Macomber"

4. _____ "The Aspern Papers," "In the Cage," "The Real Thing"

5. _____ "The Ambitious Guest," "The Birthmark," "Dr. Heidegger's Experiment"

6. _____ "The Diary of a Madman," "The Overcoat," "The Nose"

7. _____ "Livingstone's Companions," "The Smell of Death and Flowers," "Town and Country Lovers"

8. _____ "Babylon Revisited," "Diamond as Big as the Ritz"

9. _____ "Barn Burning," "A Rose for Emily," "Wash"

10. _____ "The Blue Hotel," "The Open Boat"

11. _____ "The Red-Headed League," "The Adventure of the Speckled Band"

12. _____ "The Secret Sharer," "The Lagoon"

13. _____ "The Bet," "Gooseberries," "The Kiss"

14. _____ "The Enormous Radio," "The Swimmer"

15. _____ "Impulse," "Silent Snow, Secret Snow"

16. _____ "I Want to Know Why," "I'm a Fool"

17. _____ "Going to Meet the Man," "Sonny's Blues"

18. _____ "Imagined Scenes," "In the White Night"

19. _____ "Chickamauga," "An Occurrence at Owl Creek Bridge"

20. _____ "The April Witch," "There Will Come Soft Rains"

WORLD SHORT-STORY WRITERS WORD FIND

In this grid are the names of fourteen world short-story writers whose stories or short-story collections appear below the grid. The authors' names are placed backwards, forward, diagonally, up and down. Write the author's name next to his or her short story or collection and then locate his or her name within the grid.

```
R  S  D  B  L  J  B  K  V  B  H  M  H  Y  Y  Z  K  J  G  Q  L  F  Q  X
N  Z  C  E  W  V  Y  A  Q  Z  W  F  K  F  Y  T  V  I  O  J  F  K  H  M
T  B  N  H  M  P  C  L  B  S  P  R  H  P  R  L  B  K  P  Y  S  K  J  K
D  O  Y  L  E  A  M  D  L  E  I  F  S  N  A  M  A  N  N  L  C  C  J  Y
G  A  Y  L  K  K  U  D  C  H  L  N  S  Y  S  J  C  W  N  M  I  E  G  S
C  Y  R  F  L  C  H  P  W  F  S  L  G  K  V  F  K  Q  R  S  B  N  S  G
P  D  A  N  N  X  W  O  A  M  H  X  Q  E  R  X  X  Q  B  E  R  R  G  C
L  K  Q  C  O  G  J  Q  V  S  Q  M  F  T  R  G  W  O  Z  D  N  G  N  D
T  C  X  Q  B  C  K  Q  D  G  S  M  M  F  W  K  C  G  P  H  Z  C  M  F
F  G  S  R  S  G  S  A  K  I  N  A  F  K  K  A  Q  Q  B  R  J  C  E  D
X  K  X  P  Z  T  I  Z  I  J  Q  J  N  Q  J  M  X  D  V  X  N  L  B  R
Z  C  P  S  Q  H  T  R  F  C  T  P  J  T  L  Y  X  N  M  X  T  W  Q  X
P  X  D  Y  X  F  P  M  B  Z  T  Z  D  T  M  S  N  P  H  R  F  L  F  T
F  D  X  L  F  M  Z  Z  M  M  M  W  B  V  W  V  D  B  P  R  H  J  W  S
R  B  T  Y  R  C  Q  C  X  H  V  S  T  D  M  F  F  B  H  S  C  M  Z  B
V  M  V  Q  G  H  Z  T  N  G  X  B  G  V  D  C  B  F  D  L  R  R  S  L
J  T  D  D  F  L  D  H  K  Q  H  T  W  D  Q  W  M  F  D  Z  S  K  F  G
```

STORY	AUTHOR
ARABY	_____
CAPTAINS ALL	_____
DISORDER AND EARLY SORROW	_____
HER FIRST BALL	_____
METAMORPHOSIS	_____
ODESSA TALES	_____
THE DEAD FIDDLER	_____
THE KISS	_____
THE MAN WHO WOULD BE KING	_____
THE NECKLACE	_____
THE OPEN WINDOW	_____
THE RED-HEADED LEAGUE	_____
THE ROCKING HORSE WINNER	_____
THE SECRET SHARER	_____

AMERICAN SHORT-STORY WRITERS

In this grid are the names of the twenty-six American short-story writers whose stories or short-story collections appear below the grid. The names are placed backwards, forward, diagonally, up and down. Write the author's name next to his or her short story or collection and then locate his or her name within the grid.

```
S G Y R Y C F H S B M T S B Y C B R B T V T S R
G Z X D R H J S P L R G K P K N Q A E R Y H E M
B J H A G R H O T Y M L D H H Y J H L T C K Z V
L O N D O N E S L O T H U R B E R E N D R A L Q
W E P O Z Z W N C S C T Y W W E M B O A W O Q K
I Q X Y S B G O K N A K S E B M L I P H Q I P D
P R G K E K N V T L T L T T T R H L N G E R N L
W G V Q K N C N G W U T I O E R F P O G B N N C
R D F I O L R A M Q A A T N N I A J S W W O R S
P P Q R N W G O J V W I F C G Q N H Y D S A F Y
R B Q M Y G E F H X G W N T T E R B N R B D Y T
M A L A M U D L J T R J H B C J R C E G S T N X
T W L P Y Q Q D T T W F V V Y V B D R C P W Y Y
N C Q D D N R X K Y R A Z L K C N D G N K T X X
S C N V K G L K C F Y J H D P A W R J H G Z J P
L S P T T S G N G L R X H S S P J Y W V P Z F W
B W X J G Q L N D V K J L V L Z J W L L G X T C
```

SHORT STORY (or Collection)	*AUTHOR*
1. A FATHER TO BE	_____
2. A GOOD MAN IS HARD TO FIND	_____
3. A PERFECT DAY FOR BANANAFISH	_____
4. AFTER TWENTY YEARS	_____
5. BARN BURNING	_____
6. DEEP HAVEN	_____
7. FLIGHT	_____
8. HAIRCUT	_____
9. SONNY'S BLUES	_____
10. TELL ME A RIDDLE	_____
11. THE BIG BLONDE	_____

AMERICAN SHORT-STORY WRITERS (continued)

12. THE BRIDE OF INNISFALLEN   _____

13. THE CELEBRATED JUMPING FROG OF
    CALAVERAS COUNTY   _____

14. THE JILTING OF GRANNY WEATHERALL   _____

15. THE LADY OR THE TIGER?   _____

16. THE LEGEND OF SLEEPY HOLLOW   _____

17. THE LOTTERY   _____

18. THE LUCK OF ROARING CAMP   _____

19. THE OPEN BOAT   _____

20. THE PIT AND THE PENDULUM   _____

21. THE PRISON   _____

22. THE SECRET LIFE OF WALTER MITTY   _____

23. THE SHORT LIFE OF FRANCIS MACOMBER   _____

24. TO BUILD A FIRE   _____

25. WINESBURG, OHIO   _____

26. YOUNG GOODMAN BROWN   _____

THE CHARACTERS OF SHORT STORIES

Match these twenty characters with their short stories.

1. _____ Sammy
2. _____ Sherlock Holmes
3. _____ Amelia Evans
4. _____ Abner Snopes
5. _____ The Young Lawyer
6. _____ Mrs. Hazel Morse
7. _____ Nick Adams
8. _____ Mr. Fitweiler
9. _____ Laurie
10. _____ An older waiter
11. _____ Gabriel Conroy
12. _____ Tadzio
13. _____ Jabez Stone
14. _____ Roderick
15. _____ Jody Tiflin
16. _____ Della
17. _____ Emily
18. _____ Father Brown
19. _____ A semi-barbaric king
20. _____ Ichabod Crane

A. "Barn Burning"

B. "Big Two-Hearted River"

C. "Charles"

D. "The Gift"

E. "The Devil and Daniel Webster"

F. "I Stand Here Ironing"

G. "The Bet"

H. "The Fall of the House of Usher"

I. "A & P"

J. "The Adventure of the Speckled Band"

K. "The Gift of the Magi"

L. "Death in Venice"

M. "The Lady or the Tiger?"

N. "The Catbird Seat"

O. "The Dead"

P. "The Ballad of the Sad Café"

Q. "Big Blonde"

R. "A Clean, Well-Lighted Place"

S. "The Legend of Sleepy Hollow"

T. "The Invisible Man"

MORE CHARACTERS OF SHORT STORIES

Match these twenty characters with their short stories.

1. _____ Smith

2. _____ Prince Prospero

3. _____ Gregor Samsa

4. _____ Sanger Rainsford

5. _____ Mathilde Loisel

6. _____ C. Auguste Dupin

7. _____ Luster Sexton

8. _____ Ebenezer Dorset

9. _____ Framton Nuttel

10. _____ Jabez Wilson

11. _____ John Oakhurst

12. _____ Paul

13. _____ The oiler, Billy

14. _____ Colonel Sartoris

15. _____ Ned Merrill

16. _____ Akaky Bashmachkin

17. _____ Louise Mallard

18. _____ Seymour Glass

19. _____ Samson Vyrin

20. _____ Giovanni Guasconti

A. "The Necklace"

B. "The Open Boat"

C. "The Red-Headed League"

D. "The Loneliness of the Long Distance Runner"

E. "The Outcasts of Poker Flat"

F. "Rappaccini's Daughter"

G. "A Perfect Day for Bananafish"

H. "The Rocking-Horse Winner"

I. "The Purloined Letter"

J. "The Station Master"

K. "The Swimmer"

L. "The Most Dangerous Game"

M. "The Story of an Hour"

N. "The Masque of the Red Death"

O. "The Overcoat"

P. "The Ransom of Red Chief"

Q. "The Metamorphosis"

R. "The Open Window"

S. "The Split Cherry Tree"

T. "A Rose for Emily"

SHORT-STORY WRITERS' CRYPTOLOGY

In this exercise one letter stands for another. There are twenty short-story writers' names in this list. Find the letters that were substituted in the author's name. The first name is done for you.

1. IJS

2. JFJWWJM

3. VOEOVKR

4. QSNSPP

5. ZSVDWTNOL

6. PZKMXSM

7. BOKEAWSM

8. ZOMPS

9. JEGSW

10. J. ZSWML

11. IOMASM

12. GPJFAPJW

13. XOERNDW

14. PNODW

15. FMOWS

16. IJMPSM

17. EJWRJW

18. GPSDWXSFA

19. EOMRWSM

20. OWRSMGJW

1. <u> P </u> <u> O </u> <u> E </u>

2. ___ ___ ___ ___ ___ ___ ___

3. ___ ___ ___ ___ ___ ___ ___

4. ___ ___ ___ ___ ___ ___

5. ___ ___ ___ ___ ___ ___ ___ ___

6. ___ ___ ___ ___ ___ ___

7. ___ ___ ___ ___ ___ ___ ___ ___

8. ___ ___ ___ ___ ___

9. ___ ___ ___ ___ ___

10. ___ . ___ ___ ___ ___ ___

11. ___ ___ ___ ___ ___ ___

12. ___ ___ ___ ___ ___ ___ ___

13. ___ ___ ___ ___ ___ ___

14. ___ ___ ___ ___ ___

15. ___ ___ ___ ___ ___

16. ___ ___ ___ ___ ___ ___

17. ___ ___ ___ ___ ___ ___

18. ___ ___ ___ ___ ___ ___ ___ ___ ___

19. ___ ___ ___ ___ ___ ___ ___

20. ___ ___ ___ ___ ___ ___ ___ ___

Letter Substitution Code Used:

Letter: A B C D E F G H I J K L M N O P Q R S T U V W X Y Z

Substitute: ___ ___ ___ ___ S ___ ___ ___ ___ ___ ___ ___ ___ ___ ___ J I ___ ___ ___ ___ ___ ___ ___ ___ ___

POE'S CHALLENGE . . . THE SHORT-STORY QUOTES

Edgar Allan Poe, the master of the short story, challenges you to correctly answer these excerpts taken from memorable short stories. The short story's author is given after the excerpt. Write the letter assigned to the short story next to the quote. Poe promises he will not scare you if you do well on this challenge.

A. "A & P"
B. "Barn Burning"
C. "Bartleby the Scrivener"
D. "A Cask of Amontillado"
E. "The Catbird Seat"
F. "A Christmas Carol"
G. "The Devil and Daniel Webster"
H. "Dr. Heidegger's Experiment"
I. "The Fall of the House of Usher"
J. "The Gift of the Magi"
K. "I Stand Here Ironing"
L. "The Jilting of Granny Weatherall"
M. "The Lady or the Tiger?"
N. "The Lottery"
O. "Luck"

P. "The Masque of the Red Death"
Q. "The Most Dangerous Game"
R. "The Necklace"
S. "The Open Boat"
T. "The Open Window
U. "The Quiet Man"
V. "The Ransom of Red Chief"
W. "Raymond's Run"
X. "The Red-Headed League"
Y. "Rikki-Tikki-Tavi"
Z. "Rip Van Winkle"
AA. "The Rocking-Horse Winner"
BB. "The Secret Life of Walter Mitty"
CC. "Through the Tunnel"
DD. "To Build a Fire"

1. _____ "I never hope to see such a sight as that again, Mr. Holmes. From north, south, east, and west, every man who had a shade of red in his hair had trampled into the city to answer the advertisement." (Sir Arthur Conan Doyle)

2. _____ "I'm not myself—I'm somebody else—that's not me yonder—no that's somebody else got into my shoes—I was myself last night, but I fell asleep on the mountain, and they've changed my gun . . ." (Washington Irving)

3. _____ "I never told you, mother, that if I can ride my horse, and get there then I'm absolutely sure—oh, absolutely! Mother, did I ever tell you? I am lucky!" (D. H. Lawrence)

4. _____ ". . . I dig my sneaker into the grass and stare at Gretchen who's staring back, we both wondering just who did win." (Toni Cade Bambara)

5. _____ "God bless us, Every One." (Charles Dickens)

6. _____ "For the love of God, Montresor!" (Edgar Allan Poe)

7. _____ "Yes, friends, ye are old again, and lo! the Water of Youth is all lavished on the ground. Well—I bemoan it not; for if the Fountain gushed at my very doorstep, I would not stoop to bathe my lips in it." (Nathaniel Hawthorne)

8. _____ "This case is closed. I can't find against you, Snopes, but I can give you advice. Leave this country and don't come back to it." (William Faulkner)

9. _____ "In walks these three girls in nothing but bathing suits. I'm in the third checkout slot, with my back to the door, so I don't see them until they're over by the bread." (John Updike)

10. _____ "Splendid. One of us is to furnish a repast for the hounds. The other will sleep in this very excellent bed. On guard, Rainsford." (Richard Connell)

11. _____ "While I gazed, this fissure rapidly widened—there came a fierce breath of the whirlwind—the entire orb of the satellite burst at once upon my sight—my brain reeled as I saw the mighty walls rushing asunder . . ." (Edgar Allan Poe)

12. _____ "Oh, my poor Mathilde. But mine was only paste. Why, at most it was worth five hundred francs!" (Guy de Maupassant)

13. _____ "Isn't it a dandy, Jim? I hunted all over town to find it. You'll have to look at the time a hundred times a day now. Give me your watch. I want to see how it looks on it." (O. Henry)

14. _____ "But you're the Union's story and New Hampshire's pride! He musn't get you, Mr. Webster! He musn't get you." (Stephen Vincent Benet)

15. _____ "Get along and doctor your sick. Leave a woman alone. I'll call for you when I want you . . . Where were you forty years ago when I pulled through milk leg and double pneumonia?" (Katherine Anne Porter)

16. _____ "So I leave it all with you. Which came out of the opened door?" (Frank Stockton)

17. _____ "I wish you would manage the time to come in and talk with me about your daughter. I'm sure you can help me understand her. She's a youngster who needs help and whom I'm deeply interested in helping." (Tillie Olsen)

18. _____ "I say again, as I said at the banquet, Scoresby's an absolute fool." (Mark Twain)

19. _____ "Seize him and unmask him—that we may know whom we have to hang, at sunrise, from the battlements!" (Edgar Allan Poe)

20. _____ "You drank and smoked at my apartment and you know it! You called Mr. Fitweiler an old windbag and you were going to blow him up . . ." (James Thurber)

21. _____ "Remember, take the slips and keep them folded until each person has taken one." (Shirley Jackson)

22. _____ "Well, if he'd just signal us to try the surf again, or to go to sea and wait, or go north, or go south, there would be some reason in it. But look at him! He just stands there and keeps his coat revolving like a wheel. The ass!" (Stephen Crane)

23. _____ "Out through that window, three years ago to a day, her husband and her two young brothers went off, for their day's shooting. They never came back." (Saki)

24. _____ "I am Shawn Kelvin of Knockanore Hill. Is there an O'Grady amongst you thinks himself a better man? Come then." (Maurice Walsh)

25. _____ "I would prefer not to." (Herman Melville)

26. _____ "Day had broken cold and gray, exceedingly cold and gray, when the man turned aside from the main Yukon train and climbed the high earth-bank, where a dim and little-traveled trail led eastward through the fat spruce timberland." (Jack London)

27. _____ "Here's a dead mongoose. Let's have a funeral." (Rudyard Kipling)

28. _____ "It looked like a good thing: but wait till I tell you. We were down South, in Alabama—Bill Driscoll and myself—when this kidnapping idea struck us." (O. Henry)

29. _____ "The pounding of the cylinders increased: ta-pocketa-pocketapocketa-pocketa-pocketa." (James Thurber)

30. _____ "Mummy, I can stay under water for two minutes—three minutes at least." (Doris Lessing)

WORLD SHORT-STORY WRITERS

Write the letter of the short-story writer's name who wrote the short story in each number.

_____ 1. "The Man Who Would Be King"

    A. Mann   B. Mansfield C. Saki   D. Kipling

_____ 2. "Captains All"

    A. Singer   B. Jacobs   C. Chekhov   D. Conrad

_____ 3. "The Red-Headed League"

    A. Doyle   B. Lawrence C. Mansfield   D. Joyce

_____ 4. "The Secret Sharer"

    A. Lawrence   B. Kipling   C. Conrad   D. Joyce

_____ 5. "Metamorphosis"

    A. Saki   B. Kafka   C. Mann   D. Chekhov

_____ 6. "The Dead Fiddler"

    A. Singer   B. Doyle   C. Conrad   D. Mann

_____ 7. "Odessa Tales"

    A. Kafka   B. Babel   C. Joyce   D. Conrad

_____ 8. "Araby"

    A. Chekhov   B. Joyce   C. Kipling   D. Babel

_____ 9. "The Kiss"

    A. Mansfield   B. Babel   C. Singer   D. Chekhov

_____ 10. "The Necklace"

    A. DeMaupassant B. Singer   C. Chekhov   D. Kipling

_____ 11. "The Open Window"

    A. Kafka   B. Babel   C. Saki   D. Mann

_____ 12. "The Rocking-Horse Winner"

    A. Mansfield   B. Lawrence C. DeMaupassant D. Chekhov

_____ 13. "Her First Ball"

    A. Joyce   B. Lawrence C. Babel   D. Mansfield

_____ 14. "Disorder and Early Sorrow"

    A. Mann   B. Singer   C. Kipling   D. Mansfield

SECTION 6

THE POET'S CORNER

THE WORDS OF POETRY
PART ONE

Here is your chance to show your poetic inclination! The following twenty excerpts are a real challenge to even the most poetic in the room since they cover so broad a spectrum of poetry. However, the learning experience will be worthwhile. The poet's name follows the poetic excerpt. Write the letter assigned to each poem in the blank next to the appropriate number. Good luck!

A. "Ballad of Birmingham"
B. "Because I Could Not Stop for Death"
C. "Beowulf"
D. "Bonny Barbara Allan"
E. "The Canonization"
F. "Casey at the Bat"
G. "The Collar"

H. "Crossing the Bar"
I. "Daddy"
J. "Death, be not proud"
K. "Death of the Ball Turret Gunner"
L. "Do Not Go Gentle into that Good Night"
M. "Dover Beach"

N. "Dulce et Decorum Est"
O. "Fire and Ice"
P. "The Hollow Men"
Q. "I Knew a Woman"
R. "If"
S. "Jabberwocky"
T. "Leda and the Swan"

1. _____ "O mother, mother, make my bed,
      O make it soft and narrow:
   Since my love died for me today,
      I'll die for him tomorrow."
   Anonymous

2. _____ Beware the Jubjub bird, and shun
      The fruminous Bandersnatch!"
   Lewis Carroll

3. _____ Ah, love, let us be true
   To one another! for the world, which seems
   To lie before us like a land of dreams,
   So various, so beautiful, so new,
   Hath really neither joy, nor love, nor light,
   Nor certitude, nor peace, nor help for pain,
   Matthew Arnold

4. _____ We are the stuffed men
   Leaning together
   Headpiece filled with straw. Alas!
   T. S. Eliot

5. _____   Why swell'st thou then?
   One short sleep passed, we wake eternally,
   And death shall be no more; death, thou shalt die.
   John Donne

6. _____ "No, baby, no, you may not go,
   For I fear those guns will fire.
   But you may go to the church instead
   And sing in the children's choir."
   Dudley Randall

7. _____ I struck the board and cried, "No more;
         I will abroad!
   What? shall I ever sigh and pine?
   My lines and life are free, free as the road,
      Loose as the wind, as large as store.
         Shall I be still in suit?
   George Herbert

8. _____ He kindly stopped for me—
The Carriage held but just ourselves—
And Immortality.
Emily Dickinson

9. _____ From there he sought the folk of the
South-Danes, the Honor Scyldings, over the sea-swell.
Anonymous

10. _____ And you, my father, there on the sad height,
Curse, bless, me now with your fierce tears, I pray.
Dylan Thomas

11. _____ From what I've tasted of desire
I hold with those who favor fire.
Robert Frost

12. _____ For God's sake hold your tongue, and let me love,
    Or chide my palsy, or my gout,
My five gray hairs, or ruined fortune, flout,
    With wealth your state, your mind with arts improve . . .
John Donne

13. _____ The outlook wasn't brilliant for the Mudville nine that day.
Ernest Lawrence Thayer

14. _____ A sudden blow: the great wings beating still
Above the staggering girl, her thighs caressed
By the dark webs, her nape caught in his bill,
He holds her helpless breast upon his breast.
William Butler Yeats

15. _____ For though from far out our bourne of Time and Place
    The flood may bear me far,
I hope to see my Pilot face to face
    When I have crossed the bar.
Alfred Lord Tennyson

16. _____ If you can fill the unforgiving minute
    With sixty seconds' worth of distance run,
Yours is the Earth and everything that's in it,
    And—which is more—you'll be a Man, my son!
Rudyard Kipling

17. _____ You do not do, you do not do
Any more, black shoe
In which I have lived like a foot
For thirty years, poor and white
Barely daring to breathe or Achoo.
Sylvia Plath

18. _____ I knew a woman, lovely in her bones,
When small birds sigh back at them;
Ah, when she moved more ways than one:
The shapes a bright container can contain!
Theodore Roethke

19. _____ From my mother's sleep I fell into the state,
And I hunched in its belly till my wet fur froze.
Randall Jarrell

20. _____ Bent double, like old beggars under sacks,
Knock-kneed, like coughing hags, we cursed through sludge
Till on the haunting flares we turned our backs
And towards our distant rest began to trudge.
Wilfred Owen

THE WORDS OF POETRY
PART TWO

Match the twenty poems below with their excerpts by writing the correct letter in the blank next to the number. The poet's name follows the excerpt.

A. "Ballad of the Landlord"
B. "Base Details"
C. "Battle Hymn of the Republic"
D. "Bells for John Whiteside's Daughter"
E. "Boy at the Window"
F. "Buffalo Bill's Defunct"
G. "Chicago"

H. "Dream Deferred"
I. "Earth"
J. "Elegy Written in a Country Churchyard"
K. "Fern Hill"
L. "The Flea"
M. "For the Union Dead"
N. "The Gift Outright"

O. "In Honor of David Anderson Brooks, My Father"
P. "The Inferno"
Q. "Kubla Khan"
R. "The Lamb"
S. "Last Words"
T. "The Lifeguard"

1. _____ Mine eyes have seen the glory of the coming of the Lord
Julia Ward Howe

2. _____ The curfew tolls the knell of parting day,
    The lowing herd wind slowly o'er the lea,
The ploughman homeward plods his weary way,
    And leaves the world to darkness and to me.
Thomas Gray

3. _____ Oh as I was young and easy in the mercy of his means,
        Time held me green and dying
    Though I sang in my chains like the sea.
Dylan Thomas

4. _____ And when the war is done and youth stone dead,
I'll toddle safely home and die—in bed.
Siegfried Sassoon

5. _____ I do not want a plain box, I want a sarcophagus
With tigery stripes, and a face on it
Round as the moon, to stare up.
Sylvia Plath

6. _____ Once my nose crawled like a snail on the glass;
        my hand tingled
        to burst the bubbles
        drifting from the noses of the cowed, compliant fish.
Robert Lowell

7. _____ The man of snow is, nonetheless, content
Having no wish to go inside and die.
Still, he is moved to see the youngster cry.
Richard Wilbur

8. _____ The land was ours before we were the land's.
She was our land more than a hundred years
Before we were her people. She was ours,
In Massachusetts, in Virginia,
But we were England's, still colonials
Possessing what we still were unpossessed by,
Possessed by what we now no more possessed.
Robert Frost

9. _____ There was such speed in her little body
And such lightness in her football,
It is no wonder her brown study
Astonishes us all.
John Crowe Ransom

10. _____ Does it dry up
like a raisin in the sun?
Or fester like a sore—
And then run?
Langston Hughes

11. _____ And having answered so I turn once more to those who sneer at my city,
Carl Sandburg

12. _____ he was a handsome man

and what I want to know is

how do you like your blueeyed boy
Mister Death
e. e. cummings

13. _____ A dryness is upon the house
My father loved and tended.
Beyond his firm and sculptured door
His light and lease have ended.
Gwendolyn Brooks

14. _____ In the midway of this our mortal life,
I found me in a gloomy wood, astray.
Dante

15. _____ Mark but this flea, and mark in this,
How little that which thou deniest me is;
It sucked me first, and now sucks thee,
And in this flea our two bloods mingled be;
John Donne

16. _____ A damsel with a dulcimer
In a vision once I saw:
It was an Abyssinian maid,
And on her dulcimer she played
Singing of Mount Abora.
Samuel Taylor Coleridge

17. _____ Gave thee life and bid thee feed,
By the stream and o'er the mead;
Gave thee clothing of delight,
Softest clothing wooly bright.
William Blake

18. _____ Landlord, landlord,
My roof has sprung a leak.
Don't you 'member I told you about it
Why last week?
Langston Hughes

19. _____ "A planet doesn't explode of itself . . ."
John Hall Wheelock

20. _____ I wash the black mud from my hands.
On a light given off by the grave
I kneel in the quick of the moon
At the heart of a distant forest
And hold in my arms a child
Of water, water, water.
James Dickey

THE WORDS OF POETRY
PART THREE

These poets whose names follow their excerpts are just waiting for you to identify their poems. Write the poem's letter in the space next to the poem.

A. "Lines Composed a Few Miles Above Tintern Abbey"
B. "London, 1802"
C. "The Love Song of J. Alfred Prufrock"
D. "Mirror"
E. "Musée des Beaux Arts"
F. "My Last Duchess"
G. "My Papa's Waltz"
H. "Nothing Gold Can Stay"

I. "The Nymph's Reply to the Shepherd"
J. "O Captain! My Captain!"
K. "Ode on a Grecian Urn"
L. "Ode to a Nightingale"
M. "Ode to the West Wind"
N. "On First Looking into Chapman's Homer"

O. "On His Blindness"
P. "On My First Son"
Q. "On the Pulse of the Morning"
R. "Out, Out—"
S. "Ozymandias"
T. "The Passionate Shepherd to His Love"

1. _____ Nature's first green is gold
Her hardest hue to hold.
Her early leaf's a flower;
But only so an hour.
Robert Frost

2. _____   "Don't let him cut my hand off—
The doctor, when he comes. Don't let him, sister!"
Robert Frost

3. _____ The whiskey on your breath
Could make a small boy dizzy;
But I hung on like death:
Such waltzing was not easy.
Theodore Roethke

4. _____ I am silver and exact. I have no preoccupations.
Whatever I see I swallow immediately
Just as it is, unmisted by love or dislike.
Sylvia Plath

5. _____ Milton! thou should'st be living at this hour:
England hath need of thee: she is a fen
Of stagnant waters
William Wordsworth

6. _____ I met a traveller from an antique land,
Who said—"Two vast and trunkless legs of stone
Stand in the desert . . .
Percy Bysshe Shelley

7. _____ Five years have past; five summers, with the length
Of five long winters! and again I hear
These waters, rolling from their mountain-springs
With a soft inland murmur
William Wordsworth

8. _____ When I consider how my light is spent
   Ere half my days in this dark world and wide,
John Milton

9. _____ Shall I part my hair behind? Do I dare to eat a peach?
T. S. Eliot

10. _____ Farewell, thou child of my right hand, and joy;
My sin was too much hope of thee, loved boy;
Seven years thou wert lent to me, and I thee pay,
Exacted by thy fate, on the just day.
Ben Jonson

11. _____ My captain does not answer, his lips are pale and still
My father does not feel my arm, he has no pulse nor will
The ship is anchored safe and sound, its voyage closed and done
From fearful trip the victor ship comes in with object won;
Walt Whitman

12. _____ Thou still unravush'd bride of quietness,
    Thou foster-child of silence and slow time
Sylvan history, who canst thus express
A flowery tale more sweetly than our rhyme:
John Keats

13. _____ Scatter, as from an unextinguished hearth
Ashes and sparks, my words among mankind!
Be through my lips to unawakened Earth
The trumpet of a prophecy! O Wind,
If Winter comes, can Spring be far behind?
Percy Bysshe Shelley

14. _____ Come live with me and be my love,
And we will all the pleasures prove
That valleys, groves, hills, and fields
Woods, or steept mountain yields.
Christopher Marlowe

15. _____ Much have I traveled in the realms of gold,
And many goodly states and kingdoms seen;
Round many western islands have I been
Which bards in fealty to Apollo hold.
John Keats

16. _____ Looking as if she were alive. I call
That piece a wonder, now: Fra Pandolf's hands
Worked busily a day, and there she stands.
Will't please you sit and look at her?
Robert Browning

17. _____ Here on the pulse of this new day
You may have the grace to look up and out
And into your sister's eyes, into
Your brother's face, your country
And say simply
Very simply
With hope
Good morning.
Maya Angelou

18. _____ If all the world and love were young,
And truth in every shepherd's tongue
These pretty pleasures might me move
To live with thee and be thy love.
Sir Walter Raleigh

19. _____ Thou was not born for death, immortal Bird!
John Keats

20. _____ About suffering they were never wrong,
The Old Masters: how well they understood
Its human position; how it takes place
While someone else is eating or opening a window . . .
W. H. Auden

THE WORDS OF POETRY
PART FOUR

Match these poetic excerpts with their titles. The poet's name follows the excerpt. Write the correct letter next to the number.

A. "Lilacs"
B. "The Man He Killed"
C. "The Raven"
D. "A Refusal to Mourn the Death, by Fire, of a Child in London"
E. "Richard Cory"
F. "The Rime of the Ancient Mariner"

G. "The River-Merchant's Wife: A Letter"
H. "The Road Less Taken"
I. "Sir Patrick Spens"
J. "The Solitary Reaper"
K. "Song of Myself"
L. "Sonnets from the Portuguese"
M. "Stopping by Woods on a Snowy Evening"

N. "There's been a death in the opposite house"
O. "The Tiger"
P. "To an Athlete Dying Young"
Q. "To a Skylark"
R. "Ulysses"
S. "The Unknown Citizen"
T. "We Real Cool"

1. _____ How do I love thee? Let me count the ways.
   Elizabeth Barrett Browning

2. _____ "Tis some visitor tapping at my chamber door—"
   Edgar Allan Poe

3. _____ Water, water, everywhere,
   And all the boards did shrink;
   Water, water, everywhere,
   Nor any drop to drink.
   Samuel Taylor Coleridge

4. _____ And he was always quietly arrayed,
   And he was always human when he talked;
   But still he fluttered pulses when he said,
   "Good morning," and he glittered when he walked.
   Edwin Arlington Robinson

5. _____   We
   Thin gin.   We
   Jazz June.   We
   Die soon.
   Gwendolyn Brooks

6. _____ The time you won your town the race
   We chaired you through the marketplace;
   Man and boy stood cheering by,
   And home we brought you shoulder-high.
   A. E. Housman

7. _____ I walk down the garden paths,
   And all the daffodils
   Are blowing, and the bright blue squills.
   I walk down the patterned garden-paths
   In my stiff, brocaded gown.
   Amy Lowell

8. _____ Alone she cuts and binds the grain
   And sings a melancholy strain;
   O listen! for the vale profound
   Is overflowing with the sound.
   William Wordsworth

9. _____ I took the one less traveled by,
And that has made all the difference.
Robert Frost

10. _____ It little profits that an idle king,
By this still hearth, among these barren crags,
Matched with an aged wife, I mete and dole
Unequaled laws unto a savage race,
That hoard, and sleep, and feed, and know not me.
Alfred Lord Tennyson

11. _____ The majesty and burning of the child's death.
I shall not murder
The mankind of her going with a grave truth
Nor blaspheme down the stations of the breath
With any further
Elegy of innocence and youth.
Dylan Thomas

12. _____ I celebrate myself, and sing myself,
And what I assume you shall assume
For every atom belonging to me as good belongs to you.
Walt Whitman

13. _____ If you are coming through the narrows of the river Kiang
Please let me know before hand,
And I will come out to meet you
        As far as Cho-fu-sa.
Ezra Pound

14. _____ I shot him dead because—
Because he was my foe.
Just so: my foe of course he was;
Thomas Hardy

15. _____ He was found by the Bureau of Statistics to be
One against whom there was no official complaint
And all the reports on his conduct agree
That, in the modern sense of an old-fashioned word . . .
W. H. Auden

16. _____ "O, who is this has done this deed,
    This ill deed done to me,
To send me out this time o' the year,
    To sail upon the sea?"
Anonymous

17. _____ And miles to go before I sleep
And miles to go before I sleep.
Robert Frost

18. _____ Somebody flings a mattress out—
The children hurry by;
They wonder if it died on that—
I used to when a boy.
Emily Dickinson

19. _____ In what distant deeps or skies
Burnt the fire of thine eyes?
Or what wings dare he aspire?
What the hand, dare seize the fire?
William Blake

20. _____ Hail to thee, blithe spirit!
Bird thou never wert.
Percy Bysshe Shelley

Name _____ **Date** _____ **Period** _____

LOVE POEMS

Match the following love poems with their authors. The first line of the poem follows the author's name. The number two (2) before a poetic line indicates that that line is the second line of the poem since the first line contains the title within it.

1. _____ "The Passionate Shepherd to His Love"

2. _____ "The Nymph's Reply to the Shepherd"

3. _____ "Dover Beach"

4. _____ "A Valediction: Forbidding Mourning"

5. _____ "Sonnets from the Portuguese: Number 43"

6. _____ "Love Poem"

7. _____ "A Red, Red Rose"

8. _____ "Meeting at Night"

9. _____ "To His Coy Mistress"

10. _____ "The Garden of Love

a. John Donne . . . As virtuous men pass mildly away
b. Andrew Marvell . . . Had we but world enough, and time,
c. Elizabeth Barrett Browning . . . How do I love thee? Let me count the ways.
d. Robert Burns . . . (2) That's newly sprung in June:
e. Robert Browning . . . The gray sea and the long black land
f. Matthew Arnold . . . The sea is calm tonight,
g. John Frederick Nims . . . My clumsiest dear, whose hands shipwreck vases,
h. Sir Walter Raleigh . . . If all the world and love were young,
i. Christopher Marlowe . . . Come live with me and be my love,
j. William Blake . . . (2) And saw what I never had seen:

Name _____ Date _____ Period _____

WAR POEMS

Test your knowledge of war poems by matching these poems with their poets. The first line of the poem written by that author is found next to the author's name. If a number two (2) appears before a poetic line, it is because the first line of that poem contains the poem's title.

1. _____ "Anthem for Dead Youth"

2. _____ "Naming of Parts"

3. _____ "Channel Firing"

4. _____ "Dulce et Decorum Est"

5. _____ "Death of the Ball Turret Gunner"

6. _____ "For the Union Dead"

7. _____ "Base Details"

8. _____ "The Death of a Soldier"

9. _____ "Do Not Weep, Maiden, for War Is Kind"

10. _____ "Dreamers"

a. Randall Jarrell . . . From my mother's sleep I fell into the State,
b. Wilfred Owen . . . Bent double, like old beggars under sacks,
c. Siegfried Sassoon . . . If I were fierce, and bald, and short of breath
d. Henry Reed . . . (2) We had daily cleaning. And to-morrow morning,
e. Robert Lowell . . . The old South Boston Aquarium stands
f. Wallace Stevens . . . Life contracts and death is expected,
g. Thomas Hardy . . . That night your great guns, unawares,
h. Siegfried Sassoon . . . Soldiers are citizens of death's grey land,
i. Wilfred Owen . . . What passing bells for those who die as cattle?
j. Stephen Crane . . . (2) Because your lover threw wild hands toward the sky

NATURE POEMS

Match these nature poems with their authors. The first line of each poem appears next to the author's name. The number two (2) next to a poetic line indicates that the line given is the poem's second line since the first line contains the title.

1. _____ "Stopping by Woods on a Snowy Evening"

2. _____ "Lines Composed a Few Miles Above Tintern Abbey"

3. _____ "Ode to the West Wind"

4. _____ "Lines Written in Early Spring"

5. _____ "To Autumn"

6. _____ "Loveliest of Trees"

7. _____ "Spring"

8. _____ "Nothing Gold Can Stay"

9. _____ "The Sick Rose"

10. _____ "Barter"

a. Gerard Manley Hopkins . . . Nothing is so beautiful as spring—
b. William Wordsworth . . . I heard a thousand blended notes,
c. Robert Frost . . . Whose woods these are I think I know.
d. John Keats . . . Season of mists and mellow fruitfulness,
e. Percy Bysshe Shelley . . . (2) Thou, from whose unseen presence the leaves dead
f. William Wordsworth . . . Five years have past; five summers, with the length
g. William Blake . . . (2) The invisible worm
h. Robert Frost . . . Nature's first green is gold,
i. Sara Teasdale . . . Life has loveliness to sell,
j. A. E. Housman . . . (2) Is hung with bloom along the bough,

DEATH POEMS

John Donne's "Death Be Not Proud" may be one of the best-known poems about death, but many poems use death as a theme. Match these poems about death with their authors. The first line of each poem follows the author's name. If the title is contained within the initial poetic line, the second line of the poem, indicated by (2), follows the author's name.

1. _____ "Elegy Written in a Country Churchyard"

2. _____ "On My First Son"

3. _____ "Do Not Go Gentle into That Good Night"

4. _____ "Bells for John Whiteside's Daughter"

5. _____ "Because I Could Not Stop for Death"

6. _____ "Death of a Vermont Farm Woman"

7. _____ "The Emperor of Ice Cream"

8. _____ "The Man He Killed"

9. _____ "Is my team ploughing"

10. _____ "I Heard a Fly Buzz—When I Died"

a. Barbara Howes . . . Is it time now to go away?
b. Emily Dickinson . . . (2) The stillness in the room
c. John Crowe Ransom . . . There was such speed in her little body,
d. Thomas Gray . . . The curfew tolls the knell of parting day,
e. Wallace Stevens . . . Call the roller of big cigars,
f. Emily Dickinson . . . (2) He kindly stopped for me;
g. John Donne . . . Farewell, thou child of my right hand, and joy;
h. Dylan Thomas . . . Old age should burn and rave at close of day;
i. A. E. Housman . . . (2) That I was used to drive
j. Thomas Hardy . . . Had he and I but met

ANIMAL POEMS

Animals have been a favorite topic of poets through the ages. Match these poems about animals with their authors.

1. _____ "The Eagle"   a. Emily Dickinson

2. _____ "The Oxen"   b. Walt Whitman

3. _____ "Toads"   c. William Cullen Bryant

4. _____ "The Lamb"   d. William Butler Yeats

5. _____ "To a Waterfowl"   e. William Blake

6. _____ "A Noiseless Patient Spider"   f. Philip Larkin

7. _____ "A bird came down the Walk"   g. Alfred, Lord Tennyson

8. _____ "The Fish"   h. Thomas Hardy

9. _____ "The Caged Skylark"   i. Elizabeth Bishop

10. _____ "The Wild Swans at Coole"   j. Gerard Manley Hopkins

Write the titles of five more poems you can think of that have animals in the titles.

1. _____

2. _____

3. _____

4. _____

5. _____

POEMS WITH ALLUSIONS IN TITLES

Match these poetry titles containing allusions with their authors. The first line of each poem is listed next to the author. The number two (2) appears before any line that is the poem's second line since the title is contained within the first line.

1. _____ "Kubla Khan"

2. _____ "Scottsboro"

3. _____ "Icarus"

4. _____ "Abraham to Kill Him"

5. _____ "The Destruction of Sennacherib"

6. _____ "Leda and the Swan"

7. _____ "Journey of the Magi"

8. _____ "Ulysses"

9. _____ "Penelope"

10. _____ "Hero and Leander"

a. William Butler Yeats . . . A sudden blow: the great wings beating still

b. Stephen Spender . . . He will watch the hawk with an indifferent eye

c. Alfred, Lord Tennyson . . . It little profits that an idle king,

d. Anonymous . . . Paper come out—done strewed de news

e. Samuel Taylor Coleridge . . . (2) A stately pleasure-dome decree:

f. Dorothy Parker . . . In the pathway of the sun,

g. John Donne . . . "A cold coming we had of it,

h. Emily Dickinson . . . (2) Was distinctly told

i. Lord Byron . . . The Assyrian came down like the wolf on the fold,

j. T. S. Eliot . . . Both robbed of air, we both lie in one ground,

POEMS OF CHILDHOOD AND ADOLESCENCE

Match these poems dealing with childhood and adolescence with their authors. The first line of each poem follows the poet's name. If the title is contained within the poem's first line, the second line of the poem, shown by (2), follows the author's name.

1. _____ "My Papa's Waltz"

2. _____ "We Real Cool"

3. _____ "Ballad of Birmingham"

4. _____ "Buffalo Bill's Defunct"

5. _____ "Nikki-Rosa"

6. _____ "On the Death of Friends in Childhood"

7. _____ "A Poem for Emily"

8. _____ "In Just—"

9. _____ "Out, Out—"

10. _____ "The Refusal to Mourn the Death, by Fire, of a Child in London"

a. Miller Williams . . . Small fact and fingers and farthest one from me,
b. e. e. cummings . . . (2) who used to ride a watersmooth-silver
c. Robert Frost . . . The buzz-saw snarled and rattled in the yard
d. Nikki Giovanni . . . childhood remembrances are always a drag
e. e. e. cummings . . . (2) spring when the world is mud—
f. Donald Justice . . . We shall not ever meet them bearded in heaven,
g. Theodore Roethke . . . The whiskey on your breath
h. Dudley Randall . . . "Mother dear, may I go downtown
i. Dylan Thomas . . . Never until the mankind making
j. Gwendolyn Brooks . . . Left school. We

POEMS WITH MEN'S NAMES IN THEIR TITLES

Match these poem titles containing men's names with the first line of the poem. The number two (2) before a poetic line signifies that that line is the second line of the poem since the first line contains the poem's title.

1. _____ "Richard Cory"

2. _____ "To the Memory of Mr. Oldham"

3. _____ "Terence, this is stupid stuff"

4. _____ "Sir Patrick Spens"

5. _____ "Ozymandias"

6. _____ "John Anderson My Jo"

7. _____ "On First Looking into Chapman's Homer"

8. _____ "Mr. Z"

9. _____ "Mr. Flood's Party"

10. _____ "The Love Song of J. Alfred Prufrock"

a. Let us go then, you and I, (T. S. Eliot)
b. Much have I traveled in the realms of gold, (John Keats)
c. Taught early that his mother's skin was the sign of error, (M. Carl Holman)
d. (2) Over the hill between the town below (Edwin Arlington Robinson)
e. (2) We people on the pavement looked at him: (Edwin Arlington Robinson)
f. I met a traveler from an antique land (Percy Bysshe Shelley)
g. When we were first acquent, (Robert Burns)
h. The king sits in Dumferline town, (Anonymous)
i. Farewell, too little and too lately known, (John Dryden)
j. (2) You eat your victuals fast enough (A. E. Housman)

Name _____ **Date** _____ **Period** _____

PLACES IN POEMS

Match these poem titles with their authors. The first line of each poem follows the author's name. The number two (2) next to the poetic line indicates that the line is the second line of the poem since the first line contains the poem's title.

1. _____ "My Arkansas"

2. _____ "Harlem (A Dream Deferred)"

3. _____ "London"

4. _____ "A Supermarket in California"

5. _____ "Chicago"

6. _____ "Sailing to Byzantium"

7. _____ "Iowa Farmer"

8. _____ "London, 1802"

9. _____ "Ballade for the Duke of Orleans"

10. _____ "next to of course god america I"

a. William Blake . . . I wander through each chartered street,
b. Richard Wilbur . . . Flailed from the heart of water in a bow,
c. Maya Angelou . . . There is a deep brooding
d. William Butler Yeats . . . This is no country for old men. The young
e. William Wordsworth . . . Milton! thou should'st be living at this hour:
f. e. e. cummings . . . (2) love you land of the pilgrims' and so forth oh
g. Langston Hughes . . . (2) Does it dry up
h. Margaret Walker . . . (2) We looked out far over acres of wheat.
i. Allan Ginsberg . . . What thoughts I have of you tonight, Walt Whitman, for
j. Carl Sandburg . . . Hog butcher for the world

POEMS WITH WOMEN'S NAMES IN THEIR TITLES

Match these poem titles containing women's names with their authors. The first line of each poem is given next to the author's name. The number two (2) appears before a poetic line that is the second line of the poem since the initial line contains the poem's title.

1. _____ "Circe"

2. _____ "Barbara Allen"

3. _____ "Hazel Tells LaVerne"

4. _____ "To Lucasta, Going to the Wars"

5. _____ "Upon Julia's Voice"

6. _____ "Corinna's Going A-Maying"

7. _____ "Penelope"

8. _____ "Crazy Jane Talks with the Bishop"

9. _____ "Astrophel and Stella"

10. _____ "Pocahontas to Her English Husband, John Rolfe"

a. Anonymous . . . It was in and about the Martinmas time,
b. Robert Herrick . . . (2) As, could they hear, the Damned would make no noise,
c. Dorothy Parker . . . In the pathway of the sun,
d. Katharyn Howd Machan . . . last night
e. Robert Herrick . . . Get up! get up for shame! the blooming morn
f. William Butler Yeats . . . And much said he and I
g. Richard Lovelace . . . Tell me not, Sweet, I am unkind
h. Paula Gunn Allen . . . Had I not cradled you in my arms
i. Olga Broumas . . . The Charm
j. Sir Philip Sidney . . . Who will in fairest book of Nature know,

THE HALF OF IT

Here are the names of twenty-five English poets printed in a rather different fashion. Though the dates of their births are listed chronologically, their names are printed without using the last thirteen letters of the alphabet. The title of a famous poem by each author is given to help you along. Write the poet's full name in the space provided.

Capital letters indicate the first letter of either the poet's first, middle, or last name. A space between letters signifies a new part of the poet's full name.

Example: 1564 . . . illiam hakeeare . . . "My Mistress' Eyes Are Nothing Like the Sun." The answer is **William Shakespeare**.

1. _____ 1552 . . . Edmd ee . . . "The Fairie Queene"

2. _____ 1564 . . . Chihe Male . . . "The Passionate Shepherd to His Love"

3. _____ 1572 . . . Jh De . . . "Death Be Not Proud"

4. _____ 1572 . . . Be J . . . "On My First Son"

5. _____ 1591 . . . be Heick . . . "Corinna's Going"

6. _____ 1608 . . . Jh Mil . . . "When I Consider How"

7. _____ 1631 . . . Jh Dde . . . "To the Memory of Mr. Oldham"

8. _____ 1688 . . . Aleade e . . . "Engraved on the Collar of a Dog Which I Gave to His Royal Highness"

9. _____ 1716 . . . hma Ga . . . "Elegy Written in a Country Churchyard"

10. _____ 1757 . . . illiam Blake . . . "The Lamb"

11. _____ 1759 . . . be B . . . "A Red, Red Rose"

12. _____ 1770 . . . illiam dh . . . "The Solitary Reaper"

13. _____ 1772 . . . amel al Cleidge . . . "The Rime of the Ancient Mariner"

14. _____ 1788 . . . Gege Gd, Ld B . . . "The Destruction of Sennacherib"

15. _____ 1792 . . . ec Bhe helle . . . "Ode to the West Wind"

16. _____ 1795 . . . Jh Kea . . . "Ode on a Grecian Urn"

17. _____ 1806 . . . Eliabeh Bae Big . . . "Sonnets from the Portuguese: Number 43"

18. _____ 1809 . . . Alfed Ld e . . . "Ulysses"

19. _____ 1812 . . . be Big . . . "My Last Duchess"

20. _____ 1822 . . . Mahe Ald . . . "Dover Beach"

21. _____ 1832 . . . Lei Call . . . "Jabberwocky"

22. _____ 1840 . . . hma Had . . . "Channel Firing"

23. _____ 1844 . . . Gead Male Hki . . . "God's Grandeur"

24. _____ 1859 . . . A. E. Hma . . . "To an Athlete Dying Young"

25. _____ 1885 . . . D. H. Laece . . . "Snake"

THE OTHER HALF OF IT

Here are the names of twenty-five American poets printed in a rather different fashion. Though the dates of their births are listed chronologically, their names are printed without using the first thirteen letters of the alphabet. The title of a famous poem by each author is given to help you along. Write the poet's full name in the space provided.

Capital letters indicate the first letter of either the first, middle, or last name. A space between letters signifies a new part of the poet's full name.

Example: **nn Sxton** is **Anne Sexton**

1. _____ 1869 . . . wn rnton Ronson . . . "Richard Cory"

2. _____ 1874 . . . Rort rost . . . "Home Burial"

3. _____ 1874 . . . y ow . . . "Patterns"

4. _____ 1878 . . . r Snur . . . "Chicago"

5. _____ 1879 . . . W Stvns . . . "The Emperor of Ice-Cream"

6. _____ 1883 . . . W ros Ws . . . "The Red Wheelbarrow"

7. _____ 1885 . . . zr Poun . . . "In a Station of the Metro"

8. _____ 1886 . . . Sr Sssoon . . . "Dreamers"

9. _____ 1887 . . . rnn oor . . . "Poetry"

10. _____ 1888 . . . on row Rnso . . . "Bells for John Whiteside's Daughter"

11. _____ 1892 . . . n St. Vnnt y . . . "What My Lips Have Kissed, and Where, and Why"

12. _____ 1894 . . . uns . . . "Buffalo Bill's Defunct"

13. _____ 1902 . . . nston us . . . "Harlem (A Dream Deferred)"

14. _____ 1902 . . . On Ns . . . "Very Like a Whale"

15. _____ 1903 . . . ount un . . . "Yet Do I Marvel"

16. _____ 1907 . . . Toor Rot . . . "My Papa's Waltz"

17. _____ 1911 . . . zt sop . . . "The Fish"

18. _____ 1913 . . . ur Ruysr . . . "Myth"

19. _____ 1913 . . . r Spro . . . "Auto Wreck"

20. _____ 1914 . . . Rn rr . . . "The Death of the Ball Turret Gunner"

21. _____ 1917 . . . wnoyn roos . . . "We Real Cool"

22. _____ 1917 . . . Rort ow . . . "For the Union Dead"

23. _____ 1921 . . . Rr Wur . . . "Ballade for the Duke of Orleans"

24. _____ 1926 . . . n nsr . . . "A Supermarket in California"

25. _____ 1928 . . . y nou . . . "On the Pulse of the Morning"

SECTION 7

THE PLAY'S
THE THING

PLAYS . . . FRONT AND CENTER
PART ONE

You are front row and center with this exercise designed to test your knowledge of plays. Identify the name of the play and its author by writing the play's title on the first line and the author's name on the other line beneath the play's plot description. The plays are listed in alphabetical order by title. The first play is already done for you. Break a leg!

1. King of Argos and his female captive, Cassandra, are killed by angry wife.
   Agamemnon _____   _____ Aeschylus _____

2. Plane engine parts manufacturer guilty of shipping out faulty cylinders; 21 P-40 pilots are killed.

   _____   _____

3. Mozart confronts poverty and premature death.

   _____   _____

4. Sister pleads with king to bury both brothers.

   _____   _____

5. Sisters, with the help of elderberry wine, charitably put desperate old men out of their misery.

   _____   _____

6. We've drunk the soup, and eaten the fish and chips, and the English salad. The children have drunk English water. We've eaten well this evening. That's because we live in the suburbs of London and because our name is Smith.

   _____   _____

7. Velasco, the attic neighbor, helps Corrie loosen up new husband, Paul, in NYC.

   _____   _____

8. Handsome poet marries invalid daughter of harsh father.

   _____   _____

9. Residents of Cloud-cuckoo-land reach compromise with gods' emissaries about keeping human beings in line.

   _____   _____

10. At his party seaside boardinghouse resident bullied and broken by two men.

    _____   _____

11. Seven cousins who escape Nazis will make already large, poor Brooklyn family larger.

    _____   _____

12. Blind NYC apartment dweller desires firm commitment from neighbor, an actress.

    _____   _____

13. Roman leader finds hiding princess by Sphinx.

    _____   _____

14. Wife choose husband, a Christian Socialist clergyman, over eighteen-year-old poet.

    _____   _____

15. Mississippi Delta family positions for Big Daddy's estate.

    _____   _____

16. Lord Fancourt-Babberly, a.k.a. Babbs, subs for Oxford student's female relative.

   _____   _____

17. Russian family forced to sell estate; houses to be erected on land.

   _____   _____

18. State School teacher of the deaf falls in love with one of his students.

   _____   _____

19. Boarding-school teachers forced to close school following damaging rumors.

   _____   _____

20. At party psychiatrist tells people their lives are nonproductive; Celia becomes a missionary!

   _____   _____

21. Midwestern doctor, disenchanted with overweight wife, takes to the bottle and then goes off the bottle again.

   _____   _____

22. Helped by wife's confidence, aging, alcoholic actor, Frank Elgin, does well in New York.

   _____   _____

23. Witch hunt contributes to Abigail's fleeing Salem.

   _____   _____

24. Poet with large nose falls for the beautiful Roxanne.

   _____   _____

25. Willy, a believer in "The American Dream," takes his life.

   _____   _____

26. New England mother smothers child to prove love for child's father, her stepson.

   _____   _____

27. Jewish refugees, hiding from Nazis in Holland, betrayed by thief.

   _____   _____

28. Dispute over forged IOU causes wife and children to leave lawyer husband.

   _____   _____

29. Womanizer, given chance to repent, refuses and goes to Hell.

   _____   _____

30. Mother kills daughter's pet rabbit after refusing to attend school science awards assembly.

   _____   _____

31. Deformed and freakish John Merrick completes church model before death.

   _____   _____

32. West Indian leader, Brutus Jones, fears silver bullets.

   _____   _____

33. Turmoil in resort town over polluted Baths.

   _____   _____

34. Psychiatrist helps disturbed boy who harmed six horses.

   _____   _____

35. Goddess casts vote to set Orestes free in murder of Clytemnestra.

   _____   _____

PLAYS . . . FRONT AND CENTER
PART TWO

Identify the name of the play and its author by writing the play's title on the first line and the author's name on the other line beneath the play's plot description. The plays are listed in alphabetical order by title. The first play is already done for you. Break a leg!

1. Irish writer and family return to Dublin after nine years.
   _____*Exiles*_____   _____James Joyce_____

2. Orphanage in honor of drunken husband burns; son has syphilis and is going insane.
   _____   _____

3. Mother arranges gentleman caller for her crippled daughter.
   _____   _____

4. Real estate firm's contracts stolen by struggling salesman.
   _____   _____

5. Boxer must choose between the ring and the violin.
   _____   _____

6. Jack Jefferson, black boxer, must flee to Europe with girlfriend.
   _____   _____

7. Ship's boiler room worker confronts zoo's gorilla.
   _____   _____

8. Captain Shotover and industrialist meet during World War I.
   _____   _____

9. Woman's husband and her former lover vie for professorship; wife kills herself.
   _____   _____

10. New England is setting for Aeschylus-like Oresteia plot.
    _____   _____

11. University professor's wife, intrigued by all-male North London household, becomes prostitute and professor goes back to America alone!
    _____   _____

12. British soldier involved in brothel situation.
    _____   _____

13. Matronly Norwegian immigrant assists daughter, the writer, to get published.
    _____   _____

14. Former drunken traveling salesman-turned-teetotaler surprises derelicts in Harry Hope's saloon.
    _____   _____

15. Jack can't marry until Lady Bracknell approves.
    _____   _____

16. High school teacher's teachings put Darwin's theory of evolution on trial in Hillsboro.
    _____   _____

17. After a drunken Irish captain does not receive his inheritance, his wife and daughter leave Dublin.

   _____   _____

18. Old man listens to tapes showing his life's failures.

   _____   _____

19. Presumed dead for twenty years, Mrs. Erlynne, under an alias, attempts to befriend her daughter.

   _____   _____

20. Greedy Southern business family "borrows" $88,000 from brother-in-law to conclude a business deal.

   _____   _____

21. Actor Tyrone's family battles alcohol, consumption, and mental problems.

   _____   _____

22. Jimmy Porter, frustrated college grad turned street market manager, leaves wife, who later has miscarriage.

   _____   _____

23. Athenian women agree to cease sexual activities with husbands until peace with Sparta is achieved.

   _____   _____

24. Salvation Army gets financial boost from Undershaft's armaments sales.

   _____   _____

25. Don Juan tells Jack Tanner all about the Life Force.

   _____   _____

26. Henry VIII lies about Sir Thomas More, who is subsequently put to death.

   _____   _____

27. Norwegian architect dead after he falls from the tower he designed.

   _____   _____

28. Dolly Levi tries to find the perfect match for Horace Vandergelder.

   _____   _____

29. Spurned wife of Jason sends poisonous gifts to king and then kills her two sons.

   _____   _____

30. Annie Sullivan teaches a young blind girl some discipline.

   _____   _____

31. Forged signature finally gives navy man his transfer; Pulver is his replacement.

   _____   _____

32. Mystery abounds as Monkswell Manor guest, Mrs. Boyle, is murdered in this guest house.

   _____   _____

33. Vivie learns that her mother still is employed in the "world's oldest profession."

   _____   _____

34. Thomas à Becket is slain.

   _____   _____

35. Incompetence runs rampant as air force trainer plane flies over atomic-bomb testing site by mistake.

   _____   _____

PLAYS . . . FRONT AND CENTER
PART THREE

Identify the name of the play and its author by writing the play's title on the first line and the author's name on the other line beneath the play's plot description. The plays are listed in alphabetical order by title. The first play is already done for you. Break a leg!

1. New York City male roomies, a clean freak and a slob, attempt to put up with each other.

   _____ *The Odd Couple* _____   _____ Neil Simon _____

2. Blinded father and his daughter, Antigone, wander to a sacred grove.

   _____   _____

3. Jocasta commits suicide after she learns that she has married her son.

   _____   _____

4. Stage manager helps us learn about Emily's death in childbirth and other events in Grover's Corner.

   _____   _____

5. Canine, Nana, and the Darling children greet an unexpected night visitor.

   _____   _____

6. Irish pub girls are entranced with fictitious story of Christy Mahon's killing his father; townsmen later want to string Mahon up.

   _____   _____

7. Cockney flower-girl takes speech lessons.

   _____   _____

8. Mama's insurance money goes to buy house while son wanted money for a liquor store.

   _____   _____

9. Stuffy Mrs. Malaprop does a number on the English language.

   _____   _____

10. Hamlet's friends await their fate by flipping coins.

    _____   _____

11. Woman burned at the stake in France.

    _____   _____

12. Young writer who once placed dead bird at lover's feet commits suicide.

    _____   _____

13. Antrobus family members experience several ages of mankind.

    _____   _____

14. Middle-aged men recount the days of their banner-winning high school basketball campaign.

    _____   _____

15. San Francisco waterfront saloon is home to some rather interesting and very human characters.

    _____   _____

16. Jurors known only by their numbers acquit nineteen-year-old accused of killing his father.

   _____   _____

17. Russian brother-in-law's estate manager attempts to shoot the owner, a professor, when told estate will be sold.

   _____   _____

18. Brooklyn longshoreman betrays wife's Italian immigrant relatives to the authorities before fatal fight.

   _____   _____

19. While waiting by a country road for a message, two tramps think about hanging themselves.

   _____   _____

20. Two New England college professors and their wives engage in exchanging vicious insults in the early morning hours.

   _____   _____

21. Permanently hospitalized, paralyzed young man desires to die while authorities try to block request.

   _____   _____

22. Teenaged daughter is asked to shoot her pet to please her father, but she shoots herself instead.

   _____   _____

23. After expulsion from school and ensuing family and financial problems, son is cleared of postal-order theft charge.

   _____   _____

24. One man impales himself on a knife held by the other as two fight over Central Park bench on a Sunday afternoon.

   _____   _____

THE CHARACTERS STEP FORWARD

Match these characters with the plays in which they are found. Write the correct letter in the blank next to the number.

1. _____ Gogo

2. _____ Ranevskaya

3. _____ Nora

4. _____ Werle

5. _____ Solness

6. _____ Chris Keller

7. _____ Willy Loman

8. _____ Carbone

9. _____ Brutus

10. _____ Yank

11. _____ Cabot

12. _____ Strang

13. _____ Wolfgang

14. _____ Undershaft

15. _____ Doolittle

16. _____ Dauphin

17. _____ Hamlet

18. _____ Pegeen

19. _____ Bracknell

20. _____ Stage Manager

21. _____ Amanda

22. _____ Blanche

23. _____ Big Daddy

24. _____ Annie Sullivan

25. _____ John Proctor

A. *Desire Under the Elms*

B. *The Playboy of the Western World*

C. *The Wild Duck*

D. *Cat on a Hot Tin Roof*

E. *The Cherry Orchard*

F. *A View from the Bridge*

G. *Pygmalion*

H. *Our Town*

I. *The Importance of Being Earnest*

J. *The Emperor Jones*

K. *The Master Builder*

L. *Waiting for Godot*

M. *A Doll's House*

N. *Joan of Arc*

O. *Rosencrantz and Guildenstern Are Dead*

P. *Equus*

Q. *Amadeus*

R. *All My Sons*

S. *The Hairy Ape*

T. *The Crucible*

U. *The Glass Menagerie*

V. *A Streetcar Named Desire*

W. *The Miracle Worker*

X. *Major Barbara*

Y. *Death of a Salesman*

PLAYWRIGHTS' CRYPTOLOGY

All names in this list are associated with playwrights. Find the letters that were substituted in the original word.

1. YCPBJNJ   1. ___ ___ ___ ___ ___ ___ ___

2. VSQUUJN   2. ___ ___ ___ ___ ___ ___ ___

3. VLCRRQNW   3. ___ ___ ___ ___ ___ ___ ___

4. VSQF   4. ___ ___ ___ ___

5. VQNLNJ   5. ___ ___ ___ ___ ___ ___

6. RBKLJN   6. ___ ___ ___ ___ ___ ___

7. QJVMSZPHV   7. ___ ___ ___ ___ ___ ___ ___ ___ ___

8. YBPPJN   8. ___ ___ ___ ___ ___ ___

9. JPBCL   9. ___ ___ ___ ___ ___

10. NQMBKJ   10. ___ ___ ___ ___ ___ ___

11. BGVJK   11. ___ ___ ___ ___ ___

12. SQKVGJNNZ   12. ___ ___ ___ ___ ___ ___ ___ ___

13. SJPPYQK   13. ___ ___ ___ ___ ___ ___ ___

14. VSQDJVRJQNJ   14. ___ ___ ___ ___ ___ ___ ___ ___ ___ ___ ___

15. XCKVCK   15. ___ ___ ___ ___ ___ ___

16. QPGJJ   16. ___ ___ ___ ___ ___

17. YQNPCFJ   17. ___ ___ ___ ___ ___ ___ ___

18. VCRSCMPJV   18. ___ ___ ___ ___ ___ ___ ___ ___

19. GNJMSL   19. ___ ___ ___ ___ ___ ___

20. QNBVLCRSQKJV   20. ___ ___ ___ ___ ___ ___ ___ ___ ___ ___ ___ ___

Letter Substitution Code Used:

Letter: A B C D E F G H I J K L M N O P Q R S T U V W X Y Z

Substitute: ___

PLAYWORDS

Here are forty-one quotes from well-known plays. How good an ear do you have for Playwords? The quotes are listed alphabetically according to the play's title. The playwright's name follows the quote. Be prepared for a good dose of Williams, Ibsen, Shaw, Miller, and Wilder. Write the play's name next to the quote. Good luck.

1. _____ "For me! Where do you live, where have you come from? For me!—I was dying every day and you were killing my boys and you did it for me? What the hell do you think I was thinking of, the goddam business? What is that, the world—the business? What the hell do you mean, you did it for me? Don't you have a country? Don't you live in the world? . . ." (Arthur Miller)

2. _____ "Creon is burying one to desecrate the other." (Sophocles)

3. _____ "Time's up, Major. You've managed those regiments so well that youre sure to be asked to get rid of some of the infantry of the Timok division. Send them home by way of Lom Palanka. Saranoff: dont get married until I come back: I shall be here punctually at five in the evening on Tuesday fortnight. Gracious ladies, good evening." (George Bernard Shaw)

4. _____ "I'll tell you the truth. I've resented Big Daddy's partiality to Brick ever since Brick was born, and the way I've been treated like I was just barely good enough to spit on and sometimes not even good enough for that . . . Big Daddy is dying of cancer and it's spread all through him . . ." (Tennessee Williams)

5. _____ "You'd divide the land into one acre lots and rent them for at least twenty-five roubles a year. I'll bet you that if you advertise it now there won't be a lot left by the fall, they'll be snapped up almost at once . . . And then, the old cherry orchard will have to be cut down . . ." (Anton Chekhov)

6. _____ "I don't know, but it was always kind of funny and she said things like that and all the girls would talk about it when Miss Dobie went and visited Miss Wright late at night. . . . And there are always funny sounds and we'd stay awake and listen because we couldn't help hearing and I'd get frightened because the sounds were like—" (Lillian Hellman)

7. _____ "And I have been thinking, for these five minutes,
How I could face my guests. I wish it was over.
I mean . . . I am glad you came . . . I am glad Alex told us . . .
And Peter had to know . . ." (T. S. Eliot)

8. _____ "Doc was a rich boy when I married him. His mother left him $25,000 when she died. It took him a lot to get his office started and everything . . . then, he got sick. But Doc's always good to me . . . now." (William Inge)

9. _____ "Abby, we've got to tell. Witchery's a hangin' error, a hangin' like they done in Boston two years ago. We must tell the truth, Abby! You'll only be whipped for dancin', and the other things!" (Arthur Miller)

10. _____ "Ah, never that!
No, that would be too ugly, if along
This monstrous nose a tear should trickle down!" (Edmond Rostand)

11. _____ "Oh, I could understand that, Willy. But you're a road man, Willy, and we do a road business." (Arthur Miller)

12. _____ "The Gestapo have found the radio that was stolen. Mr. Dussel says they'll trace it back . . . to the thief, and then it's just a matter of time 'til they get us. Everyone is low. Even poor Pim can't raise their spirits. I have often been downcast myself . . . but never in despair. I can shake off everything if I write." (Frances Goodrich and Albert Hackett)

13. _____ "Nora! Nora! Empty. She's gone. The greatest miracle?" (Henrik Ibsen)

14. _____ "You kin bet yo whole roll on one thin, white man. Dis baby plays out his string to de end and when he quits, he quits wid a bang de way he ought. Silver bullet ain't none too good for him . . . Silver bullet bring me luck anyway . . ." (Eugene O'Neill)

15. _____ "Can you say it any other way, Peter? Our water, which we provide to the trusting souls who pay us huge fees to restore them to health, is poison either for drinking or for bathing." (Henrik Ibsen)

16. _____ "There was a Jim O'Connor we both knew in high school—If that is the one Tom is bringing to dinner—you'll have to excuse me, I won't come to the table." (Tennessee Williams)

17. _____ "She done me doit. She done me doit, didn't she? I'll git square wit her! I'll get her some way! Git offen me, youse guys! Lemme up! I'll show her who's a ape." (Eugene O'Neill)

18. _____ "Shot herself! Shot herself in the temple! Can you imagine!" (Henrik Ibsen)

19. _____ "Poor devil! God rest his soul in peace. Ah, the damned pity, the wrong kind, as Hickey said. Be God, there's no more hope. I'll never be a success in the grandstand—or anywhere else. Life is too much for me!" (Eugene O'Neill)

20. _____ "You know why I did it. I had the book in my hand, Hunter's *Civic Biology*. I opened it up, and read my sophomore science class Chapter 17, Darwin's *Origin of Species*. All it says is that man wasn't just stuck here like a geranium in a flower pot; that living comes from a long miracle, it just didn't happen in seven days." (Jerome Lawrence and Robert E. Lee)

21. _____ "I am going to make a new will, Regina, leaving you eighty-eight thousand dollars in Union Pacific bonds. The rest will go to Zan. It's true that your brothers have borrowed your share for a little while. After my death I advise you to talk to Ben and Oscar. They won't admit anything . . ." (Lillian Hellman)

22. _____ "Will you listen to your father, Jamie? After thirty-five years of marriage! He isn't a great actor for nothing, is he? What's come over you, James?" (Eugene O'Neill)

23. _____ "I was happy in the Salvation Army for a moment. I escaped from the world into a paradise of enthusiasm and prayer and soul saving; but the moment our money ran short, it all came back to Badger." (George Bernard Shaw)

24. _____ "I solemnly say that I am not a happy man. Ann looks happy; but she is only triumphant, successful, victorious. This is not happiness, but the price for which the strong sell happiness. What we have both done this afternoon is to renounce happiness, renounce freedom, renounce tranquillity, above all, renounce the romantic possibilities of an unknown future, for the cares of a household and a family." (George Bernard Shaw)

25. _____ "Sir Thomas, Sir Thomas . . . You know it amazes me that you, who were once so effective in the world and are now so much retired from it, should be opposing yourself to the whole new movement of the times." (Robert Bolt)

26. _____ "So that's the sum total, as far, as far back as I can see. Nothing really built. And nothing sacrificed for the chance to build, either. Nothing, nothing—it all comes to nothing." (Henrik Ibsen)

27. _____ "So you will come to my house at five-thirty. At about six I shall take you both with me to the Harmonia Gardens Restaurant on the Battery; Mr. Vandergelder will be there and everything will be arranged." (Thornton Wilder)

28. _____ "Wah. Wah." (William Gibson)

29. _____ "Captain, this is Ensign Pulver. I just threw your palm trees overboard . . ." (Thomas Heggen and Joshua Logan)

30. _____ "Lord, have mercy upon us.
Christ, have mercy upon us.
Lord, have mercy upon us.
Blessed Thomas, pray for us." (T. S. Eliot)

31. _____ "Two did not return. In the shattered tail of the plane, all that remained were two charred helmets and a handful of dust. I ask you now to rise as I award these medals posthumously to the gallant heroes who gave us the last measure of devotion, Privates Stackpole and Whitehead." (Max Hyman)

32. _____ "Hear this; since you have thrown your blindness at me:
Your eyes can't see the evil to which you've come
nor where you live, nor who is in your house.
Do you know your parents?" (Sophocles)

33. _____ "Thank you, Mrs. Webb; thank you, Emily. There are some more things we want to explore about this town. I think this is a good time to tell you that the Cartwright interests have just begun building a new bank in Grover's Corners . . ." (Thornton Wilder)

34. _____ "I ain't done nothing wrong by speaking to the gentleman. Ive a right to sell flowers if I keep off the kerb." (George Bernard Shaw)

35. _____ "Been thinking that we maybe could meet the notes on a little old two-story somewhere, with a yard where Travis could play in the summertime, if we use part of the insurance for a down payment and everybody kind of pitch in . . ." (Lorraine Hansberry)

36. Well, well, Mrs. Malaprop, I will dispute the point no further with you." (Richard Brinsley Sheridan)

37. _____ "But what voices do you need to tell you what the blacksmith can tell you: that you must strike while the iron is hot? I tell you we must make a dash at Compiegne and relieve it as we relieved Orleans. Then Paris will open its gates; or if not, we will break through them. What is your crown worth without your capital?" (George Bernard Shaw)

38. _____ "Mr. Antrobus, don't mind what I say. I'm just an ordinary girl, you know what I mean, I'm just an ordinary girl. But you're a bright man, you're a very bright man, and of course you invented the alphabet and the wheel, and, my God, a lot of things . . ." (Thornton Wilder)

39. _____ "Stella, I can't live with him. You can, he's your husband. But how could I stay here with him, after last night, with just those curtains between us?" (Tennessee Williams)

40. _____ "Give me the number of the Immigration Bureau. Thanks. I want to report something. Illegal immigrants. Two of them. That's right. Four-forty-one Saxon Street, Brooklyn . . ." (Arthur Miller)

41. _____ "Confidential . . . I am commanded by My Lord's Commissioner of Investigation if the circumstances of the case leaves no other conclusion possible than that the postal order was taken by your son . . . My Lords deeply regret that they must therefore request you to withdraw your son from the college." (Terrence Ratigan)

NAME THAT PLAYWRIGHT

Identify the authors of these twenty plays by writing the correct letter in the blank next to each number.

_____ 1. *Rosencrantz and Guildenstern Are Dead*
     A. Ibsen   B. Shaffer   C. Marlowe   D. Stoppard

_____ 2. *The Zoo Story*
     A. Shaw   B. Albee   C. Racine   D. Pinter

_____ 3. *The Birds*
     A. Shaffer   B. Sartre   C. Aeschylus   D. Aristophanes

_____ 4. *Mother Courage and Her Children*
     A. Pinter   B. Miller   C. Eliot   D. Brecht

_____ 5. *The Little Foxes*
     A. Shaffer   B. Hellman   C. Pinter   D. Jonson

_____ 6. *The Oresteia*
     A. Racine   B. Miller   C. Hansberry   D. Aeschylus

_____ 7. *The Birthday Party*
     A. Pinter   B. Miller   C. Racine   D. Albee

_____ 8. *Major Barbara*
     A. Shaw   B. Jonson   C. Pinter   D. Eliot

_____ 9. *Romeo and Juliet*
     A. Shaffer   B. Ibsen   C. Shakespeare   D. Miller

_____ 10. *The Misanthrope*
     A. Jonson   B. Shakespeare   C. Molière   D. Hellman

_____ 11. *Volpone*
     A. Miller   B. Racine   C. Jonson   D. Sartre

_____ 12. *Doctor Faustus*
     A. Sophocles   B. Pinter   C. Marlowe   D. Miller

_____ 13. *Murder in the Cathedral*
     A. Eliot   B. Stoppard   C. Miller   D. Jonson

_____ 14. *No Exit*
     A. Brecht   B. Euripedes   C. Shakespeare   D. Sartre

_____ 15. *An Enemy of the People*
     A. Aristophanes   B. Albee   C. Sartre   D. Ibsen

_____ 16. *Medea*
     A. Sophocles   B. Euripedes   C. Stoppard   D. Miller

_____ 17. *Phedre*
     A. Aristophanes   B. Sophocles   C. Albee   D. Racine

_____ 18. *Oedipus Rex*
     A. Shaffer   B. Euripedes   C. Sophocles   D. Ibsen

_____ 19. *All My Sons*
     A. Miller   B. Sophocles   C. Hellman   D. Stoppard

_____ 20. *Equus*
     A. Shaffer   B. Sophocles   C. Molière   D. Shakespeare

A TRIP TO BROADWAY

Match the twenty-five Broadway plays with their songs. Write the correct letter in the space next to each question.

A. *Applause*
B. *Babes in Arms*
C. *Bye Bye Birdie*
D. *Calamity Jane*
E. *Can Can*
F. *Carousel*
G. *Fiddler on the Roof*
H. *Gentlemen Prefer Blondes*
I. *Hair*
J. *HMS Pinafore*
K. *How to Succeed in Business Without Really Trying*
L. *Jesus Christ Superstar*

M. *Joseph and the Amazing Technicolor Dreamcoat*
N. *Kiss Me Kate*
O. *La Cage Aux Folles*
P. *Man of La Mancha*
Q. *The Music Man*
R. *My Fair Lady*
S. *Oklahoma!*
T. *The Pajama Game*
U. *Promises, Promises*
V. *Shenandoah*
W. *The Sound of Music*
X. *Sweet Charity*
Y. *Zorba*

1. _____ "Good Morning Star Shine" . . . "Easy to Be Hard" . . . "Aquarius" . . . "Let the Sunshine In" . . .

2. _____ "I'll Never Fall in Love Again" . . . "Turkey Lurkey Time" . . . "Upstairs" . . . "Where Can You Take a Girl?" . . .

3. _____ "So in Love" . . . "Brush Up Your Shakespeare" . . . "We Open in Venice" . . . "Too Damn Hot" . . . "Always True to You in My Fashion" . . .

4. _____ "C'est Magnifique" . . . "I Love Paris" . . . "It's All Right With Me" . . . "Never Give Anything Away" . . . "Come Along with Me" . . .

5. _____ "My Funny Valentine" . . . Johnny One Note" . . . "Lady Is a Tramp" . . . "Where or When" . . .

6. _____ "For I'm Called Little Buttercup—Dear Little Buttercup" . . . "I am the Monarch of the Sea" . . . "When I was a Lad I served a Term" . . .

7. _____ "On the Street Where You Live" . . . "Get Me to the Church on Time" . . . "Wouldn't It be Luverly" . . . "The Rain in Spain" . . .

8. _____ "People Will Say We're in Love" . . . "The Surrey with the Fringe on the Top" . . . "Oh, What a Beautiful Mornin'" . . .

9. _____ "Hey There" . . . "I'm Not at All in Love" . . . "Steam Heat" . . . "Hernando's Hideaway" . . .

10. _____ "One More Angel in Heaven" . . . "Close Every Door" . . . "Song of the King" . . . "Any Dream Will Do" . . .

11. _____ "Do Re Mi" . . . "Climb Every Mountain" . . . "My Favorite Things" . . .

12. _____ "But Alive" . . . "Who's that Girl?" . . . "The Best Night of My Life" . . .

13. _____ "My Secret Love" . . . "The Black Hills of Dakota" . . . "The Deadwood Stage" . . .

14. _____ "You'll Never Walk Alone" . . . "If I Loved You" . . . "June Is Bustin' Out All Over" . . . "Blow High, Blow Low" . . .

15. _____ "If I Were a Rich Man" . . . "Matchmaker, Matchmaker" . . . "Sunrise Sunset"

16. _____ "A Lot of Livin' to Do" . . . "One Last Kiss" . . . "An English Teacher" . . . "Put On a Happy Face" . . . "One Boy" . . . "The Telephone Hour" . . .

17. _____ "Diamond's Are a Girl's Best Friend" . . . "Coquette" . . . "A Little Girl from Little Rock" . . .

18. _____ "Brotherhood of Man" . . . "I Believe in You" . . . "Happy to Keep His Dinner Warm" . . .

19. _____ "We Are What We Are" . . . "I Am What I Am" . . . "The Best of Times" . . .

20. _____ "Life Is" . . . "The First Time" . . . "The Top of the Hill" . . . "No Boom Boom"

21. _____ "I Don't Know How to Love Him" . . . "Everything's All Right" . . . "Superstar"

22. _____ "We Make a Beautiful Pair" . . . "Raise the Flag of Dixie" . . . "The Pickers Are Comin'" . . . "Freedom"

23. _____ "The Impossible Dream" . . . "Dulcinea" . . . "Knight of the Woeful Countenance" . . . "Aldonza" . . .

24. _____ "Till There Was You" . . . "Lida Rose" . . . "Seventy-Six Trombones" . . . "Goodnight, My Someone" . . .

25. _____ "Big Spender" . . . "Baby, Dream Your Dream" . . . "If My Friends Could See Me Now" . . . "I Love to Cry at Weddings" . . .

MUSIC TO YOUR EARS

Sherlock Holmes enjoyed his trips to the music halls since it gave him a break from his busy schedule and allowed his cerebral side to rest (a bit). His mind never seemed to stop working.

Enjoy the sounds of the following songs, all taken from Broadway plays. Write the play's corresponding letter in the space provided. Score one front-row-center seat for each correct answer. Good luck.

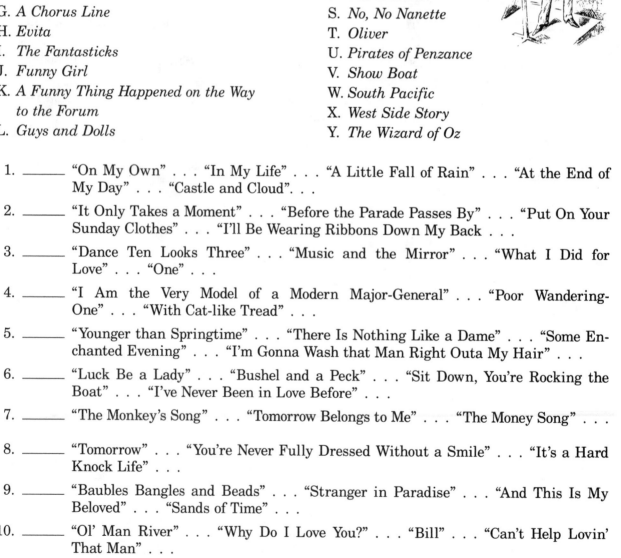

A. *Annie*
B. *Annie Get Your Gun*
C. *Anything Goes*
D. *Brigadoon*
E. *Cabaret*
F. *Camelot*
G. *A Chorus Line*
H. *Evita*
I. *The Fantasticks*
J. *Funny Girl*
K. *A Funny Thing Happened on the Way to the Forum*
L. *Guys and Dolls*

M. *Hello Dolly*
N. *The King and I*
O. *Kismet*
P. *Les Misérables*
Q. *Mame*
R. *The Mikado*
S. *No, No Nanette*
T. *Oliver*
U. *Pirates of Penzance*
V. *Show Boat*
W. *South Pacific*
X. *West Side Story*
Y. *The Wizard of Oz*

1. _____ "On My Own" . . . "In My Life" . . . "A Little Fall of Rain" . . . "At the End of My Day" . . . "Castle and Cloud". . .

2. _____ "It Only Takes a Moment" . . . "Before the Parade Passes By" . . . "Put On Your Sunday Clothes" . . . "I'll Be Wearing Ribbons Down My Back . . .

3. _____ "Dance Ten Looks Three" . . . "Music and the Mirror" . . . "What I Did for Love" . . . "One" . . .

4. _____ "I Am the Very Model of a Modern Major-General" . . . "Poor Wandering-One" . . . "With Cat-like Tread" . . .

5. _____ "Younger than Springtime" . . . "There Is Nothing Like a Dame" . . . "Some Enchanted Evening" . . . "I'm Gonna Wash that Man Right Outa My Hair" . . .

6. _____ "Luck Be a Lady" . . . "Bushel and a Peck" . . . "Sit Down, You're Rocking the Boat" . . . "I've Never Been in Love Before" . . .

7. _____ "The Monkey's Song" . . . "Tomorrow Belongs to Me" . . . "The Money Song" . . .

8. _____ "Tomorrow" . . . "You're Never Fully Dressed Without a Smile" . . . "It's a Hard Knock Life" . . .

9. _____ "Baubles Bangles and Beads" . . . "Stranger in Paradise" . . . "And This Is My Beloved" . . . "Sands of Time" . . .

10. _____ "Ol' Man River" . . . "Why Do I Love You?" . . . "Bill" . . . "Can't Help Lovin' That Man" . . .

11. _____ "All Through the Night" . . . "You're the Top" . . . "I Get a Kick Out of You" . . .

12. _____ "Try to Remember" . . . "Soon It's Gonna Rain" . . . "Much More" . . .

MUSIC TO YOUR EARS (continued)

13. _____ "Almost Like Being in Love" . . . "I'll Go Home with Bonnie Jean" . . . "The Heather on the Hill" . . .

14. _____ "I Want to Be Happy" . . . "Tea for Two" . . . "My Boy and I" . . .

15. _____ "We're Off to See the Wizard" . . . "Over the Rainbow" . . . "Ding Dong the Witch Is Dead" . . .

16. _____ "Food, Glorious Food" . . . "Consider Yourself" . . . "You've Got to Pick a Pocket or Two" . . .

17. _____ "If He Walked into My Life" . . . "The Man in the Moon" . . . "Bosom Buddies" . . . "It's Today" . . . "We Need a Little Christmas" . . .

18. _____ "There's No Business Like Show Business" . . . "Anything You Can Do" . . . "I Got the Sun in the Morning" . . .

19. _____ "Don't Rain on My Parade" . . . "His Love Makes Me Beautiful" . . . "People" . . .

20. _____ "Comedy Tonight" . . . "Everybody Ought to Have a Maid" . . . "Lovely" . . . "Love, I Hear" . . .

21. _____ "Three Little Maids from School Are We" . . . "If You Want to Know Who We Are" . . . "The Sun Whose Rays" . . .

22. _____ "Shall We Dance?" . . . "I Whistle a Happy Tune" . . . "Hello Young Lovers" . . . "March of the Siamese Children" . . . "My Lord and Master" . . .

23. _____ "Gee, Officer Krupke" . . . "America" . . . "I Feel Pretty" . . . "Tonight" . . .

24. _____ "If Ever I Should Leave You" . . . "I Loved You Once in Silence" . . . "The Simple Joys of Maidenhood" . . . "How to Handle a Woman" . . .

25. _____ "Don't Cry for Me Argentina" . . . "Another Suitcase in Another Hall" . . .

THE PLAYWRIGHT MEETS HIS CREATION

Match these playwrights with their plays by writing the correct letter in the space next to the number.

_____	1. Medoff	A.	*The Elephant Man*
_____	2. Sophocles	B.	*Krapp's Last Tape*
_____	3. Zindel	C.	*Juno and the Paycock*
_____	4. Rostand	D.	*The Homecoming*
_____	5. Behan	E.	*The Children's Hour*
_____	6. O'Casey	F.	*Antigone*
_____	7. Chekhov	G.	*Cyrano de Bergerac*
_____	8. Pinter	H.	*Glengarry Glen Ross*
_____	9. Osborne	I.	*Children of a Lesser God*
_____	10. Odets	J.	*The Cherry Orchard*
_____	11. Thomas	K.	*Look Back in Anger*
_____	12. Shaw	L.	*The Skin of our Teeth*
_____	13. Wilder	M.	*The Effect of Gamma Rays on Man-in-the-Moon Marigolds*
_____	14. Pomerance	N.	*Don Juan*
_____	15. Beckett	O.	*Charley's Aunt*
_____	16. Molière	P.	*Exiles*
_____	17. Joyce	Q.	*Come Back, Little Sheba*
_____	18. Inge	R.	*Golden Boy*
_____	19. Hellman	S.	*The Hostage*
_____	20. Mamet	T.	*Pygmalion*

Name _____ **Date** _____ **Period** _____

THE PLAYWRIGHT PROBLEM

The problem here is that the playwright's names need to be unscrambled. Spell these names correctly.

1. NLEMHLA

2. NNOJSO

3. EEABL

4. EPRASKASEHE

5. IOETL

6. WSHA

7. INAECR

8. ABHYNSRRE

9. LSCHESUAY

10. NSEBI

11. SIHPSREATOAN

12. IELRML

13. RHBETC

14. AFFHRSE

15. RIÈELMO

16. RMWELAO

17. OCOSHSELP

18. ENTPRI

19. TSEARR

20. PDESEIURE

1. ___ ___ ___ ___ ___ ___ ___

2. ___ ___ ___ ___ ___ ___

3. ___ ___ ___ ___ ___

4. ___ ___ ___ ___ ___ ___ ___ ___ ___ ___ ___

5. ___ ___ ___ ___ ___

6. ___ ___ ___ ___

7. ___ ___ ___ ___ ___ ___

8. ___ ___ ___ ___ ___ ___ ___ ___ ___

9. ___ ___ ___ ___ ___ ___ ___ ___ ___

10. ___ ___ ___ ___ ___

11. ___ ___ ___ ___ ___ ___ ___ ___ ___ ___ ___ ___

12. ___ ___ ___ ___ ___ ___

13. ___ ___ ___ ___ ___ ___

14. ___ ___ ___ ___ ___ ___ ___

15. ___ ___ ___ ___ ___ ___ ___

16. ___ ___ ___ ___ ___ ___ ___

17. ___ ___ ___ ___ ___ ___ ___ ___ ___

18. ___ ___ ___ ___ ___ ___

19. ___ ___ ___ ___ ___ ___

20. ___ ___ ___ ___ ___ ___ ___ ___ ___

CAN YOU FIND ME?

The names of twenty-one playwrights are hidden in this grid. See how many of them you can find.

```
H E L L M A N F H B N K Z S H A K E S P E A R E
D T B P G V E S V O M Q Z T H A R Y Q J J T P Q
M Y X R G Y R U S W N K D Y D T N C F P T L J K
G A P S E G D N R K M G Y J R R D S K P T S X N
T Q R R K C O X W I S T M A B N E S B I S P C Q
V Q W L H J H W G L P V S M H X J B G E H Y S C
G K D S O P W T C C L E Z P N W G V S F R E R V
B V G W W V G P K R F D P Z Y G F V F N R Z X
G T V H Q H E S L X B S M E C V H Z C A N F Y X
C Z Q Y P V J S G V E Z D P S Z K D H D L Z M G
Q B S H E K S B D L K J H R W L Y P R S W M C S
L V C V Z R D X C R R C L S E R O A S C G D V N
Z Z V N E F E O J H X M Q N E T P J E W N J B D
L Q F T D E H I H X Y L I L S P T K W L F N W J
X D N H B P L B L B S C L I O N Z F T A I F V W
X I J L O Q S B L O A I R T X C R D J R H O T W
P S A S H A F F E R M A S A E S C H Y L U S T G
```

AESCHYLUS
ALBEE
ARISTOPHANES
BRECHT
ELIOT
EURIPEDES

HANSBERRY
HELLMAN
IBSEN
JONSON
MARLOWE

MILLER
MOLIÈRE
PINTER
RACINE
SARTRE

SHAFFER
SHAKESPEARE
SHAW
SOPHOCLES
STOPPARD

PULITZER PRIZE-WINNING PLAYWRIGHTS

Match the dramatists with their plays.

1. _____ Wasserstein	A. *Glengarry Glen Ross*
2. _____ Simon	B. *Fences*
3. _____ Albee	C. *The Subject Was Roses*
4. _____ Sackler	D. *Beyond the Horizon*
5. _____ Chase	E. *Harvey*
6. _____ Zindel	F. *Death of a Salesman*
7. _____ Gilroy	G. *Driving Miss Daisy*
8. _____ Wilson (August)	H. *Lost in Yonkers*
9. _____ Miller (Arthur)	I. *The Heidi Chronicles*
10. _____ MacLeish	J. *Talley's Folly*
11. _____ Wilson (Lanford)	K. *The Great White Hope*
12. _____ Wilder	L. *A Streetcar Named Desire*
13. _____ Inge	M. *Our Town*
14. _____ O'Neill	N. *J.B.*
15. _____ Mamet	O. *Picnic*
16. _____ Uhry	P. *That Championship Season*
17. _____ Williams	Q. *A Delicate Balance*
18. _____ Miller (Jason)	R. *The Effect of Gamma Rays on Man-in-the-Moon Marigolds*

SECTION 8

SHAKESPEARE—WHERE THERE'S WILL, THERE ARE WORDS

William Shakespeare

A SHAKESPEARE PRIMER

Here are twenty-five questions to get you into a Shakespeare frame of mind. Write the answers in the blank next to the question.

1. _____ Shakespeare was born in this year.

2. _____ His birthplace was in this English town.

3. _____ Shakespeare was born in the same year as this playwright who wrote *Tamburlaine* and *Dr. Faustus*.

4. _____ This queen reigned during most of Shakespeare's life.

5. _____ I authored the *Chronicles of England, Scotland,* and *Ireland* from which Shakespeare drew information for his plays.

6. _____ Shakespeare's troupe performed most of their plays in this playhouse built in 1599.

7. _____ I circumnavigated the earth during Shakespeare's lifetime.

8. _____ After annexing Virginia this explorer was knighted.

9. _____ This was Shakespeare's mother's maiden name.

10. _____ This was Shakespeare's wife's maiden name.

11. _____ This queen was executed in 1587.

12. _____ Mr. and Mrs. William Shakespeare had how many children?

13. _____ This was the name of the fleet defeated by the English navy.

14. _____ This was the beautiful estate purchased by Shakespeare in 1597 in Stratford-upon-Avon.

15. _____ In 1592, 1603, and 1609 the theaters closed because of this.

16. _____ I was Shakespeare's patron.

17. _____ This was the year King James I assumed the British throne.

18. _____ This was the number of actresses who performed in Shakespeare's plays.

19. _____ Shakespeare wrote how many sonnets?

20. _____ This is what happened to the Globe Playhouse during a performance of *King Henry VIII* in 1613.

21. _____ Besides writing histories and comedies, Shakespeare also wrote these.

22. _____ This is the number of male heirs that Shakespeare left.

23. _____ This is the year Shakespeare died.

24. _____ Shakespeare was born and died on the same day, fifty-two years apart. Give the month and day.

25. _____ What is the missing word in the last line of Shakespeare's epitaph? "And curst be he who moves my _____."

WHAT'S IN A NAME?
PART ONE

Twenty-five characters from Shakespeare's plays are described below. Match the name with the correct description by writing the correct name in the space next to the number.

Achilles	Banquo	Julius Caesar	Cressida
Titus Andronicus	Bassanio	Cassio	Desdemona
Antonio	Sir Toby Belch	Claudio	Edgar
Antony	Bianca	Cleopatra	Sir John Falstaff
Apothecary	Nick Bottom	Cordelia	Fortinbras
Ariel	Brutus	Coriolanus	Gaunt
Aufidius			

1. _____ Othello's wife who is killed in bed.

2. _____ Egyptian queen and mistress of a triumvirate member.

3. _____ Antonio's friend and Portia's suitor.

4. _____ Roman dictator who is killed at the Capitol.

5. _____ The Earl of Gloucester's legitimate son and brother to illegitimate Edmund.

6. _____ The king who succeeds Claudius, Hamlet's uncle.

7. _____ Just before his death, he delivers his eulogy on England and offers some advice to Richard II.

8. _____ His ghost appears at Macbeth's banquet.

9. _____ Coriolanus defeats him, but then is killed by him and the conspirators.

10. _____ King Lear's youngest, best loved, and most honest daughter.

11. _____ The most famous Greek warrior. He is proclaimed conqueror of Hector although Hector was killed by the Myrmidons.

12. _____ The Merchant of Venice.

13. _____ "An ayrie sprite" freed by Prospero. He has the ability to calm a storm at sea.

14. _____ Chalchas' daughter who defects to the Greek side during the Trojan siege of Troy.

15. _____ A contemptuous Roman general who is banished and ultimately killed.

WHAT'S IN A NAME? (PART ONE) (continued)

16. _____ A weaver of Athens who is given the head of an ass by Puck. He plays the part of Pyramus in the Interlude before the duke.

17. _____ An aging Roman general who returns to Rome in triumph after his sixth victory over the Goths.

18. _____ He sells a dram of deadly poison to a teenaged boy in Mantua, Italy.

19. _____ According to Antony the "noblest Roman of them all."

20. _____ He was both a rowdy, heavy drinking friend of the Prince of Wales and the head of the London thieves.

21. _____ Because of this man's appointment by Othello, Iago plots revenge against Othello.

22. _____ Though he is arrested for fornication with Juliet, he is ultimately pardoned by the Duke.

23. _____ He fell in love with the Queen of Egypt and stabs himself toward the play's conclusion.

24. _____ Cassio's mistress.

25. _____ Olivia's drunken uncle who gulls Malvolio.

WHAT'S IN A NAME?
PART TWO

Match Shakespeare's characters with their descriptions by writing the correct name in the blank next to the number.

Gertrude	Hippolyta	Katherina Minola	Mercutio
Earl of Gloucester	Horatio	Laertes	Nurse
Goneril	Iago	King Lear	Oberon
Hamlet	Imogen	Lorenzo	Octavia
Helena	Isabella	Macbeth	Ophelia
Henry, Prince of Wales	Juliet	Macduff	Othello
Henry VIII			

1. _____ The Queen of the Amazons.

2. _____ The villain of villains. He is the knave who tricks Othello into believing that Desdemona, Othello's wife, has been unfaithful to Othello.

3. _____ Prince of Denmark who sees his father's ghost.

4. _____ He misjudges the intentions of his two sons, Edgar and Edmund. He wants to kill himself until he is rescued by Edgar. He ultimately dies broken-hearted after he learns of his other son's deception.

5. _____ This king, divorced from Katherine, marries Anne Bullen and befriends Cranmer.

6. _____ He is killed by Tybalt.

7. _____ The shrew that Petruchio tames.

8. _____ A man of "vaulting ambition," he kills King Duncan and arranges for the deaths of others in Scotland.

9. _____ Antony's devoted wife who is the victim of political maneuverings.

10. _____ He decides that his three daughters will inherit his kingdom. He ultimately goes mad and dies after trying to revive his daughter, Cordelia, who was executed.

11. _____ Claudio's sister, a novice in the convent; she is asked to give up her chastity to save her brother's life.

12. _____ The Moor who is duped by Iago into such jealousy that he smothers his wife, Desdemona.

13. _____ Suspicious of Macbeth, he leads the army and kills Macbeth in a one-on-one fight.

14. _____ She is the teenager who marries a sixteen-year-old. She takes a potion that gives her the appearance of death.

15. _____ Hamlet's mother, wife of Claudius, and Queen of Denmark, she dies by drinking poison.

16. _____ King Lear's eldest daughter who stabs herself to death.

17. _____ Hamlet's confidant.

18. _____ Earlier known as Hal, this king-to-be revels and plays tricks with Falstaff, kills Hotspur, and rescues his father, the king. Later, as the king, he banishes Falstaff and wins Katherine as part of his peace agreement with France.

19. _____ She is the daughter of Cymbeline who marries Posthumus without her father's permission.

20. _____ The Athenian maid who loves Demetrius.

21. _____ Son of Polonius and brother of Ophelia, he stabs Hamlet with a poisoned sword.

22. _____ Juliet's talkative confidante.

23. _____ King of the Faeries who is married to Titania.

24. _____ She is in love with Hamlet. She drowns herself after hearing that Hamlet killed her father, Polonius.

25. _____ Bassanio's friend who elopes with Shylock's daughter, Jessica, after they steal some of Shylock's jewelry and money.

WHAT'S IN A NAME?
PART THREE

Match the twenty characters from Shakespeare's plays with their descriptions by writing the names in the correct spaces.

Paris	Priam	Regan	Theseus
Petruchio	Prospero	Romeo	Titania
Pistol	Proteus	Rosencrantz	Touchstone
Polonius	Puck	Shylock	Tybalt
Portia	Mistress Quickly	Christopher Sly	Viola

1. _____ He loans Antonio money in *The Merchant of Venice*.

2. _____ A sixteen-year-old male who lives in Verona, Italy.

3. _____ The King of Troy.

4. _____ Falstaff's ancient.

5. _____ Oberon's fairy who pours the flower "love-in-idleness" over Lysander.

6. _____ The Duke of Athens.

7. _____ King Lear's daughter who is married to the Duke of Cornwall.

8. _____ The wife of Brutus.

9. _____ The father of Ophelia and Laertes.

10. _____ He tames the shrew.

11. _____ Dukes Frederick's court Fool.

12. _____ The Queen of the Fairies.

13. _____ The hostess of the tavern in Eastcheap.

14. _____ A gentleman of Verona, he is in love with Julia.

15. _____ Sebastian's twin sister.

16. _____ He kills Mercutio.

17. _____ The drunken tinker in the Induction to *The Taming of the Shrew*.

18. _____ The young man Juliet's parents arranged for her to marry.

19. _____ The father of Miranda. He and Miranda had lived on an island for twelve years.

20. _____ A supposed friend of Hamlet's.

Name _____ Date _____ Period _____

HOW TRAGIC OF YOU, WILL!

Shakespeare is well known for his enduring tragedies. Here are thirty-five questions that deal with his major tragedies. Write the letter of the tragedy that correctly answers each question. If a question asks for a specific character's name, write the appropriate letter only. You may use an answer more than once. The first one is done for you.

A. *Antony and Cleopatra*   E. *King Lear*   H. *Richard II*
B. *Coriolanus*   F. *Macbeth*   I. *Romeo and Juliet*
C. *Hamlet*   G. *Othello*   J. *Timon of Athens*
D. *Julius Caesar*

1. __C__ I am friends with Rosencrantz and Guildenstern in Denmark.

2. _____ This play contains the famous dagger speech.

3. _____ I have three daughters—Goneril, Regan, and Cordelia.

4. _____ I am killed on the Ides of March.

5. _____ Friar John's inability to deliver a letter spells disaster in this play.

6. _____ My mother marries my father's murderer.

7. _____ They fall in love at Capulet's party.

8. _____ *The Murder of Gonzago,* a.k.a. *The Mousetrap,* is performed to assess the degree of guilt.

9. _____ This titular character is known as the Moor.

10. _____ A soothsayer warns this titular character at the Senate.

11. _____ Because he did not act sooner, this character might be called a melancholy procrastinator.

12. _____ Caius Martius has his name changed to this play's title after he defeats the Volscians.

13. _____ He dies by Laertes' poisonous sword.

14. _____ A dropped handkerchief leads to more trouble in this play.

15. _____ Brutus and Cassius disagree in this play.

16. _____ A potion allows this character to appear dead for forty-two hours.

17. _____ Kent and Edgar rule the land at this play's end.

18. _____ As this play opens, an angry crowd must be calmed by Menenius.

19. _____ Banquo's ghost scares this titular character.

20. _____ This character finds gold in a cave.

21. _____ The Earl of Gloucester, Edgar, and Edmund play important roles in this play.

22. _____ This play opens in Egypt.

23. _____ In this play Brutus is called the "noblest Roman of them all."

24. _____ Iago and Desdemona are important characters in this tragedy.

25. _____ The appearance of three witches opens this play.

26. _____ As this play commences, Henry Bolingbroke and Thomas Mowbray are at odds.

27. _____ After the former king is killed, the new king, Henry IV, plans to repent in the Holy Land.

28. _____ This titular character wants to kill himself by falling on his sword.

29. _____ The plebeians' reactions drive this man to join forces with their enemy.

30. _____ As asp brings an end to this character's life.

31. _____ This character finances the expedition of Alciabiades, banished by the Athenian Senate.

32. _____ The feuding families will erect statues to honor these dead teens.

33. _____ Agents of Aufidius kill this titular character.

34. _____ This character's wife cannot kill King Duncan because he looks too much like her own father.

35. _____ This character takes John of Gaunt's son's inheritance to finance the Irish War.

WILL PAIRS THEM UP

Do you know the names of the two gentlemen of Verona? This exercise tests your knowledge of famous pairs from Shakespeare's plays. Match the pairs by writing the correct letter in the appropriate space next to the number.

1. _____ Hamlet

2. _____ Romeo

3. _____ Macbeth

4. _____ King Ferdinand

5. _____ Proteus

6. _____ Hermia

7. _____ Bassanio

8. _____ Petruchio

9. _____ Claudio (*Much Ado About Nothing*)

10. _____ Juliet

11. _____ Antonio (*Twelfth Night*)

12. _____ Claudio (*Measure for Measure*)

13. _____ Leontes

14. _____ Prince Hal

15. _____ Casca

16. _____ Rosencrantz

17. _____ Achilles

18. _____ Emilia

19. _____ Malcolm

20. _____ Sebastian (*The Tempest*)

A. Nurse

B. Valentine

C. Desdemona

D. Sir John Falstaff

E. Antonio (*The Tempest*)

F. Hortensio

G. Horatio

H. Banquo

I. Don Pedro

J. Helena

K. Guildenstern

L. Lucio

M. Polixenes

N. Siward

O. Brutus

P. Antonio (*The Merchant of Venice*)

Q. Sebastian (*Twelfth Night*)

R. Biron, Longaville, and Dumain

S. Benvolio

T. Patroclus

WILL SETS THE SCENE

How familiar are you with the locations of Shakespeare's plays? Match the twenty-five plays with their settings.

A. *All's Well That Ends Well*
B. *Antony and Cleopatra*
C. *As You Like It*
D. *The Comedy of Errors*
E. *Coriolanus*
F. *Cymbeline*
G. *Hamlet*
H. *Julius Caesar*
I. *King Lear*

J. *Love's Labour's Lost*
K. *Macbeth*
L. *Measure for Measure*
M. *The Merchant of Venice*
N. *A Midsummer Night's Dream*
O. *Much Ado About Nothing*
P. *Othello*
Q. *Pericles*

R. *Romeo and Juliet*
S. *The Taming of the Shrew*
T. *The Tempest*
U. *Titus Andronicus*
V. *Troilus and Cressida*
W. *Twelfth Night*
X. *Two Gentlemen of Verona*
Y. *The Winter's Tale*

COMEDIES

1. _____ Navarre, the King's palace, and the country near it

2. _____ Epheseus

3. _____ Verona; Milan; and a forest between Milan and Mantua

4. _____ Athens, and a wood near it

5. _____ Partly at Venice and partly at Belmont, the seat of Portia

6. _____ Padua, and Petruchio's country house

7. _____ Messina

8. _____ Oliver's House; Duke Frederick's court; and the Forest of Arden

9. _____ A city in Illyria, and the sea coast near it

10. _____ Troy, and the Greek camp before it

11. _____ Rousillon; Paris; Florence; Marseilles

12. _____ Vienna

13. _____ Dispersed in various countries

14. _____ Britain; Rome

15. _____ Sicilia and Bohemia

16. _____ [A ship at sea;] an uninhabited island

TRAGEDIES

17. _____ Rome and the country near it

18. _____ Verona; Mantua

19. _____ Rome; the neighborhood of Sardis; the neighborhood of Philippi

20. _____ Elsinore

21. _____ Venice; a seaport in Cyprus

22. _____ Britain

23. _____ Scotland; England

24. _____ In several parts of the Roman Empire

25. _____ Rome and the neighborhood; Corioli and the neighborhood; Antium

Name _____ **Date** _____ **Period** _____

SHAKESPEARE STAGES A BRAWL

Shakespeare's play *The Tempest* was about a storm at sea. This exercise uses the word *storm* to be a fight or argument between two or more people in Shakespeare's plays. Match the combatants by writing the correct letter in the appropriate space next to the number.

1. _____ Prince Hal

2. _____ Henry V

3. _____ Titus Andronicus

4. _____ Romeo

5. _____ Julius Caesar

6. _____ Achilles

7. _____ Hamlet

8. _____ Othello

9. _____ Cornwall

10. _____ Macduff

11. _____ Antony

12. _____ Volsces

13. _____ Antonio

14. _____ Angelo

15. _____ Somerset

A. Laertes

B. Hotspur

C. Macbeth

D. Marcius

E. Brutus

F. Hector

G. The French

H. Tybalt

I. Octavius

J. Shylock

K. Richard

L. Iago

M. Goths

N. Gloucester's servant

O. Claudio

SHAKESPEARE'S SENSATIONAL SALES

The Merchant of Venice has some goods for sale. Each of the items is from one of Shakespeare's plays. For instance if a potion guaranteed to give one the appearance of death for forty-two hours were for sale, your answer would be *Romeo and Juliet* since that was how the man who married Romeo to Juliet hoped to save Juliet from marrying Paris. Correctly match the item with the play in which it is found by writing the correct letter in the space next to its corresponding number.

A. *All's Well That Ends Well*
B. *Antony and Cleopatra*
C. *As You Like It*
D. *A Comedy of Errors*
E. *Coriolanus*
F. *Cymbeline*
G. *Hamlet*
H. *Julius Caesar*

I. *King Lear*
J. *Macbeth*
K. *Measure for Measure*
L. *The Merchant of Venice*
M. *The Merry Wives of Windsor*
N. *A Midsummer Night's Dream*
O. *Much Ado About Nothing*

P. *Othello*
Q. *Romeo and Juliet*
R. *The Taming of the Shrew*
S. *The Tempest*
T. *Timon of Athens*
U. *Twelfth Night*
V. *Two Gentlemen of Verona*

1. _____ Ariel's magic

2. _____ an unusual bracelet

3. _____ a death penalty rule banning fornication

4. _____ a ring given to Diana by the King of France

5. _____ a purple flower that has amorous powers

6. _____ a phony love letter found by Malvolio

7. _____ Forest of Arden plants

8. _____ masks worn by dancers at a Messina, Italy, ball

9. _____ a laundry hamper

10. _____ a promissory note to forfeit a pound of flesh

11. _____ a lute broken by Katherina

12. _____ rocks from Valentine's cave

13. _____ Angelo's gold chain

14. _____ the oaken garland given to Marcius

15. _____ covered dishes of warm water used at a Greek feast

16. _____ a killer asp

17. _____ Laertes' sword

18. _____ witches' brew

19. _____ the cord used to hand Cordelia

20. _____ Desdemona's handkerchief

21. _____ an unread, unopened emperor's scroll

22. _____ Friar Laurence's emissary's undelivered note

THE END JUSTIFIES THE SCENES

Shakespeare's plays' endings do not always fit the title of his play *All's Well That Ends Well*. In fact, some of his plays end quite sadly or even deadly—especially if you know how *Hamlet* ends.

This exercise asks you to match the play with its ending. Write the correct letter in the space next to the number.

A. *All's Well That Ends Well*   H. *Henry VIII*   O. *Othello*
B. *Antony and Cleopatra*   I. *Julius Caesar*   P. *Richard II*
C. *As You Like It*   J. *King Lear*   Q. *Romeo and Juliet*
D. *Coriolanus*   K. *Macbeth*   R. *The Taming of the Shrew*
E. *Hamlet*   L. *The Merchant of Venice*   S. *Timon of Athens*
F. *Henry IV, Part I*   M. *A Midsummer Night's Dream*   T. *Two Gentlemen of Verona*
G. *Henry VI, Part I*   N. *Much Ado About Nothing*

1. _____ The Bishop of Winchester escorts the Earl of Armagnac's daughter to England.

2. _____ King Henry IV will go to the Holy Land to "wash this blood off from his guilty hand."

3. _____ King Henry and Prince Hal will fight Owen Glendower and the Earl of March in Wales.

4. _____ Cranmer delivers a moving speech about the upcoming reign of Queen Elizabeth.

5. _____ The Montagues and the Capulets resolve to end their feud.

6. _____ Antony and Octavius approach the dead bodies.

7. _____ Fortinbras will be the next King of Denmark.

8. _____ Cassio orders the execution of Iago.

9. _____ Cordelia is killed and her father dies.

10. _____ The titular character's head is presented to Scotland's new king.

11. _____ Octavius says the two lovers should have a common grave.

12. _____ Word that the titular character has died in a cave reaches the Greek city.

13. _____ Aufidius plans to pay homage to the titular character killed by the conspirators.

14. _____ A double wedding in Italy is in the works.

15. _____ Petruchio kisses Katherina.

16. _____ Puck delivers a monologue.

17. _____ Antonio's ships have safely reached the Italian port city.

18. _____ Don Juan has been captured and will be punished.

19. _____ Four couples will be married.

20. _____ The king will find Diana a husband.

THE BARD'S BUNGLES

Each of the twenty statements concerning actions that take place in Shakespeare's plays contains an error. Correct the error by crossing out the incorrect portion of the statement and writing the correct information on the line below the statement. The first one is done for you.

1. Romeo and Juliet, two people in their ~~twenties~~, are married by Friar Leo.

    _____ teens _____

2. When *Julius Caesar* begins, Caesar returns to Rome after his victories over Brutus.

    _____

3. The ghost of Hamlet's uncle urges him to seek revenge.

    _____

4. Iago is angry with Othello because Othello has been having an affair with Iago's wife, Emilia.

    _____

5. In Act I, both Macbeth and Banquo receive four predictions from the witches.

    _____

6. At the conclusion of *Antony and Cleopatra,* Caesar demands that Antony and his wife, Octavius, be buried in the same grave.

    _____

7. The citizens of Rome are angry with the senate because of the high taxes.

    _____

8. Timon of Athens dies happily surrounded by his loyal friends.

    _____

9. Cordelia and her father, King Lear, die happily in each other's arms.

    _____

10. The plot of *Troilus and Cressida* involves the Punic Wars.

    _____

11. Cranmer, the Archbishop of Canterbury, annuls the marriage of Henry VIII and Jane Seymour.

    _____

12. Richard III kills Richmond on Bosworth Field.

    _____

13. *Henry V* shows the former Prince Hal's continuing downfall.

    _____

14. Hotspur kills both Henry IV and his son.

    _____

15. At the conclusion of Richard II, Richard is in prison awaiting his execution.

_____

16. Prospero's servant, Ferdinand, has magical powers.

_____

17. Banished by Imogen's father, Posthumus gives her a beautiful dress before he leaves.

_____

18. The action in *All's Well That Ends Well* takes place in England.

_____

19. Claudio's foil in *Much Ado About Nothing* is Antonio.

_____

20. Baptista Minola, the father of Katherina and Bianca, says Bianca cannot marry until Katherina dies.

_____

LOVE—SHAKESPEAREAN STYLE

This exercise tests your knowledge of Shakespeare's love bugs. Match the husbands and wives or lovers by writing the appropriate letter in the space next to the number.

1. _____ Henry VI

2. _____ Pistol

3. _____ Henry

4. _____ Aaron

5. _____ Romeo

6. _____ Troilus

7. _____ Hamlet

8. _____ Iago

9. _____ Othello

10. _____ King of France

11. _____ Antony

12. _____ Proteus

13. _____ Petruchio

14. _____ Portia

15. _____ Claudio

16. _____ Rosalind

17. _____ Viola

18. _____ Bertram

19. _____ Imogen

20. _____ Virgilia

A. Juliet (*Romeo and Juliet*)

B. Emilia

C. Julia

D. Cressida

E. Margaret of Anjou

F. Juliet (*Measure for Measure*)

G. Helena

H. Katherina

I. Orsino

J. Ophelia

K. Katherine

L. Hostess Quickly

M. Cordelia

N. Desdemona

O. Posthumus

P. Bassanio

Q. Orlando

R. Coriolanus

S. Cleopatra

T. Tamora

WILL'S TRAGIC WORDS

What book of literary exercises would be complete without tragic words from the master, William Shakespeare? Identify the play for each of the quotes by writing the correct corresponding letter. Answers may be used more than once.

TRAGEDIES

A. *Antony and Cleopatra* (1607)
B. *Coriolanus* (1608)
C. *Hamlet* (1601)
D. *Julius Caesar* (1599)
E. *King Lear* (1605)
F. *Macbeth* (1606)

G. *Othello* (1604)
H. *Romeo and Juliet* (1596)
I. *Timon of Athens* (1607)
J. *Titus Andronicus* (1590)
K. *Troilus and Cressida* (1601)

1. _____ "O swear not by the moon, the inconstant moon,
   That monthly changes in her circled orb,
   Lest that thy love prove likewise variable."

2. _____ "Methought I heard a voice cry, 'Sleep no more
   (Name) does murder sleep,' the innocent sleep,
   Sleep that knits up the ravell'd sleave of care,
   The death of each day's life, sore labor's bath . . .'"

3. _____ "The worst is not
   So long as we can say, 'This is the worst.'"

4. _____ "And what's he then that says I play the villain,
   When this advice is free I give and honest,
   Probal to thinking, and indeed the course
   To win the Moor again?"

5. _____ "Frailty, thy name is woman!"

6. _____ "This was the noblest Roman of them all."

7. _____ "I am dying, Egypt, dying."

8. _____ "What is the city but the people?"

9. _____ "She is a woman, therefore may be woo'd;
   She is a woman, therefore may be won;
   She is Lavinia, therefore must be lov'd."

10. _____ "The fault, dear Brutus, is not in the stars,
    But in ourselves, that we are underlings."

11. _____ "Alas, poor Yorick. I knew him, Horatio: a fellow of infinite jest, of most excellent
    fancy; . . ."

12. _____ "When shall we three meet again
    In thunder, lightning, or in rain?"

13. _____ "I am Misanthropos, and hate mankind.
    For thy part, I do wish thou wert a dog,
    That I might love thee something."

14. _____ "Where's my serpent of old Nile?"

15. _____ "Child Roland to the dark tower came.
    His word was still, Fie, foh, and fum,
    I smell the blood of a British man."

16. _____ "But yet the pity of it, Iago! O Iago, the pity of it, Iago!"

17. _____ "Something is rotten in the state of Denmark."

18. _____ "Deny thy father and refuse thy name . . ."

19. _____ "What's in a name? That which we call a rose
By any other word would smell as sweet;"

20. _____ "We are accounted poor citizens, the patricians good. What authority surfeits on
would relieve us; if they would yield us but the superfluity while it were wholesome,
we might guess they relieved us humanely; but they think we are too dear. The lean-
ness that afflicts us, the object of our misery, is as an inventory to particularize
their abundance; our sufferance is a gain to them."

21. _____ "Here I stand your slave,
A poor, infirm, weak, and despis'd old man;"

22. _____ "Is this a dagger which I see before me,
The handle toward my hand? Come, let me clutch thee:
I have thee not, and yet I see thee still,
Art thou not, fatal vision, sensible
To feeling as to sight? or art thou but
A dagger of the mind a false creation,
Proceeding from the heat-oppressed brain?"

23. _____ "Reputation, reputation, reputation!
Oh! I have lost my reputation. I have lost the immortal part of myself, and what re-
mains is bestial."

24. _____ "Romans, make way! The good __(Name)__,
Patron of virtue, Rome's best champion,
Successful in the battles that he fights,
With honour and with fortune is return'd
From where he circumscribed with his sword
And brought yoke the enemies of Rome."

25. _____ "Why, I was writing of my epitaph;
It will be seen to-morrow. My long sickness
Of health and living now begins to mend,
And nothing brings me all things. Go, live still;
Be Alcibiades your plague, you his,
And last so long enough!"

26. _____ "Most probable
That so she died; for her physician tells me
She hath pursu'd conclusions infinite
Of easy ways to die. Take up her bed;
And bear her woman from the monument . . .
Our army shall in solemn show attend this funeral;"

27. _____ "A soothsayer bids you beware the ides of March."

28. _____ "I lov'd Ophelia. Forty thousand brothers
Could not, with all their quantity of love,
Make up my sum. What wilt thou do for her?"

29. _____ "Love not yourselves; away,
Rob one another. There's more gold. Cut throats;
All that you meet are thieves. To Athens go,
Break open shops; nothing can you steal,
But thieves do lose it. Steal [no] less for this
I give you; and gold confound you howso'er!"

30. _____ "My rage is gone,
And I am struck with sorrow. Take him up.
Help, three o' th' chiefest soldiers; I'll be one.
Beat thou the drum, that it speak mournfully.
Trail your steel pikes. Though in this city he
Hath widow'd and unchilded many a one,
Which to this hour bewail the injury,
Yet he shall have a noble memory.
Assist."

31. _____ "There's language in her eye, her cheek, her lip."

32. _____ "Draw, Benvolio; beat down their weapons.
Gentlemen, for shame, forbear this outrage!
Tybalt, Mercutio, the Prince expressly hath
Forbid this bandying in Verona streets.
Hold, Tybalt! Good Mercutio!"

33. _____ "I bear a charmed life, which must not yield
To one of woman born."

34. _____ "The Greeks are strong, and skillful to their strength,
Fierce to their skill, and to their fierceness valiant;
But I am weaker than a woman's tear,
Tamer than sleep, fonder than ignorance,
Less valiant than the virgin in the night,
And skilless as upractis'd infancy."

35. _____ "O, never
Shall sun that morrow see!
Your face, my thane, is as a book where men
May read strange matters. To beguile the time,
Look like the time; bear welcome in your eye,
Your hand, your tongue; look like the innocent flower
But be the serpent under't . . ."

36. _____ "Ay, every inch a king."

37. _____ "Life's uncertain voyage."

38. _____ "Thy husband he is dead; and for his death
Thy brothers are condemn'd, and dead by this.
Look, Marcus! ah, son Lucius, look on her!
When I did name her brothers, then fresh tears
Stood on her cheeks, as doth the honey-dew
Upon a gath'red lily almost withered."

39. _____ "My sweet Patroclus, I am thwarted quite
From my great purpose in to-morrow's battle.
Here is a letter from Queen Hecuba.
A token from her daughter, my fair love,
Both taxing me and gaging me to keep
An oath that I have sworn."

40. _____ "A plague o' both your houses!"

41. _____ "Et tu, Brute?"

42. _____ "To be, or not to be: that is the question . . ."

43. _____ "Howl, howl, howl! O, you are men of stones!
Had I your tongues and eyes, I'd use them so
That heaven's vault should crack. She's gone for ever!
I know when one is dead, and when one lives;
She's dead as earth."

44. _____ "Tomorrow, and tomorrow, and tomorrow,
Creeps in this petty pace from day to day
To the last syllable of recorded time,
And all our yesterdays have lighted fools
The way to dusty death. Out, out, brief candle!
Life's but a walking shadow, a poor player
That struts and frets his hour upon the stage
And then is heard no more: it is a tale
Told by an idiot, full of sound and fury,
Signifying nothing."

45. _____ "Good-night, good-night! parting is such sweet sorrow
That I shall say good-night till it be morrow."

46. _____ "O cursed, cursed slave!
Whip me, ye devils,
From the possession of this heavenly sight!
Blow me about in winds! roast me in sulphur!
Wash me in steep—down gulfs of liquid fire!
O Desdemon! dead, Desdemon! dead!
Oh! Oh!"

47. _____ "If beauty have a soul, this is not she.
If soul guide vows, if vows are sanctimony,
If sanctimony be the gods' delight,
If there be rule in unity itself,
This is not she."

48. _____ "My name is Caius Marcius, who hath done
To thee particularly and to all the Volsces
Great hurt and mischief; thereto witness may
My surname . . ."

49. _____ "Tribunes, I thank you; and this suit I make,
That you create our emperor's eldest son,
Lord Saturnine; whose virtue will, I hope,
Reflect on Rome as [Titan's] rays on earth,
And ripen justice in this commonweal.
Then, if you will elect by my advice,
Crown him and say, 'Long live our emperor!'"

50. _____ "Long have I been forlorn, and all for thee.
Welcome, dread Fury, to my woeful house;
Rapine and Murder, you are welcome too.
How like the Empress and her sons you are!
Well are you fitted, had you but a Moor;
Could not all hell afford you such a devil?"

SECTION 9

POTPOURRI—
ACTIVITIES TO
PLEASE THE SENSES

Name _____ **Date** _____ **Period** _____

SCRAMBLED AMERICAN AUTHORS
PART ONE

Here are the scrambled names of twenty-five American authors. Unscramble them and write their names in the space after each number.

1. _____ onelsil

2. _____ ebaynrrsh

3. _____ weetjt

4. _____ seannord

5. _____ rabtesdret

6. _____ nocphi

7. _____ hotccnir

8. _____ yreg

9. _____ nigvir

10. _____ dunop

11. _____ ormeo

12. _____ hotr

13. _____ minso

14. _____ itnaw

15. _____ asmorn

16. _____ elcmucrsl

17. _____ dwacllel

18. _____ breefr

19. _____ silwe

20. _____ eoast

21. _____ glaserin

22. _____ grithw

23. _____ cokzi

24. _____ ezozsnc

25. _____ aeoucrk

SCRAMBLED AMERICAN AUTHORS
PART TWO

Do your best to unscramble the names of these twenty-five American authors by writing their names in the space next to each number.

1. _____ gine

2. _____ esedrir

3. _____ kbcu

4. _____ olewbl

5. _____ eabel

6. _____ seehyr

7. _____ trofs

8. _____ ootkp

9. _____ eryli

10. _____ itsne

11. _____ lywte

12. _____ shna

13. _____ reeminch

14. _____ escamlih

15. _____ teebiat

16. _____ iadzerltgf

17. _____ narldre

18. _____ melnhal

19. _____ hetacr

20. _____ sidicoknn

21. _____ doolnn

22. _____ yaccnl

23. _____ wensolk

24. _____ osgwalg

25. _____ steod

SCRAMBLED AMERICAN AUTHORS
PART THREE

Unscramble the names of these twenty-five American authors. Write your answers in the blank next to the number.

1. _____ oxtesn

2. _____ wotse

3. _____ leolin

4. _____ gelwolnolf

5. _____ taplh

6. _____ kinebstec

7. _____ risnge

8. _____ vecrhee

9. _____ saonkjc

10. _____ llerhe

11. _____ ecopat

12. _____ ibnadwl

13. _____ geamhyniw

14. _____ necar

15. _____ cibree

16. _____ yunnor

17. _____ eudkip

18. _____ basgnurd

19. _____ hyponnc

20. _____ ronrsi

21. _____ lllowe

22. _____ bruehrt

23. _____ sobkor

24. _____ seughh

25. _____ nrakot

SCRAMBLED AMERICAN AUTHORS
PART FOUR

There are twenty-five names of famous American authors waiting for you to unscramble them. Write your answers in the blanks next to the numbers.

1. _____ gusrbouhr

2. _____ krabaa

3. _____ darn

4. _____ anclrisi

5. _____ nilwrasg

6. _____ llmaiy

7. _____ rytnos

8. _____ liveleml

9. _____ himletcl

10. _____ yasorna

11. _____ ealufnrk

12. _____ vacerr

13. _____ rarlejl

14. _____ cattol

15. _____ tabhr

16. _____ deogd

17. _____ ooyrnc

18. _____ beetn

19. _____ limrel

20. _____ krapre

21. _____ theoker

22. _____ soonrirm

23. _____ terpor

24. _____ innsobor

25. _____ eaypl

© 1994 by The Center for Applied Research in Education

Name _____ Date _____ Period _____

SCRAMBLED BRITISH AND IRISH AUTHORS
PART ONE

Display your knowledge of British and Irish authors by unscrambling the names of these forty authors. Write the correct name in the blank next to the number.

1. _____ spyep
2. _____ modthisgl
3. _____ nowingrb
4. _____ oynrb
5. _____ wamlore
6. _____ sadnodi
7. _____ tosersit
8. _____ sofrert
9. _____ ligipnk
10. _____ nadlor
11. _____ soonnj
12. _____ norocon
13. _____ hammagu
14. _____ dreoegilc
15. _____ anehb
16. _____ otile
17. _____ ofdee
18. _____ leolwr
19. _____ tropet
20. _____ shyr

21. _____ tocst
22. _____ neelrawc
23. _____ neond
24. _____ caceruh
25. _____ nestau
26. _____ kabel
27. _____ nerege
28. _____ osceya
29. _____ kias
30. _____ soasons
31. _____ slewi
32. _____ coyej
33. _____ seofrert
34. _____ woelsbl
35. _____ kratheyac
36. _____ prakesashee
37. _____ delwi
38. _____ thorsrowdw
39. _____ eselet
40. _____ ranhides

SCRAMBLED BRITISH AND IRISH AUTHORS
PART TWO

Unscramble the names of these forty famous British and Irish authors. Write your answers in the blank next to each number.

1. _____ enprti
2. _____ oylarm
3. _____ rdonac
4. _____ etectbk
5. _____ farsehf
6. _____ nesgy
7. _____ lomttesl
8. _____ gawhu
9. _____ netsesnov
10. _____ niglodg
11. _____ pepo
12. _____ ekicdsn
13. _____ snurb
14. _____ luxyeh
15. _____ sinkur
16. _____ fiwts
17. _____ wash
18. _____ opelortl
19. _____ neestr
20. _____ troben

21. _____ aygr
22. _____ fanliemsd
23. _____ ribear
24. _____ espnres
25. _____ lowof
26. _____ postdarp
27. _____ syate
28. _____ leelyhs
29. _____ drnyed
30. _____ lolrarc
31. _____ wone
32. _____ tekas
33. _____ rowadc
34. _____ keotlni
35. _____ nidyes
36. _____ steerbw
37. _____ defnilgi
38. _____ mothsa
39. _____ aprsk
40. _____ neonsynt

SCRAMBLED WORLD AUTHORS

Name _____ Date _____ Period _____

Unscramble the names of these twenty-five world authors. Write the names in the blank next to the number.

1. _____ cabicocco

2. _____ sehse

3. _____ peresedui

4. _____ nurom

5. _____ seibn

6. _____ hecvokh

7. _____ tapnaresk

8. _____ traseecnv

9. _____ sopea

10. _____ togeeh

11. _____ namn

12. _____ fkkaa

13. _____ mmrig

14. _____ yovkostedys

15. _____ cleamehi

16. _____ zazakaksint

17. _____ apanlui

18. _____ argaic qarzume

19. _____ seyulchas

20. _____ ikikosns

21. _____ hopnaartsise

22. _____ riganb

23. _____ morhe

24. _____ herbtc

25. _____ modegirr

Name ———————————————————————— Date ——————— Period ———

AN ASSORTMENT OF EXCERPTS

See how many of these excerpts from an assortment of literary genres you can answer correctly. The work's date, author, and his or her nationality are given for you. Match the work's letter with the excerpt.

A. *The Aeneid*
B. *The Autobiography of Malcolm X*
C. *Beowulf*
D. *The Canterbury Tales*
E. *The Faerie Queene*
F. *Idylls of the King*
G. *Journal of the Plague Year*
H. *The Life of Samuel Johnson*
I. *The Little Prince*

J. *A Modest Proposal*
K. *Morte d'Arthur*
L. *Odyssey*
M. *Paradise Lost*
N. *Piers Plowman*
O. *Poor Richard's Almanack*
P. *The Rape of the Lock*
Q. *Walden*

1. ——— "Such then," said Una, "as she seemeth here,
Such is the face of falshood, such the sight
Of fawle Duessa, when her borrowed light
Is laid away, and countertes aunce knowne." [1590–1596; Edmund Spenser; English]

2. ——— As I had the honor and happiness of enjoying his friendship for upwards of twenty years; as I had the scheme of writing his life constantly in view . . . [1791; James Boswell; English]

3. ——— Speak to me, Muse, of the adventurous man who wandered long after he sacked the sacred citadel of Troy. [Ninth century B.C.; Homer; Ionian]

4. ——— Arms and the man I sing, who came from Troy [19 B.C.; Vergil; Roman]

5. ——— A small leak will sink a great ship
He that lieth down with dogs, shall rise up with fleas. [1732–1757; Ben Franklin; American]

6. ——— O wretched maid!
Was it for this you took such constant care
The bodkin; comb and essence to prepare?
For this your locks in paper durance bound,
For this with torturing irons wreathed around? [1714; Alexander Pope; English]

7. ——— When all treasures are tried, Truth is the best.
Now I have told thee what truth is, that no treasure is better,
I may no longer linger with thee; now look thee on our Lord. [c. 1367–c. 1387; Anonymous]

8. ——— Then murmured Arthur, "Place me in the barge."
So to the barge they came. There those three Queens
Put forth their hands, and took the King, and wept. [1875; Alfred Lord Tennyson; English]

9. ——— Now that I have told you soothly in a clause
th'estaat, th'array, the nombre, and eek the cause
Why that assembled was this compaignye
In Southwerk at this gentil hostelyre
That highte the Tabard . . . (Prologue) [1387; Geoffrey Chaucer; English]

10. _____ I profess in the sincerity of my heart that I have not the least personal interest in endeavouring to promote this necessary work, having no other motive than the public good of my country, by advancing our trade, providing for infants, relieving the poor, and giving some pleasure to the rich. I have no children by which I can propose to get a single penny; [1729; Jonathan Swift; English]

11. _____ Ah, Sir Lancelot, this day have I sore missed thee. And alas that ever I was against thee, for now have I my death, whereof Sir Gawain warned in my dream. [1469; Sir Thomas Mallory; English]

12. _____ Of man's First disobedience, and the Fruit
of that Forbidden Tree, whose mortal taste
Brought death into the World, and all our woe, . . . [1667; John Milton; English]

13. _____ From there he sought the folk of the South-Danes, the Honor Scyldings, over the sea swell [Early eighth century; Anonymous]

14. _____ "My little man, where do you come
from? What is this 'where I live' of
which you speak? Where do you want
to take your sheep?" [1943; Antoine de Saint Exupery; French]

15. _____ It was about the beginning of September, 1664,
that I, among the rest of my neighbours,
heard, in ordinary discourse, that the plague
was returned again in Holland . . . [1722; Daniel Defoe; English]

16. _____ When my mother was pregnant with me, she told me later, a party of hooded Ku Klux Klan riders galloped up to our home in Omaha, Nebraska, one night. [1964; (as told to Alex Haley); American]

17. _____ When I wrote the following pages, or rather the bulk of them, I lived alone, in the woods, a mile from any neighbor, in a house which I had built myself . . . [1854; Henry David Thoreau; American]

BODY PARTS IN LITERARY TITLES

Name the author of each literary title containing a body part.

1. _____ *A Farewell to Arms*

2. _____ *The Man with the Golden Arm*

3. _____ *The Heart Is a Lonely Hunter*

4. _____ *The Skin of Our Teeth*

5. _____ "The Tell-Tale Heart"

6. _____ *Heart of Darkness*

7. _____ *Arms and the Man*

8. _____ *Crimes of the Heart*

9. _____ *Rabble in Arms*

10. _____ *The Left Hand of Darkness*

11. _____ *The Heart of the Matter*

12. _____ *None but the Lonely Heart*

13. _____ *Their Eyes Were Watching God*

14. _____ *Bury My Heart at Wounded Knee*

15. _____ *The Bluest Eye*

16. _____ *My Left Foot*

17. _____ *Jaws*

18. _____ *Bones of the Buffalo*

19. _____ *The Lives of a Cell*

20. _____ *Death of the Heart*

21. _____ *Eye of the Needle*

22. _____ *Eye of the Storm*

23. _____ *House and Its Head*

24. _____ *In the Prison of Her Skin*

25. _____ *Charlotte Temple*

COLORS IN LITERATURE

Fill in the correct color for each of these titles.

1. *A Study in* _____ by Sir Arthur Conan Doyle

2. *The* _____ *Devil* by John Webster

3. "The _____ Man's Burden" by Rudyard Kipling

4. *Ma Railey's* _____ *Bottom* by August Wilson

5. *The* _____ *Knight* by Joseph Wambaugh

6. *The Color* _____ by Alice Walker

7. *Biloxi* _____ by Neil Simon

8. _____ -*Jacket* by Herman Melville

9. _____ *Fang* by Jack London

10. "The Ransom of _____ Chief" by O. Henry

11. *Good as* _____ by Joseph Heller

12. *The* _____ *Letter* by Nathaniel Hawthorne

13. *To Be Young, Gifted, and* _____ by Lorraine Hansberry

14. *House of* _____ *Leaves* by John Guare

15. *Riders of the* _____ *Sage* by Zane Grey

16. *The* _____ *Album* by Joan Didion

17. *The* _____ *Badge of Courage* by Stephen Crane

18. *The* _____ *Pastures* by Marc Connelly

19. *The Hunt for* _____ *October* by Tom Clancy

20. *Anne of* _____ *Gables* by Lucy M. Montgomery

21. *The* _____ *and the* _____ by Stendhal

22. *Sir Gawain and the* _____ *Knight* by the Pearl Poet

23. _____ *Beauty* by Anna Sewell

24. *Great* _____ *Hope* by Howard Sackler

25. *The* _____ *Cell* by Sharon Olds

26. *Man in the* _____ *Flannel Suit* by Sloan Wilson

27. _____ *Magic* by Amira Baraka (LeRoi Jones)

28. *A Clockwork* _____ by Anthony Burgess

29. _____ *Sky at Morning* by Richard Bradford

30. _____ *Boy* by Richard Wright

31. _____ *Light* by Garrett Hongo

THE COMMON DENOMINATOR
(A Sherlock Holmes Primer)

Is there a detective inside you just waiting to get that big break? Can you compete with the likes of Holmes, Poirot, Marple, and Father Brown?

This contest will test your creativity and your ability to locate clues in the titles written by famous authors. Here's how you can work your way toward induction into the Detectives' Hall of Fame. We want to warn you that this is no picnic!

Each author in the group of four authors has written a literary title that shares something in common with the titles written by the other authors in the group. See if you can detect what is common to all four titles. Write the common denominator after the group's number.

Here is a sample group to get you started:

John Gunther   Thomas Mann   Arthur Miller   Willa Cather

Their commonality is that all have written a work with the word *Death* in the title.

John Gunther: *Death Be Not Proud*   Arthur Miller: *Death of a Salesman*
Thomas Mann: *Death in Venice*   Willa Cather: *Death Comes for the Archbishop*

Start looking for those clues. Good luck, Sherlock!

Group 1:
Anton Chekhov _____
Fyodor Dostoyevsky _____
Ivan Turgenev _____
Bertolt Brecht _____

Group 2:
George Bernard Shaw _____
Zora Neale Hurston _____
Thornton Wilder _____
Dee Brown _____

Group 3:
John Updike _____
Tennessee Williams _____
Eugene O'Neill _____
C. S. Lewis _____

Group 4:
J. D. Salinger _____
Anthony Burgess _____
John Steinbeck _____
Fannie Flagg _____

Group 5:

William Faulkner _____

Thomas Wolfe _____

James Baldwin _____

William Styron _____

Group 6:

Edith Wharton _____

Nathaniel Hawthorne _____

Charles Dickens _____

Henrik Ibsen _____

Group 7:

John Fowles _____

Rudyard Kipling _____

Mac Hyman _____

George Bernard Shaw _____

Group 8:

Dashiell Hammett _____

Harper Lee _____

Jack Higgins _____

Aristophanes _____

Group 9:

George Eliot _____

Joseph Conrad _____

Charles Dickens _____

Kingsley Amos _____

Group 10:

Robert Browning _____

Edwin O'Connor _____

James Fenimore Cooper _____

Edward Bulwer-Lytton _____

Group 11:

Jean Rhys _____

Henry David Thoreau _____

Rachael Carson _____

Mark Twain _____

THE COMMON DENOMINATOR (continued)

Group 12:

Mark Twain _____

Saul Bellow _____

Lewis Carroll _____

Walker Percy _____

Group 13:

Erich Maria Remarque _____

Kenneth Roberts _____

John Millington Synge _____

Percy Bysshe Shelley _____

Group 14:

Anna Sewell _____

Alice Walker _____

Stendhal _____

W. H. Hudson _____

Group 15:

Aldous Huxley _____

Rachael Carson _____

William Shakespeare _____

Barbara Pym _____

Group 16:

D. H. Lawrence _____

Alberto Moravia _____

Euripedes _____

Louisa May Alcott _____

Group 17:

Nikos Kazantzakis _____

Theodore Dreiser _____

Thomas Kyd _____

Elizabeth Barrett Browning _____

Group 18:

Conrad Richter _____

Alfred Lord Tennyson _____

William Faulkner _____

Garrett Hongo _____

How many common groups can you compose? Try it!

CREATURES IN LITERARY TITLES

Check your knowledge of titles containing creatures. Name as many of these authors as you can.

1. _____ *Tarzan of the Apes*
2. _____ *King Rat*
3. _____ *The Little Foxes*
4. _____ *One Flew Over the Cuckoo's Nest*
5. _____ *To Kill a Mockingbird*
6. _____ *The Sea Wolf*
7. _____ *The Octopus*
8. _____ *The Hairy Ape*
9. _____ *The Birds*
10. _____ *The Yearling*
11. _____ *Cat's Cradle*
12. _____ *Of Mice and Men*
13. _____ *I Know Why the Caged Bird Sings*
14. _____ *Cat on a Hot Tin Roof*
15. _____ *Rabbit, Run*
16. _____ *The Day of the Locust*
17. _____ *Sweet Bird of Youth*
18. _____ *Lord of the Flies*
19. _____ *Androcles and the Lion*
20. _____ *Portrait of the Artist as a Young Dog*
21. _____ *The Wild Swans at Coole*
22. _____ "The Ugly Duckling"
23. _____ *Hound of the Baskervilles*
24. _____ *The Maltese Falcon*
25. _____ *The Eagle Has Landed*
26. _____ *The Lion, the Witch, and the Wardrobe*
27. _____ *The Young Lions*
28. _____ *Painted Bird*
29. _____ *Thorn Birds*
30. _____ *The Frogs*
31. _____ *The Night of the Iguana*
32. _____ *Monkeys*
33. _____ *Madame Butterfly*
34. _____ *Animal Farm*

THE FLOW OF LITERATURE

Do you think about some common themes flowing through the titles of literary works? Bodies of water and their associations seem to be popular. The following titles contain a word associated with water. First write the correct word associated with a body of water in the space and then match the title with its author. The first one is already done.

1. __*d*__ The Old Man and the <u>Sea</u>

2. _____ Life on the _____

3. _____ Drums Along the _____

4. _____ An Occurrence at Owl _____ Bridge

5. _____ The Open _____

6. _____ The _____ Around Us

7. _____ Watch on the _____

8. _____ The _____ Wolf

9. _____ The Lady of the _____

10. _____ Show _____

11. _____ Twenty Thousand Leagues under the _____

12. _____ Two Years Before the _____

13. _____ On the _____

14. _____ Crossing Brooklyn _____

15. _____ The Bridge on the _____ Kwai

a. Jack London

b. Edna Ferber

c. Lillian Hellman

d. Ernest Hemingway

e. Stephen Crane

f. Mark Twain

g. Rachel Carson

h. Richard Dana

i. Walt Whitman

j. Jules Verne

k. Nevil Shute

l. Pierre Boulle

m. Walter Edmonds

n. Ambrose Bierce

o. Sir Walter Scott

Name _____ **Date** _____ **Period** _____

THE DEATHS OF LITERATURE

Can you remember the author of each of these titles all containing words associated with death?

1. _____ *Death of a Salesman*

2. _____ *Death on the Nile*

3. _____ *Death in Venice*

4. _____ *Death Comes for the Archbishop*

5. _____ *Death of Ivan Ilych*

6. _____ "The Death of the Hired Man"

7. _____ *Rosencrantz and Guildenstern Are Dead*

8. _____ *A Death in the Family*

9. _____ *The Death of the Heart*

10. _____ *As I Lay Dying*

11. _____ *Death and the King's Horseman*

12. _____ *Sizwe Banzi Is Dead*

13. _____ "Because I Could Not Stop for Death"

14. _____ *Dead Souls*

15. _____ *The Naked and the Dead*

THE "-ISM'S" OF LITERATURE
PART ONE

Match the fifteen literary "-ism's" with their correct definitions.

anachronism   euphemism   New Criticism   spoonerism
aphorism   existentialism   pragmatism   syllogism
barbarism   humanism   realism   transcendentalism
didacticism   imagism   romanticism

1. _____ A word used in coarse or unrefined speech.

2. _____ An interchange of two sounds, usually at the beginning of two words. An example is a "rig bat" instead of a "big rat."

3. _____ The poetic theory and practice prevalent around 1912–1927 advocating that poetry should employ the language of common speech. It was a revolt against sentimentality. Ezra Pound was a leader of this movement.

4. _____ A representation of something (a word, expression, etc.) out of its proper time. Talking about compact discs in a story set in the 1800s is an example of this term.

5. _____ Depicting life as it really is.

6. _____ An argument employing two premises and a logical conclusion. An example is: All men are human. John is a man. John is human.

7. _____ Literature intended to teach.

8. _____ Thought in which human interests, natures, ideals, and values are prominent.

9. _____ Interpretation and evaluation using close reading and examination of the text.

10. _____ Human beings are free to shape their own lives. Concrete existence has more importance than abstract existence.

11. _____ A less offensive or more refined way of referring to something. Instead of saying, "He croaked," a more refined way is to say, "He met his Maker."

12. _____ A concise statement of a principle or truth.

13. _____ Philosophy espousing that basic truths can be reached through intuition. Alcott, Emerson, and Thoreau were advocates of this philosophy.

14. _____ Philosophy that stresses practical consequences and values. William James was a leader in this movement.

15. _____ A movement that began as a revolt against classicism. Feeling and imagination, not fact and reason, are key components of this philosophy.

THE "-ISM'S" OF LITERATURE
PART TWO

Match the following literary "-ism's" with their correct definitions.

archaism	expressionism	plagiarism	solecism
classicism	naturalism	provincialism	surrealism
criticism	malapropism	rationalism	symbolism
empiricism	neoclassicism	regionalism	

1. _____ Representing objects or concepts through symbols.

2. _____ A style of writing, popular in the seventeenth and eighteenth centuries, employing the style of classical writers.

3. _____ Named after a character in Richard Brinsley Sheridan's *The Rivals,* this term means to use words ludicrously. Saying "a wolf in sheik's clothing," instead of the proper "a wolf in sheep's clothing" is an example of this.

4. _____ A movement reflecting the style of the ancient Greeks and Romans.

5. _____ The ungrammatical use of words. Saying brung instead of brought is an example.

6. _____ Analysis and evaluation of a literary work.

7. _____ A movement that emphasized the mind and emotions over the external realities.

8. _____ A method that uses experience and observation to gain knowledge.

9. _____ An extreme form of realism in which the unpleasant side of life is shown. Characters in this environment (Clyde Griffiths in Dreiser's *An American Tragedy*) find the forces prohibiting success in life to be rather overwhelming.

10. _____ Reason is the authority in a person's decisions.

11. _____ Representation of a particular geographical region or setting.

12. _____ Movement showing the inner mind's actions. The irrational and the fantastic are generally part of this.

13. _____ A word or expression common to a particular section or region. It can also mean an unsophisticated or sheltered approach to life.

14. _____ A word or phrase that is no longer in common, everyday use.

15. _____ Using another's words or ideas and passing them off as one's own.

KIDDIE LIT CHARACTERS

Turn back the hands of time and recall books you read as a child. Match up the stories with their authors.

TITLES	AUTHORS
1. _____ *Cinderella*	a. Mary Mapes Dodge
2. _____ *Children's and Household Tales*	b. Carlo Collodi
3. _____ *Uncle Remus*	c. Thomas Hughes
4. _____ *Pinocchio*	d. J. M. Barrie
5. _____ *Tom Brown's School Days*	e. Charles Perrault
6. _____ *Hans Brinker*	f. Mary O'Hara
7. _____ *Peter Pan*	g. Dr. Seuss
8. _____ *Winnie-the-Pooh*	h. Joel Chandler Harris
9. _____ *Mary Poppins*	i. Brothers Grimm
10. _____ *Charlotte's Web*	j. Lewis Carroll
11. _____ *Green Eggs and Ham*	k. Jean de Brunhoff
12. _____ *My Friend Flicka*	l. Louisa May Alcott
13. _____ *Little Women*	m. P. L. Travers
14. _____ *Alice in Wonderland*	n. A. A. Milne
15. _____ *Babar the Elephant*	o. E. B. White

LITERATURE 101 . . . AND OTHER NUMBERS

This exercise will test your literary knowledge and research abilities. Fill in the numbers that are missing in the titles of these novels, plays, short stories, poems, and books of true experience. Their authors are given to assist you. An adjective form of the number word is used when needed. Thus *four* could also be *fourth* and *one* could also be *first*. Good luck!

TITLE	AUTHOR	GENRE
1. *19___ __*	George Orwell	(novel)
2. *A Tale of _____ Cities*	Charles Dickens	(novel)
3. *Around the World in _____ Days*	Jules Verne	(novel)
4. *And Then There Were _____*	Agatha Christie	(novel)
5. *Walden _____*	B. F. Skinner	(novel)
6. *The _____ Musketeers*	Alexander Dumas	(novel)
7. *_____ for the Seesaw*	William Gibson	(play)
8. *_____ Flew Over the Cuckoo's Nest*	Ken Kesey	(novel)
9. *Chapter _____*	Neil Simon	(play)
10. *Born on the _____ of July*	Ron Kovic	(book of true experience)
11. *Slaughterhouse-_____*	Kurt Vonnegut, Jr.	(novel)
12. *The Moon and _____pence*	W. Somerset Maugham	(novel)
13. *_____ Quartets*	T. S. Eliot	(poetry)
14. *_____*	Booth Tarkington	(novel)
15. *Fahrenheit _____*	Ray Bradbury	(novel)
16. *_____ Years Before the Mast*	Richard Henry Dana, Jr.	(novel)
17. *_____ Coaches Waiting*	Mary Stewart	(novel)
18. *The _____ Steps*	John Buchan	(novel)
19. *_____ Writer's Beginnings*	Eudora Welty	(autobiography)
20. *The _____ Tailors*	Dorothy Sayers	(novel)
21. *The _____ Storey Mountain*	Thomas Merton	(autobiography)
22. *_____ Leagues Under the Sea*	Jules Verne	(novel)
23. "*_____ O'Clock*"	A. E. Housman	(poem)
24. *_____ Gentlemen of Verona*	William Shakespeare	(play)
25. "*_____ Art*"	Elizabeth Bishop	(poem)
26. *Catch-_____*	Joseph Heller	(novel)

27. _____ *Characters in Search of an Author*   Luigi Pirandello   (play)

28. *Butterfield* _____   John O'Hara   (novel)

29. _____ *Weeks in Another Town*   Irwin Shaw   (novel)

30. *The Crying of Lot* _____   Thomas Pynchon   (novel)

31. *The* _____ *Minutes*   Irving Wallace   (novel)

32. "*Big* _____ *-Hearted River*"   Ernest Hemingway   (short story)

33. *A Cool* _____   Nathanael West   (novel)

34. *My* _____ *Years in a Quandary*   Robert Benchley   (essays)

35. *The* _____ *Protocol*   Frederick Forsyth   (novel)

36. _____ *Years of Solitude*   Gabriel Garcia Marquez   (novel)

37. _____ *Is Enough*   Tom Braden   (autobiography)

38. _____ *Day in the Life of Ivan Denisovich*   Alexander Solzhenitsyn   (novel)

39. _____ *Cousins*   Louisa May Alcott   (novel)

40. *Dinner at* _____   Edna Ferber with
     George S. Kaufman   (play)

41. _____ *Day in the Afternoon of the World*   William Saroyan   (novel)

42. _____ *Stories*   J. D. Salinger   (short stories)

43. *The* _____ *Sisters*   Anton Chekhov   (play)

44. _____ *-Penny Opera*   Bertolt Brecht and Kurt Weill   (play)

45. *The* _____ *Million*   O. Henry   (short stories)

46. *Postman Always Rings* _____   James M. Cain   (novel)

47. _____ *Against Thebes*   Aeschylus   (play)

48. *The House of the* _____ *Gables*   Nathaniel Hawthorne   (novel)

49. *The* _____ *Circle*   Alexander Solzhenitsyn   (novel)

50. _____ *Angry Men*   William Rose   (play)

LOCATION . . . LOCATION . . . LOCATION

The fifty states have provided the settings for some of literature's most memorable stories. Below are five sets of matching columns including the titles, authors, and states featured in the books. On the sheets provided write the letters corresponding to the correct title and author. Good luck!

SET #1

STATE	TITLE	AUTHOR
1. Alabama	a. *I Know Why the Caged Bird Sings*	k. Edna Ferber
2. Alaska	b. *The Lord's Oysters*	l. Frank Norris
3. Arizona	c. *The Song of the Lark*	m. Erskine Caldwell
4. Arkansas	d. *To Kill a Mockingbird*	n. Jack London
5. California	e. *The Octopus*	o. Marjorie Kinnan Rawlings
6. Colorado	f. *The Call of the Canyon*	p. Harper Lee
7. Connecticut	g. *The Yearling*	q. Zane Grey
8. Delaware	h. *Tobacco Road*	r. Maya Angelou
9. Florida	i. *American Beauty*	s. Willa Cather
10. Georgia	j. *The Call of the Wild*	t. Gilbert Byron

SET #2

11. Hawaii	a. *The Jungle*	k. MacKinlay Kantor
12. Idaho	b. *The Friendly Persuasion*	l. James Jones
13. Illinois	c. *All the King's Men*	m. Grace Jordan
14. Indiana	d. *In Cold Blood*	n. John Barth
15. Iowa	e. *Home Below Hell's Canyon*	o. Truman Capote
16. Kansas	f. *From Here to Eternity*	p. Elizabeth Coatsworth
17. Kentucky	g. *The Jaybird*	q. Upton Sinclair
18. Louisiana	h. *Country Neighborhood*	r. Bobbie Ann Mason
19. Maine	i. *The Sot-Weed Factor*	s. Jessamyn West
20. Maryland	j. *Shiloh and Other Stories*	t. Robert Penn Warren

SET #3

21. Massachusetts	a. *Main Street*	k. Mark Twain
22. Michigan	b. *A River Runs Through It*	l. William Faulkner
23. Minnesota	c. *Tiverton Towns*	m. William Carlos Williams
24. Mississippi	d. *The Dollmaker*	n. Willa Cather
25. Missouri	e. *The Scarlet Letter*	o. Norman McLean
26. Montana	f. *Life Along the Passaic River*	p. Nathaniel Hawthorne
27. Nebraska	g. *Meet Me in St. Louis*	q. Harriette Arnow
28. Nevada	h. *A Lost Lady*	r. Sinclair Lewis
29. New Hampshire	i. *Sartoris*	s. Sally Benson
30. New Jersey	j. *Roughing It*	t. Alice Brown

LOCATION . . . LOCATION . . . LOCATION (continued)

SET #4

31. New Mexico	a. *The Checkered Years*	k. DuBose Heyward
32. New York	b. *The Minister's Wooing*	l. Tony Hillerman
33. North Carolina	c. *The Blessing Way*	m. Bernard Malamud
34. North Dakota	d. *Look Homeward, Angel*	n. John Steinbeck
35. Ohio	e. *Porgy*	o. James Baldwin
36. Oklahoma	f. *Beloved*	p. Harriet Beecher Stowe
37. Oregon	g. *The Grapes of Wrath*	q. Mary Dodge Woodward
38. Pennsylvania	h. *Go Tell It on the Mountain*	r. Toni Morrison
39. Rhode Island	i. *A New Life*	s. Benjamin Franklin
40. South Carolina	j. *Autobiography*	t. Thomas Wolfe

SET #5

41. South Dakota	a. *A Day No Pigs Would Die*	k. James Agee
42. Tennessee	b. *Green Timber*	l. Dee Brown
43. Texas	c. *The Story of My Boyhood and Youth*	m. Jack Schaefer
44. Utah	d. *Bury My Heart at Wounded Knee*	n. William Styron
45. Vermont	e. *A Death in the Family*	o. Wallace Stegner
46. Virginia	f. *Up From Slavery*	p. Thomas Ripley
47. Washington	g. *Shane*	q. Edna Ferber
48. West Virginia	h. *Morman Country*	r. Booker T. Washington
49. Wisconsin	i. *The Confessions of Nat Turner*	s. John Muir
50. Wyoming	j. *Giant*	t. Robert Peck

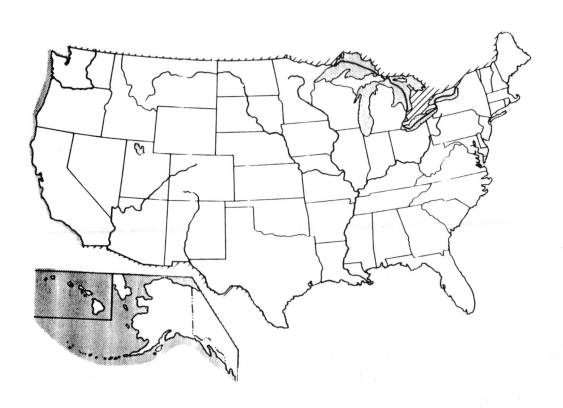

Name _____ **Date** _____ **Period** _____

LOCATION . . . LOCATION . . . LOCATION

STATE	TITLE	AUTHOR	STATE	TITLE	AUTHOR

SET # 1

STATE	TITLE	AUTHOR	STATE	TITLE	AUTHOR
1. Alabama	_____	_____	6. Colorado	_____	_____
2. Alaska	_____	_____	7. Connecticut	_____	_____
3. Arizona	_____	_____	8. Delaware	_____	_____
4. Arkansas	_____	_____	9. Florida	_____	_____
5. California	_____	_____	10. Georgia	_____	_____

SET # 2

STATE	TITLE	AUTHOR	STATE	TITLE	AUTHOR
11. Hawaii	_____	_____	16. Kansas	_____	_____
12. Idaho	_____	_____	17. Kentucky	_____	_____
13. Illinois	_____	_____	18. Louisiana	_____	_____
14. Indiana	_____	_____	19. Maine	_____	_____
15. Iowa	_____	_____	20. Maryland	_____	_____

SET # 3

STATE	TITLE	AUTHOR	STATE	TITLE	AUTHOR
21. Massachusetts	_____	_____	26. Montana	_____	_____
22. Michigan	_____	_____	27. Nebraska	_____	_____
23. Minnesota	_____	_____	28. Nevada	_____	_____
24. Mississippi	_____	_____	29. New Hampshire	_____	_____
25. Missouri	_____	_____	30. New Jersey	_____	_____

SET # 4

STATE	TITLE	AUTHOR	STATE	TITLE	AUTHOR
31. New Mexico	_____	_____	36. Oklahoma	_____	_____
32. New York	_____	_____	37. Oregon	_____	_____
33. North Carolina	_____	_____	38. Pennsylvania	_____	_____
34. North Dakota	_____	_____	39. Rhode Island	_____	_____
35. Ohio	_____	_____	40. South Carolina	_____	_____

SET # 5

STATE	TITLE	AUTHOR	STATE	TITLE	AUTHOR
41. South Dakota	_____	_____	46. Virginia	_____	_____
42. Tennessee	_____	_____	47. Washington	_____	_____
43. Texas	_____	_____	48. West Virginia	_____	_____
44. Utah	_____	_____	49. Wisconsin	_____	_____
45. Vermont	_____	_____	50. Wyoming	_____	_____

ONE-WORD TITLES

How many literary titles do you know that contain only one word in their titles? Here is your chance to show your literary expertise.

Try to complete this list by filling in at least *one title and its author* for each letter. It can be the title of a novel, play, poem, or short story. The letters Q, X, Y, and Z count three points while the other letters count a point each. You may name more than one title per letter.

Title   *Author*

A. _____

B. _____

C. _____

D. _____

E. _____

F. _____

G. _____

H. _____

I. _____

J. _____

K. _____

L. _____

M. _____

N. _____

O. _____

P. _____

Q. _____

R. _____

S. _____

T. _____

U. _____

V. _____

W. _____

X. _____

Y. _____

Z. _____

THE TWO ROADS THAT ARE TRAVELED . . .
THE FIRST ROAD

Take these two trips to see parts of the great USA through your reading. Match the states with the novel or play featuring the state as its setting and you're on your way. Give the author's name for each work if you can. The first one is done for you. Good luck and happy trails!

On your first trip, visit the states in this order:

1. Florida _____ e-*The Yearling*-Marjorie Kinnan Rawlings _____

2. Georgia _____

3. South Carolina _____

4. North Carolina _____

5. Virginia _____

6. West Virginia _____

7. Maryland _____

8. Pennsylvania _____

9. New York _____

10. Vermont _____

11. Massachusetts _____

12. New York City (not a state but worth the trip) _____

13. Long Island (not a state but populated enough to be) _____

The literary works you'll match up are:

a. *Porgy*

b. *The Scarlet Letter*

c. *The Autobiography of Ben Franklin*

d. *The Age of Innocence*

e. *The Yearling*

f. *An American Tragedy*

g. *Look Homeward, Angel*

h. *Up From Slavery*

i. *The Great Gatsby*

j. *A Day No Pigs Would Die*

k. *Deliverance*

l. *The Sot-Weed Factor*

m. *The Confessions of Nat Turner*

THE TWO ROADS THAT ARE TRAVELED . . .
THE SECOND ROAD

Now start off in Montana and do the same as in the first part.

1. Montana _____ c-*A River Runs Through It*-Norman McLean _____

2. Wyoming _____

3. South Dakota _____

4. Nebraska _____

5. Kansas _____

6. Oklahoma _____

7. Texas _____

8. Louisiana _____

9. Arkansas _____

10. Mississippi _____

11. Alabama _____

12. Tennessee _____

13. Illinois _____

14. Indiana _____

15. Ohio _____

The literary works you'll match up are:

a. *A Death in the Family*
b. *The Grapes of Wrath*
c. *A River Runs Through It*
d. *The Jungle*
e. *In Cold Blood*
f. *Beloved*
g. *O Pioneers!*
h. *Shane*

i. *To Kill a Mockingbird*
j. *As I Lay Dying*
k. *I Know Why the Caged Bird Sings*
l. *Giant*
m. *All the King's Men*
n. *Bury My Heart at Wounded Knee*
o. *The Friendly Persuasion*

ANSWER KEY
TO ACTIVITIES

Section 1

AUTHORS WHO MAKE US LAUGH AND CRY

Pages 287–304

ANSWERS TO
SOME AMERICAN AUTHORS BORN BEFORE 1800

1. John Smith
2. William Bradford
3. Anne Bradstreet
4. Michael Wigglesworth
5. Edward Taylor
6. William Byrd
7. Jonathan Edwards
8. Benjamin Franklin
9. Phyllis Wheatley
10. Francis Scott Key
11. Clement Moore
12. Washington Irving
13. James Fenimore Cooper

ANSWERS TO
SOME AMERICAN AUTHORS BORN DURING THE 1800s

1. Ralph Waldo Emerson
2. Nathaniel Hawthorne
3. John Greenleaf Whittier
4. Edgar Allan Poe
5. Harriet Beecher Stowe
6. Henry David Thoreau
7. Walt Whitman
8. Herman Melville
9. Emily Dickinson
10. Louisa May Alcott
11. Horatio Alger
12. Mark Twain
13. William Dean Howells
14. Henry James
15. Kate Chopin
16. O. Henry
17. Edith Wharton
18. Edward Stratemeyer
19. Laura Ingalls Wilder
20. Booth Tarkington
21. Theodore Dreiser
22. Stephen Crane
23. Willa Cather
24. Clarence Day, Jr.
25. Robert Frost
26. Gertrude Stein
27. Zane Grey
28. Jack London
29. Sherwood Anderson
30. Carl Sandburg
31. Upton Sinclair
32. Sinclair Lewis
33. Edna Ferber
34. Raymond Chandler
35. Katherine Anne Porter
36. Pearl S. Buck
37. Dashiell Hammett
38. F. Scott Fitzgerald
39. Marjorie Kinnan Rawlings
40. Thornton Wilder
41. William Faulkner
42. E. B. White
43. Ernest Hemingway

ANSWERS TO
SOME AMERICAN AUTHORS BORN DURING THE 1900s

1. Margaret Mitchell
2. Thomas Wolfe
3. Zora Neale Hurston
4. John Steinbeck
5. Nathanael West
6. Irving Stone
7. Erskine Caldwell
8. Theodor Geisel (Doctor Seuss)
9. Ayn Rand
10. Robert Penn Warren
11. Lillian Hellman
12. James Michener
13. Robert A. Heinlein
14. William Saroyan
15. Richard Wright
16. Tennessee Williams
17. John Cheever
18. Studs Terkel
19. William Inge
20. Bernard Malamud
21. John Hersey
22. Ralph Ellison
23. William Gibson
24. Walker Percy
25. Carson McCullers
26. J. D. Salinger
27. Shirley Jackson
28. Isaac Asimov
29. Ray Bradbury
30. Alex Haley
31. Kurt Vonnegut
32. Jack Kerouac
33. Joseph Heller
34. Norman Mailer
35. James Baldwin
36. Truman Capote
37. William Styron
38. Harper Lee
39. John Knowles
40. Elie Wiesel
41. Edward Albee
42. Chaim Potok
43. Ira Levin
44. John Barth
45. Lorraine Hansberry
46. Toni Morrison
47. Tom Wolfe
48. John Updike
49. Sylvia Plath
50. Philip Roth
51. Paul Zindel
52. Thomas Pynchon
53. Anne Tyler
54. Michael Crichton
55. Alice Walker
56. Tom Clancy
57. S. E. Hinton
58. Pat Conroy

ANSWERS TO
SOME BRITISH AUTHORS BORN BEFORE 1800

1. Geoffrey Chaucer
2. Sir Thomas Malory
3. Edmund Spenser
4. William Shakespeare
5. John Donne
6. John Milton
7. Daniel Defoe
8. Jonathan Swift
9. Alexander Pope
10. Henry Fielding
11. Thomas Gray
12. James Boswell
13. Richard Brinsley Sheridan
14. William Blake
15. William Wordsworth
16. Samuel Taylor Coleridge
17. Jane Austen
18. Lord Byron (George Gordon)
19. John Keats
20. Mary Shelley

ANSWERS TO
SOME BRITISH AUTHORS BORN DURING THE 1800s

1. Elizabeth Barrett Browning
2. Alfred Tennyson
3. William Makepeace Thackeray
4. Charles Dickens
5. Charlotte Brontë
6. Emily Brontë
7. George Eliot (Mary Ann Evans)
8. Lewis Carroll
9. Thomas Hardy
10. Bram Stoker
11. Oscar Wilde
12. George Bernard Shaw
13. Joseph Conrad
14. Sir Arthur Conan Doyle
15. Rudyard Kipling
16. Beatrix Potter
17. John Millington Synge
18. W. Somerset Maugham
19. E. M. Forster
20. James Joyce
21. A. A. Milne
22. Virginia Woolf
23. D. H. Lawrence
24. T. S. Eliot
25. Agatha Christie
26. J.R.R. Tolkien
27. C. S. Lewis

ANSWERS TO
SOME BRITISH AUTHORS BORN DURING THE 1900s

1. James Hilton
2. George Orwell (Eric Arthur Blair)
3. Evelyn Waugh
4. Mary Renault
5. Samuel Beckett
6. Daphne Du Maurier
7. W. H. Auden
8. William Golding
9. Dylan Thomas
10. James Herriot
11. Roald Dahl
12. Anthony Burgess
13. Doris Lessing
14. Peter Shaffer
15. Ted Hughes
16. Harold Pinter
17. John LeCarre
18. Simon Gray
19. Tom Stoppard
20. Ford Madox Ford

ANSWERS TO
WORLD AUTHORS BORN BEFORE 1800

1. Homer
2. Aeschylus
3. Pindar
4. Sophocles
5. Euripedes
6. Plato
7. Vergil
8. Ovid
9. Plutarch
10. Li Po
11. Omar Khayyám
12. Dante Alighieri
13. Petrarch
14. Giovanni Boccaccio
15. Michel de Montaigne
16. Miguel de Cervantes
17. Lope de Vega
18. Jean de La Fontaine
19. Molière
20. Jean Racine

21. Matsuo Bashō
22. Voltaire
23. Johann Wolfgang von Goethe

24. The Brothers Grimm . . . Jacob and Wilhelm Carl
25. Honoré de Balzac

ANSWERS TO
SOME WORLD AUTHORS BORN DURING THE 1800s

1. Alexander Dumas
2. Victor Hugo
3. Hans Christian Andersen
4. Gustave Flaubert
5. Fyodor Dostoyevsky
6. Leo Tolstoy
7. Henrik Ibsen
8. Jules Verne
9. Robert Louis Stevenson
10. Anton Chekhov
11. J. M. Barrie
12. Luigi Pirandello
13. Edmond Rostand
14. Colette (Sidonie-Gabrielle Colette)
15. Thomas Mann
16. Edgar Rice Burroughs
17. Herman Hesse
18. Kahlil Gibran
19. Franz Kafka
20. Nikos Kazantzakis
21. Boris Pasternak
22. Erich Maria Remarque

ANSWERS TO
WORLD AUTHORS BORN DURING THE 1900s

1. Antoine de Saint-Exupéry
2. Alan Paton
3. Jean-Paul Sartre
4. Jean Anouilh
5. Eugene Ionesco
6. Albert Camus
7. Morris West
8. Alexander Solzhenitsyn
9. Gabriel Garciá Márquez
10. Mordecai Richler
11. Jerzy Kosinski
12. Yevgeny Yevtushenko
13. Václav Havel
14. Colleen McCullough

ANSWERS TO AUTHORS AND THEIR INITIALS

1. A. R. Ammons   Archir Randolph . . . poet
2. W. H. Auden   Wystan Hugh . . . poet
3. J. M. Barrie   Sir James Matthew . . . dramatist and novelist
4. H. E. Bates   Herbert Ernest . . . writer
5. L. Frank Baum   Lyman . . . playwright and author of children's books
6. G. K. Chesterton   Gilbert Keith . . . journalist, novelist, and poet
7. J.R.R. Tolkien   John Ronald Reuel . . . fantasy writer and philologist
8. J. D. Salinger   Jerome David . . . novelist and short-story writer
9. C. L. Lewis   Clive Staples . . . novelist and essayist
10. A. J. Cronin   Archibald Joseph . . . novelist and physician
11. e. e. cummings   edward estlin . . . poet
12. G. W. Curtis   George William . . . editor and essayist
13. C. Day Lewis   Cecil . . . poet and detective story writer
14. T. S. Eliot   Thomas Stearns . . . poet, critic, and dramatist

15. E. M. Forster   Edward Morgan . . . novelist and short-story writer
16. A. B. Guthrie   Alfred Bertram . . . novelist
17. A. E. Housman   Alfred Edward . . . poet
18. W. Somerset Maugham   William . . . dramatist and novelist
19. H. L. Mencken   Henry Louis . . . newspaperman, editor, and critic
20. J. B. Priestly   John Boynton . . . novelist, essayist, and playwright
21. B. F. Skinner   Burrhus Frederic . . . psychologist and novelist
22. C. P. Snow   Charles Percy . . . novelist
23. H. G. Wells   Herbert George . . . novelist
24. Morris L. West   Langlo . . . novelist
25. E. B. White   Elwyn Brooks . . . humorist and essayist
26. T. H. White   Terence Hanbury . . . novelist
27. Pearl S. Buck   Sydenstricker . . . novelist
28. W.E.B. Du Bois   William Edward Burghardt . . . civil rights leader and writer
29. F. Scott Fitzgerald   Francis . . . novelist
30. D. H. Lawrence   David Herbert . . . novelist
31. A. A. Milne   Alan Alexander . . . dramatist and novelist
32. Dorothy L. Sayers   Leigh . . . detective story writer
33. P. G. Wodehouse   Pelham Grenville . . . writer and humorist
34. George M. Cohan   Michael . . . song writer and playwright
35. George S. Kaufman   Simon . . . playwright
36. J. M. Synge   John Millington . . . playwright

ANSWERS TO AMERICAN AUTHORS AND GEOGRAPHY

	SECTION	AUTHOR	TITLES
1.	Midwest	Sinclair Lewis	*Babbitt, Main Street*
2.	Midwest	Willa Cather	*O Pioneers!, My Antonia*
3.	Northeast	Nathaniel Hawthorne	*The House of the Seven Gables, The Scarlet Letter, The Blithedale Romance*
4.	Northeast	Robert Frost	"Mending Wall," "The Death of the Hired Man," "Home Burial," "Out, Out—"
5.	South	Tennessee Williams	*A Street Car Named Desire, Cat on a Hot Tin Roof*
6.	South	DuBose Heyward	*Porgy, Mamba's Daughters*
7.	South	Ellen Glasgow	*The Woman Within, Virginia*
8.	Northeast	Bronson Alcott	*Concord Days*
9.	Midwest	Edgar Lee Masters	*Spoon River Anthology*
10.	South	Erskine Caldwell	*Tobacco Road, God's Little Acre*
11.	Midwest	Hamlin Garland	*Main-Travelled Roads: Six Mississippi Valley Stories, Rose of Dutcher's Cooly*
12.	North	Washington Irving	*History of New York,* "Rip Van Winkle," "The Legend of Sleepy Hollow"
13.	Northeast	Sarah Orne Jewett	*A White Heron, Deephaven*
14.	West (Alaska)	Jack London	*White Fang, The Call of the Wild,* "To Build a Fire"

15. West	Ken Kesey	*Sometimes a Great Notion, One Flew Over the Cuckoo's Nest*
16. South	Sidney Lanier	*Tiger-Lillies, "The Marches of Glyn"*
17. South	Carson McCullers	*The Heart Is a Lonely Hunter, Reflections in a Golden Eye*
18. South	Katherine Anne Porter	*"The Jilting of Granny Weatherall," Flowering Judas*
19. South	Marjorie Kinnan Rawlings	*The Yearling, South Moon Under, When the Whipporwill*
20. South	Flannery O'Connor	*Wise Blood, The Violent Bear It Away*
21. Midwest	Theodore Dreiser	*The Financier, The Titan, The Stoic, An American Tragedy*
22. Midwest	Mark Twain	*The Adventures of Huckleberry Finn, Life on the Mississippi, The Adventures of Tom Sawyer*
23. Northeast	Henry David Thoreau	*Walden, A Week on the Concord and Merrimack Rivers*
24. South	Eudora Welty	*Delta Wedding, A Curtain of Green, Losing Battle*
25. Midwest	James Whitcomb Riley	*The Old Swimmin' Hole, Home Folks*

ANSWERS TO
DO YOU KNOW THEIR FAMOUS CONTEMPORARIES?

1. b   Horace Mann was born in 1796 and Dred Scott was born in 1795.
2. a   W. H. Auden was born in 1907 and T. S. Eliot was born in 1888. Thomas Hardy and Emile Zola were both born in 1840.
3. c
4. a
5. b   Nathaniel Hawthorne was born in 1804 and Hans Christian Andersen was born the next year.
6. a   All were born in the early 1900s.
7. b   Dylan Thomas was born in 1914 and Auden was born in 1907.
8. c
9. b   Nietzsche (1844–1900) . . . Boswell (1740–1795) . . . Ionesco (1912–   ) . . . Huxley (1825–1895)
10. d   Keats (1795–1821) . . . Shelley (1792–1822) . . . Pushkin (1799–1837)
11. d   Robert Penn Warren was appointed in 1986.
12. c   Samuel Richardson, author of *Pamela*, was born in 1689.
13. a   All were published in 1980.
14. b   The year was 1960. The deaths of the other authors were: Faulkner—1962 . . . Shaw—1950 . . . Steinbeck—1968 . . . Masters—1950 . . . T. S. Eliot—1965 . . . Sandburg—1967.
15. a   Dickens (1812–1870) . . . D. H. Lawrence (1885–1930) . . . Petrarch (1304–1374) . . . Colette (1873–1954) . . . Lord Byron (1788–1824) . . . John Donne (1572?–1631)

ANSWERS TO FAMOUS AND NOT SO FAMOUS FIRSTS

1. Q		11. K		21. jj		31. W	
2. T		12. C		22. nn		32. X	
3. aa		13. I		23. cc		33. U	
4. B		14. J		24. dd		34. S	
5. D		15. N		25. Z		35. R	
6. H		16. O		26. V		36. bb	
7. A		17. G		27. kk		37. ff	
8. Y		18. F		28. gg		38. M	
9. L		19. mm		29. hh		39. P	
10. E		20. ii		30. ll		40. ee	

41. James Baldwin
42. Edgar Rice Burroughs
43. Ralph Ellison
44. Joseph Heller
45. James Jones
46. Ken Kesey
47. Harper Lee
48. Norman Mailer
49. Carson McCullers
50. Margaret Mitchell
51. J. D. Salinger

ANSWERS TO HOW NOBEL OF YOU!

1. G	6. P	11. H	16. K
2. Q	7. R	12. S	17. O
3. I	8. M	13. D	18. T
4. B	9. L	14. E	19. C
5. F	10. A	15. N	20. J

ANSWERS TO HIDDEN AUTHORS

1. Lew Wallace

   Edith Wharton
   Miguel de Cervantes
   G. K. Chesterton
Hidden author: David Herbert Lawrence Title: *Sons and Lovers*

2. Lillian Hellman

   William Inge
   Robert Browning
   Clarence Day, Jr.
Hidden author: Ernest Hemingway Title: *In Our Time*

3. Thornton Wilder

   Sinclair Lewis
   Robert Sherwood
   Chaim Potok
Hidden author: Theodore Dreiser Title: *Sister Carrie*

4. Philip Roth

   George Orwell
   Oscar Wilde
   Jane Austen
   Hidden author: Henry David Thoreau Title: *Walden*

5. Franz Kafka

   Carson McCullers
   John Knowles
   F. Scott Fitzgerald
   Hidden author: William Faulkner Title: *As I Lay Dying*

6. Robert Penn Warren

   Arthur Miller
   Johann Wolfgang von Goethe
   Betty Smith
   Hidden author: Richard Wright Title: *Black Boy*

7. George Bernard Shaw

   Louisa May Alcott
   William Dean Howells
   Stephen Crane
   Hidden author: Nathaniel Hawthorne Title: *Fanshawe*

8. Jessamyn West

   Ken Kesey
   Lord Byron
   Frank Norris
   Hidden author: William Styron Title: *Lie Down in Darkness*

9. Jonathan Swift

   George Eliot
   Anne Morrow Lindbergh
   Emily Dickinson
   Hidden author: John Steinbeck Title: *Of Mice and Men*

10. John Milton

    John Cheever
    Walt Whitman
    John Hersey
    Hidden author: James Michener Title: *Poland*

11. William Saroyan

    Fyodor Dostoyevsky
    William Wordsworth
    Edmond Rostand
    Hidden author: Sherwood Anderson Title: *Winesburg, Ohio*

12. Edward Albee

    James Boswell
    Booth Tarkington
    Elie Wiesel
Hidden author: William Blake Title: *Songs of Innocence*

13. Edgar Allan Poe

    Robert Frost
    Kate Chopin
    Anton Chekhov
Hidden author: Chaim Potok Title: *The Chosen*

14. Molière

    Ray Bradbury
    Tennessee Williams
    William Gibson
Hidden author: Toni Morrison Title: *Beloved*

15. Richard Brinsley Sheridan

    J. D. Salinger
    Kurt Vonnegut
    Jack London
Hidden author: James Hilton Title: *The Lost Horizon*

16. Margaret Mitchell

    Jack Kerouac
    Charles Dickens
    Thomas Gray
Hidden author: William Makepeace Thackeray Title: *Vanity Fair*

17. Nathaniel Hawthorne

    Edgar Rice Burroughs
    Henrik Ibsen
    Pat Conroy
Hidden author: Lorraine Hansberry Title: *A Raisin in the Sun*

18. Thomas Pynchon

    James Herriot
    Robert Louis Stevenson
    John Updike
Hidden author: Agatha Christie Title: *Death on the Nile*

19. Truman Capote

    Henry Fielding
    Alice Walker
    Joseph Heller
Hidden author: Erskine Caldwell Title: *Tobacco Road*

20. Daniel Defoe

    Charlotte Brontë
    Gustave Flaubert
    Jean-Paul Sartre
Hidden author: Edna Ferber Title: *Giant*

ANSWERS TO LITERARY LICENSE PLATES

1. Louisa May Alcott . . . *Little Women* (novel)
2. Henry David Thoreau . . . *Civil Disobedience* (essay)
3. Samuel Taylor Coleridge . . . "The Rime of the Ancient Mariner" (poem) contains an albatross
4. Washington Irving . . . "The Legend of Sleepy Hollow" (story)
5. Jean-Paul Sartre . . . *No Exit* (play)
6. Jack London . . . *The Sea Wolf* (novel)
7. William Dean Howells . . . *The Rise of Silas Lapham* (novel)
8. John Hersey . . . *Hiroshima* (novel)
9. Charlotte Brontë . . . *Jane Eyre* (novel)
10. George Orwell (Eric Blair) . . . *Nineteen Eighty-Four* (novel)
11. Boris Pasternak . . . *Doctor Zhivago* (novel)
12. Mary Shelley . . . *Frankenstein* (novel)
13. Edmond Rostand . . . *Cyrano de Bergerac* (play)
14. Rudyard Kipling . . . "If" (poem)
15. Molière . . . *Le Misanthrope* (play)
16. Jules Verne . . . *Around the World in Eighty Days* (novel)
17. Kahlil Gibran . . . *The Prophet* (prose poem)
18. O. Henry . . . *The Four Million* (collection of twenty-five short stories)
19. Theodor Geisel . . . Dr. Seuss (Geisel's pen name)
20. Sean O'Casey . . . *Juno and the Paycock* (play)
21. Jack Kerouac . . . *On the Road* (novel)
22. William Shakespeare . . . *Richard III* (play)
23. Herman Melville . . . *Billy Budd* (novella)
24. Voltaire (Francois Marie Arouet) . . . *Candide* (novel)
25. Gertrude Stein . . . *The Autobiography of Alice B. Toklas* (Stein's autobiography)
26. William Saroyan . . . *The Human Comedy* (novel)
27. Toni Morrison . . . *Beloved* (novel)
28. Miguel de Cervantes . . . *Don Quixote* (novel)
29. Joseph Heller . . . *Catch-22* (novel)
30. Sophocles . . . *Oedipus Rex* (play)
31. James Hilton . . . *Goodbye, Mr. Chips* (novel)
32. A. A. Milne . . . *Winnie-the-Pooh* (children's book)
33. Aeschylus . . . *Seven Against Thebes* (play)
34. Jane Austen . . . *Sense and Sensibility* (novel)
35. Albert Camus . . . *The Stranger* (novel)
36. Sir Thomas More . . . *Utopia* (political romance)
37. Lord Byron (George Gordon) . . . "Childe Harold's Pilgrimage" (narrative poem)
38. Henrik Ibsen . . . *Hedda Gabler* (play)
39. James Joyce . . . *Bloomsday* (June 16, 1904) from *Ulysses* (novel)

40. Booth Tarkington . . . *Seventeen* (novel)
41. Victor Hugo . . . *The Hunchback of Notre Dame* (novel)
42. D. H. Lawrence . . . *Lady Chatterley's Lover* (novel)
43. Samuel Butler . . . *Erewhon* (novel)
44. Sinclair Lewis . . . *Babbitt* (novel)
45. Samuel Beckett . . . *Waiting for Godot* (play)
46. Henry Wadsworth Longfellow . . . Evangeline, character from Longfellow's 1847 poem, "Evangeline, A Tale of Acadia."
47. Daniel Defoe . . . *Robinson Crusoe* (novel)
48. Homer . . . *The Iliad* (epic) deals with the Trojan War
49. J. D. Salinger . . . Holden is the main character in the novel *The Catcher in the Rye.*
50. J. M. Barrie . . . *Peter Pan* (children's dramatic fantasy)
51. Machiavelli . . . *The Prince* (political treatise)
52. Lewis Carroll (Charles Lutwidge Dodgson) . . . *Jabberwocky* is the mock-heroic ballad in *Through the Looking Glass* (children's tale)
53. Richard Llewellyn . . . *How Green Was My Valley* (novel)
54. Edgar Lee Masters . . . *Spoon River Anthology* (collection of poems, or verse epitaphs, narrated by deceased citizens of this fictional place)
55. John Millington Synge . . . *The Playboy of the Western World* (play)
56. Arthur Miller . . . *The Death of a Salesman* (play) features the demise of Willy Loman, a salesman.
57. Margaret Mitchell . . . *Gone with the Wind* is a novel featuring Scarlett O'Hara, the famous heroine of the book.
58. Erskine Caldwell . . . *Tobacco Road* (novel)
59. Frank Norris . . . *The Octopus* (novel)
60. Eugene O'Neill . . . *Long Day's Journey into Night* (play)
61. Luigi Pirandello . . . *Six Characters in Search of an Author* (play)
62. Thornton Wilder . . . *Our Town* (play)
63. William Butler Yeats . . . *The Wild Swans at Coole* (poetry)
64. F. Scott Fitzgerald . . . *The Great Gatsby* (novel)
65. Charles Dickens . . . "A Christmas Carol" (short story)
66. DuBose Heyward . . . *Porgy* (novel)
67. Johann Wolfgang von Goethe . . . *Faust* (play)
68. Joseph Conrad . . . famous lines from Conrad's novel, *Heart of Darkness*
69. Erich Maria Remarque . . . *All Quiet on the Western Front* (novel)
70. James Fenimore Cooper . . . *The Pathfinder* (novel)
71. Joel Chandler Harris . . . *Uncle Remus* (book of folk tales)
72. Willa Cather . . . *A Lost Lady* (novel)
73. Edmund Spenser . . . *The Faerie Queene* (allegorical epic poem)
74. Emily Dickinson . . . poetess known as The Belle of Amherst (Massachusetts)
75. Henry Fielding . . . *Tom Jones* (novel)
76. Marjorie Kinnan Rawlings . . . *The Yearling* (novel)
77. Mark Twain (Samuel Langhorne Clemens) . . . *The Adventures of Huckleberry Finn* (novel)
78. Sir Walter Scott . . . *Ivanhoe* (novel)
79. Richard Brinsley Sheridan . . . *The Rivals* (play) included a character named Mrs. Malaprop who blundered with her word usage.
80. Geoffrey Chaucer . . . *The Canterbury Tales* (poetry within twenty-four tales)

81. Zane Grey . . . *Riders of the Purple Sage* (novel)
82. William Faulkner . . . Yoknapatawpha is Faulkner's fictional county in Mississippi.
83. George Bernard Shaw . . . *Saint Joan* (play)
84. Thomas Hardy . . . *Tess of the D'Urbervilles* (novel) and *Jude the Obscure* (novel)
85. Upton Sinclair . . . *King Coal* (novel)
86. Stephen Crane . . . *The Red Badge of Courage* (novel)
87. John Steinbeck . . . *The Grapes of Wrath* (novel)
88. Nathaniel Hawthorne . . . *The House of the Seven Gables* (novel)
89. Robert Louis Stevenson . . . *The Strange Case of Dr. Jekyll and Mr. Hyde* (novel)
90. Ernest Hemingway . . . Nick Adams is a character in Hemingway's short stories.
91. Bram Stoker . . . *Dracula* (novel)
92. Herman Hesse . . . *Steppenwolf* (novel)
93. Aristophanes . . . *The Frogs* (play)
94. Tennessee Williams . . . *A Streetcar Named Desire* (play)
95. Edith Wharton . . . *Ethan Frome* (novel)
96. Oscar Wilde . . . *The Picture of Dorian Gray* (novel)
97. Leo Tolstoy . . . *War and Peace* (novel)
98. H. G. Wells . . . *The Island of Dr. Moreau* (novel)
99. Nathanael West . . . *Miss Lonelyhearts* (novel)
100. Virginia Woolf . . . *Mrs. Dalloway* (novel)
101. William Wordsworth . . . *The Prelude* (autobiographical poem)
102. James T. Farrell . . . *Studs Lonigan* (novel)
103. Harriet Beecher Stowe . . . *Uncle Tom's Cabin* (novel)
104. Sir Arthur Conan Doyle . . . Creator of detective Sherlock Holmes

ANSWERS TO THE PARADE OF AUTHORS (PART ONE)

1. Louisa May Alcott 1832–1888
2. Nathaniel Hawthorne 1804–1864
3. Sylvia Plath 1932–1963
4. Henry David Thoreau 1817–1862
5. James Michener 1907–
6. Albert Camus 1913–1960
7. Tom Wolfe 1931–
8. Samuel Taylor Coleridge 1772–1834
9. Alan Paton 1903–1988
10. Gabriel García Márquez 1928–
11. Jonathan Swift 1667–1745
12. Daniel Defoe 1660–1731
13. Alice Walker 1944–
14. Lewis Carroll 1832–1898
15. Jane Austen 1775–1817
16. Robert Penn Warren 1905–1989
17. John Steinbeck 1902–1968
18. Sinclair Lewis 1885–1951
19. Washington Irving 1783–1859
20. J. D. Salinger 1919–
21. John Updike 1932–
22. William Dean Howells 1837–1920
23. James Fenimore Cooper 1789–1851
24. John Barth 1930–
25. T. S. Eliot 1888–1965
26. Edgar Rice Burroughs 1875–1950
27. Giovanni Boccaccio 1313–1375
28. Geoffrey Chaucer 1340–1400
29. Richard Wright 1908–1960
30. Jules Verne 1828–1905
31. William Makepeace Thackeray 1811–1863
32. William Golding 1911–1993
33. John Milton 1608–1674
34. Sir Thomas Malory ?–1471
35. Plato 427 B.C.–348 B.C.
36. Edith Wharton 1862–1937
37. Jack London 1876–1916

38. Kurt Vonnegut, Jr.   1922–
39. Herman Melville   1819–1891
40. Thomas Mann   1875–1955
41. Voltaire   1694–1778
42. George Bernard Shaw   1856–1950
43. Leo Tolstoy   1828–1910
44. Alexander Pope   1688–1744

45. George Eliot (Mary Ann Evans)
    1819–1880
46. Honoré de Balzac   1799–1850
47. Norman Mailer   1923–
48. James Baldwin   1924–1987
49. John Hersey   1914–
50. Theodore Dreiser   1871–1945

ANSWERS TO THE PARADE OF AUTHORS (PART TWO)

1. Philip Roth   1933–
2. Shirley Jackson   1919–1965
3. Katherine Anne Porter   1890–1980
4. Sherwood Anderson   1876–1941
5. Ralph Waldo Emerson   1803–1882
6. Willa Cather   1873–1947
7. Ernest Hemingway   1899–1961
8. Stephen Crane   1871–1900
9. Anton Chekhov   1860–1904
10. W. Somerset Maugham   1874–1965
11. Johann Wolfgang von
    Goethe   1749–1832
12. Homer   c. 700 B.C.–?
13. Alexander Dumas   1802–1870
14. Thomas Hardy   1840–1928
15. Vergil   70 B.C.–19 B.C.
16. John Millington Synge   1871–1909
17. John Donne   1572–1631
18. Gustave Flaubert   1821–1880
19. Walt Whitman   1819–1892
20. Jack Kerouac   1922–1969
21. Margaret Mitchell   1900–1949
22. Gertrude Stein   1874–1946
23. Ray Bradbury   1920–
24. Dashiell Hammett   1894–1961
25. William Saroyan   1908–1981
26. Toni Morrison   1931–
27. Charlotte Brontë   1816–1855

28. Thomas Wolfe   1900–1938
29. Miguel de Cervantes   1547–1616
30. E. B. White   1899–1985
31. Pearl S. Buck   1892–1973
32. Robert A. Heinlein   1907–
33. F. Scott Fitzgerald   1896–1940
34. John Cheever   1912–1982
35. William Blake   1757–1827
36. Colette (Sidonie-Gabrielle Colette)
    1873–1954
37. Agatha Christie   1890–1976
38. Victor Hugo   1802–1885
39. Plutarch   c. 48–c. 122
40. Henry Fielding   1707–1754
41. Fyodor Dostoyevsky   1821–1881
42. George Orwell (Eric Arthur Blair)
    1903–1950
43. Oscar Wilde   1854–1900
44. Jean-Paul Sartre   1905–1980
45. Dylan Thomas   1914–1953
46. Robert Louis Stevenson
    1850–1894
47. Joseph Conrad   1857–1924
48. Boris Pasternak   1890–1960
49. Sir Arthur Conan Doyle
    1859–1930
50. Lord Byron (George Gordon)
    1788–1824

ANSWERS TO THE PARADE OF AUTHORS (PART THREE)

1. Herman Hesse   1877–1962
2. Charles Dickens   1812–1870
3. William Wordsworth   1770–1850
4. Edmond Rostand   1868–1918
5. Mary Shelley   1797–1851
6. William Shakespeare   1564–1616

7. Alfred Lord Tennyson   1809–1892
8. Rudyard Kipling   1865–1936
9. Henrik Ibsen   1828–1906
10. Emily Brontë   1818–1848
11. Henry James   1843–1916

12. Zora Neal Hurston   1901–1960
13. Harriet Beecher Stowe   1811–1896
14. William Styron   1925–
15. Elizabeth Barrett Browning
    1806–1861
16. James Boswell   1740–1795
17. D. H. Lawrence   1885–1930
18. Franz Kafka   1883–1924
19. James Joyce   1882–1941
20. Thomas Pynchon   1937–
21. E. M. Forster   1879–1970
22. James Herriot   1916–
23. Edward Albee   1928–
24. Pat Conroy   1955–
25. Marjorie Kinnan Rawlings   1896–
    1953
26. Paul Zindel   1936–
27. Irving Stone   1903–1989
28. J.R.R. Tolkien   1892–1973
29. Erich Maria Remarque   1898–1970
30. Raymond Chandler   1888–1959

31. John Le Carre   1931–
32. Edgar Allan Poe   1809–1849
33. Isaac Asimov   1920–1992
34. Bram Stoker   1847–1912
35. Edward Stratemeyer   1862–1930
36. Daphne Du Maurier   1907–1989
37. Michael Crichton   1942–
38. William Faulkner   1897–1962
39. Ralph Ellison   1914–
40. Tom Clancy   1947–
41. Clarence Day, Jr.   1874–1935
42. Lillian Hellman   1905–1984
43. Horatio Alger   1832–1899
44. Truman Capote   1924–1984
45. Anne Tyler   1941–
46. Mark Twain   1835–1910
47. Upton Sinclair   1878–1968
48. Booth Tarkington   1869–1946
49. Virginia Woolf   1882–1941
50. Aeschylus   525 B.C.?–456 B.C.

ANSWERS TO THE PARADE OF AUTHORS (PART FOUR)

1. Hans Christian Andersen   1805–
   1875
2. Dante   1265–1321
3. Erskine Caldwell   1903–1987
4. Edna Ferber   1887–1968
5. Chaim Potok   1929–
6. Laura Ingalls Wilder   1867–1957
7. Elie Wiesel   1928–
8. Thornton Wilder   1897–1975
9. C. S. Lewis   1898–1963
10. Beatrix Potter   1866–1943
11. Molière   1622–1673
12. Sophocles   c. 496 B.C.–c. 406 B.C.
13. Jules Verne   1828–1905
14. Nathanael West   1903–1940
15. J. M. Barrie   1860–1937
16. Tennessee Williams   1911–1983
17. James Hilton   1900–1954
18. John Keats   1795–1821
19. Edmund Spenser   1552–1599
20. Judy Blume   1938–
21. Alex Haley   1921–1992
22. Robert Frost   1874–1963

23. Walker Percy   1916–1990
24. Carl Sandburg   1878–1967
25. Studs Terkel   1912–
26. Nikos Kazantzakis   1883–1957
27. Euripedes   485 B.C.?–406 B.C.
28. Kahlil Gibran   1883–1931
29. Luigi Pirandello   1867–1936
30. S. E. Hinton   1950–
31. O. Henry   1862–1910
32. Theodor Geisel (Doctor
    Seuss)   1904–1991
33. William Gibson   1914–
34. Ira Levin   1929–
35. John Greenleaf Whittier   1807–
    1892
36. Antoine de Saint-Exupéry   1900–
    1944
37. Kate Chopin   1851–1904
38. Emily Dickinson   1830–1886
39. Joseph Heller   1923–
40. Zane Grey   1875–1939
41. William Inge   1913–1973
42. Harper Lee   1926–

43. Carson McCullers   1917–1967
44. Bernard Malamud   1914–1986
45. Ayn Rand   1905–1982
46. Thomas Gray   1716–1771
47. A. A. Milne   1882–1956
48. Richard Brinsley Sheridan 1751–1816
49. Lorraine Hansberry   1930–1965
50. John Knowles   1926–

ANSWERS TO RIGHT FROM THE WRITER'S MOUTH
PART ONE

1. J. D. Salinger   1919–
2. Charles Dickens   1812–1870
3. Nathaniel Hawthorne   1804–1864
4. James Joyce   1882–1941
5. Fyodor Dostoyevsky   1821–1881
6. James Baldwin   1924–1987
7. Joseph Conrad   1857–1924
8. Sophocles   496 B.C.–406 B.C.
9. Tennessee Williams   1911–1983
10. William Styron   1925–
11. Robert Frost   1874–1963
12. Emily Brontë   1818–1848
13. Jack London   1876–1916
14. Eugene O'Neill   1888–1953
15. Sir Arthur Conan Doyle   1859–1930
16. Sylvia Plath   1932–1963
17. Leo Tolstoy   1828–1910
18. H. G. Wells   1866–1946
19. Sherwood Anderson   1876–1941
20. Henrik Ibsen   1826–1906
21. Emily Dickinson   1830–1886
22. Oscar Wilde   1854–1900
23. Thornton Wilder   1897–1975
24. Arthur Miller   1915–
25. Herman Melville   1819–1891
26. George Bernard Shaw   1856–1950
27. Harriet Beecher Stowe   1811–1896
28. Saki (H. H. Munro)   1870–1916
29. D. H. Lawrence   1885–1930
30. Geoffrey Chaucer   1343–1400
31. Edward Albee   1928–
32. Washington Irving   1783–1859
33. Lillian Hellman   1905–1984
34. William Shakespeare   1564–1616
35. Samuel Beckett   1906–1989
36. Vergil   70 B.C.–19 B.C.
37. O. Henry   1862–1910
38. Alexander Pope   1688–1744
39. Alfred Tennyson   1809–1892
40. James Thurber   1894–1961
41. Dante   1265–1321
42. William Faulkner   1897–1962
43. Jonathan Swift   1667–1745
44. Sir Thomas More   1478–1535
45. Daniel Defoe   1660–1731
46. Henry David Thoreau   1817–1862
47. Rudyard Kipling   1865–1936
48. John Milton   1608–1674
49. Homer   ninth century B.C.
50. Langston Hughes   1902–1967

ANSWERS TO RIGHT FROM THE WRITER'S MOUTH
PART TWO

1. Siegfried Sassoon   1886–1967
2. Jules Verne   1828–1905
3. Agatha Christie   1890–1976
4. William Blake   1757–1827
5. George Orwell   1903–1950
6. Mark Twain   1835–1910
7. T. S. Eliot   1888–1965
8. Ayn Rand   1905–1982
9. Alexander Dumas   1802–1870
10. Edgar Allan Poe   1809–1849
11. Alice Walker   1944–
12. Carl Sandburg   1878–1967
13. Herman Hesse   1877–1962
14. Albert Camus   1913–1960

15. Dylan Thomas   1914–1953
16. Matthew Arnold   1822–1888
17. F. Scott Fitzgerald   1896–1940
18. Theodore Dreiser   1871–1945
19. Lewis Carroll   1832–1898
20. Upton Sinclair   1878–1968
21. John Steinbeck   1902–1968
22. William Wordsworth   1770–1850
23. Harold Pinter   1930–
24. Sinclair Lewis   1885–1951
25. John Donne   1572–1631
26. Jane Austen   1775–1817
27. Walt Whitman   1819–1892
28. Toni Morrison   1931–
29. James Fenimore Cooper   1789–1851
30. Gwendolyn Brooks   1917–
31. J.R.R. Tolkien   1892–1973
32. Voltaire   1694–1778
33. Percy Bysshe Shelley   1792–1822

34. William Golding   1911–1993
35. Elizabeth Barrett Browning   1806–1861
36. Graham Greene   1904–1991
37. Samuel Taylor Coleridge   1772–1834
38. Henry James   1843–1916
39. Edith Wharton   1862–1937
40. Thomas Hardy   1840–1928
41. Bret Harte   1836–1902
42. George Eliot   1819–1880
43. John Keats   1795–1821
44. Truman Capote   1924–1984
45. Jean Rhys   1894–1979
46. Anton Chekhov   1860–1904
47. Edmund Spenser   1552–1599
48. Pearl S. Buck   1892–1973
49. Victor Hugo   1802–1885
50. Louisa May Alcott   1832–1888

ANSWERS TO ROUND-TABLE DISCUSSION

Group 1

T. S. Eliot   1888–1965
Eugene O'Neill   1888–1953
Katherine Mansfield   1888–1923
George Eliot   1819–1880
Answer: George Eliot

Group 2

William Dean Howells   1837–1920
Vladimir Nabokov   1899–1977
Bret Harte   1836–1902
Thomas Hardy   1840–1928
Answer: Vladimir Nabokov

Group 3

William Butler Yeats   1865–1939
Ben Jonson   1572–1637
H. G. Wells   1866–1946
Luigi Pirandello   1867–1936
Answer: Ben Jonson

Group 4

Jonathan Edwards   1703–1758
Benjamin Franklin   1706–1790
Voltaire   1694–1778
Gerard Manley Hopkins   1844–1889
Answer: Gerald Manley Hopkins

Group 5

Sir Thomas More   1478–1535
Hans Christian Andersen   1805–1875
Ralph Waldo Emerson   1803–1882
Nathaniel Hawthorne   1804–1864
Answer: Sir Thomas More

Group 6

Colette   1873–1954
W. Somerset Maugham   1874–1965
James Fenimore Cooper   1789–1851
Robert Frost   1874–1963
Answer: James Fenimore Cooper

Group 7

D. H. Lawrence   1885–1951
Emily Dickinson   1830–1886
Sinclair Lewis   1885–1951
Ezra Pound   1885–1972
Answer: Emily Dickinson

Group 8

Louisa May Alcott   1832–1888
Lewis Carroll   1832–1898
Jules Verne   1828–1910
Rachel Carson   1907–1964
Answer: Rachel Carson

Group 9

John Cheever   1912–1982
O. Henry   1862–1910
Samuel Beckett   1906–1989
Richard Wright   1908–1960
Answer: O. Henry

Group 10

William Wordsworth   1770–1850
Sean O'Casey   1880–1964
Upton Sinclair   1878–1968
E. M. Forster   1879–1970
Answer: William Wordsworth

Group 11

Daniel Defoe   1659–1731
Jonathan Swift   1667–1745
Virginia Woolf   1882–1941
Joseph Addison   1672–1719
Answer: Virginia Woolf

Group 12

Anton Chekhov   1860–1904
James Barrie   1860–1937
A. E. Housman   1859–1916
James Michener   1907–
Answer: James Michener

Group 13

Willa Cather   1873–1947
Charles Dickens   1812–1870
W.E.B. Du Bois   1868–1963
Edith Wharton   1862–1937
Answer: Charles Dickens

Group 14

Joseph Pulitzer   1847–1911
Ernest Hemingway   1899–1961
Thomas Wolfe   1900–1938
F. Scott Fitzgerald   1896–1940
Answer: Joseph Pulitzer

Group 15

Miguel de Cervantes   1547–1616
William Shakespeare   1564–1616
Plutarch   46–120
Sir Francis Bacon   1561–1626
Answer: Plutarch

ANSWERS TO AUTHORS' FUNNY NAMES

1. Albert CAMUS
2. Robert Penn WARREN
3. Eugene O'NEILL
4. LEWIS (C. S. or Sinclair)
5. J. D. SALINGER
6. Algernon Charles SWINBURNE
7. William Dean HOWELLS
8. Charles LAMB
9. William Makepeace THACKERAY
10. Aldous HUXLEY
11. Edith WHARTON
12. MOORE (George, Henry, Marianne)
13. Kurt VONNEGUT
14. George Bernard SHAW
15. René DESCARTES
16. Kate CHOPIN

17. Philip ROTH
18. Shirley JACKSON
19. James DICKEY
20. ANDERSON (Maxwell, Robert, Sherwood)
21. Willa CATHER
22. Jules VERNE
23. Gertrude STEIN
24. Robert HEINLEIN
25. Jean-Paul SARTRE
26. Joseph CONRAD
27. Charles DICKENS
28. William WORDSWORTH
29. Edmond ROSTAND
30. Alfred TENNYSON
31. Henrik IBSEN
32. BRONTË (Anne, Charlotte, Emily)
33. Zora Neale HURSTON
34. BROWNING (Robert or Elizabeth Barrett)
35. D. H. LAWRENCE
36. Marjorie Kinnan RAWLINGS
37. Irving STONE
38. J.R.R. TOLKIEN
39. Erich Maria REMARQUE
40. Raymond CHANDLER
41. William FAULKNER
42. Ralph ELLISON
43. Lillian HELLMAN
44. Horatio ALGER
45. Truman CAPOTE
46. Booth TARKINGTON
47. Hans Christian ANDERSEN
48. DANTE (Dante Alighieri)
49. Erskine CALDWELL
50. Elie WIESEL
51. Beatrix POTTER
52. WEST (Jessamyn, Dame Jessica, Morris, Nathanael)
53. Tennessee WILLIAMS
54. James HILTON
55. John KEATS
56. Walker PERCY
57. Carl SANDBURG
58. Margaret MITCHELL
59. EURIPEDES
60. Kahlil GIBRAN
61. Luigi PIRANDELLO
62. S. E. HINTON
63. William GIBSON
64. John Greenleaf WHITTIER
65. Harper LEE
66. Emily DICKINSON
67. Carson MCCULLERS
68. Sarah Orne JEWETT
69. Bernard MALAMUD
70. Ayn RAND
71. Richard Brinsley SHERIDAN
72. John KNOWLES
73. A. A. MILNE
74. Lorraine HANSBERRY
75. Jack LONDON
76. James BALDWIN
77. Saul BELLOW
78. Mary Mapes DODGE
79. William GOLDING
80. H. G. WELLS
81. Bret HARTE
82. James Gould COZZENS
83. Ring LARDNER
84. Walter DE LA MARE
85. Eldridge CLEAVER
86. James CLAVELL
87. Edgar Lee MASTERS
88. Alan SILLITOE
89. STEWART (Douglas, John, Mary)
90. Theodore DREISER
91. Booker T. WASHINGTON
92. Christopher MARLOWE
93. ARISTOTLE
94. James THURBER
95. STENDHAL (Marie Henri Beyle)
96. Denis DIDEROT
97. Maya ANGELOU
98. Ellen GLASGOW
99. Rachael CARSON
100. Eric AMBLER
101. Ian FLEMING
102. Judith KRANTZ
103. Boris PASTERNAK
104. Karl SHAPIRO
105. Alice B. TOKLAS
106. John Crowe RANSOM
107. G. K. CHESTERTON
108. Joseph ADDISON
109. Louis L'AMOUR

Section 2

CHARACTERS—LITERATURE'S LEGACIES

(Pages 305–311)

ANSWERS TO
FAMOUS LITERARY CHARACTERS AND THEIR CREATORS

Group 1

1. Jonathan Swift
2. Daniel Defoe
3. Lewis Carroll
4. John Steinbeck
5. John David Salinger
6. Sinclair Lewis
7. Edgar Rice Burroughs
8. Herman Melville
9. Voltaire
10. George Bernard Shaw
11. Ernest Hemingway
12. Gustave Flaubert

Group 2

1. Margaret Mitchell
2. Charlotte Brontë
3. Miguel de Cervantes
4. F. Scott Fitzgerald
5. Agatha Christie
6. Henry Fielding

Group 2 (continued)

7. Oscar Wilde
8. Boris Pasternak
9. Charles Dickens
10. Edmond Rostand
11. Mary Shelley
12. J.R.R. Tolkien

Group 3

1. Arthur Miller
2. Bram Stoker
3. Mark Twain
4. Beatrix Potter
5. James M. Barrie
6. Tennessee Williams
7. Nikos Kazantzakis
8. Antoine de Saint-Exupéry
9. A. A. Milne
10. Richard Brinsley Sheridan
11. Sir Arthur Conan Doyle
12. Harper Lee

ANSWERS TO
FICTIONAL AMERICAN LITERATURE CHARACTERS

1. Scarlett O'Hara
2. Holden Caulfield
3. Tom Sawyer
4. Hiawatha
5. Jaffrey Pyncheon
6. Becky Thatcher
7. Lennie Small
8. Nick Adams
9. Jo March
10. Bartleby
11. Ebenezer Scrooge
12. Uncle Remus
13. Francie Nolan
14. Martin Arrowsmith
15. Henry Fleming
16. Hester Prynne
17. Yossarian
18. Queequeg
19. Ligeia
20. Arthur Dimmesdale

ANSWERS TO DO YOU KNOW WHO I AM?

1. Atticus Finch
2. Billy Budd
3. Lemuel Gulliver
4. Eliza Doolittle
5. Hercule Poirot
6. Leopold Bloom
7. Ishmael
8. Fagin
9. Mr. Chips
10. Captain Nemo
11. Sondra Finchley
12. Big Brother
13. Tom Joad
14. Ebenezer Scrooge
15. Willy Loman
16. Catherine Earnshaw
17. Nick Adams
18. Scarlett O'Hara
19. Nora Helmer
20. Holden Caulfield
21. Bartleby
22. Elmer Gantry
23. Hester Prynne
24. Rebecca Thatcher
25. Huw Morgan

ANSWERS TO PLEASE MR. POSTMAN!

CHARACTER	NOVEL
1. Mr. Chips	*Goodbye, Mr. Chips*
2. Philip Pirrip (Pip)	*Great Expectations*
3. Lemuel Gulliver	*Gulliver's Travels*
4. Jude Fawley	*Jude the Obscure*
5. Jack Merridew	*Lord of the Flies*
6. Mr. Kurtz	*Heart of Darkness*
7. Huw Morgan	*How Green Was My Valley*
8. Mr. Henry Wilcox	*Howards End*
9. Fanny Price	*Mansfield Park*
10. Michael Henchard	*The Mayor of Casterbridge*
11. Clarissa Dalloway	*Mrs. Dalloway*
12. Edwin Drood	*The Mystery of Edwin Drood*
13. Big Brother	*Nineteen Eighty-Four*
14. Philip Carey	*Of Human Bondage*
15. Oliver Twist	*Oliver Twist*
16. Dr. Aziz	*A Passage to India*
17. Peter Pan	*Peter Pan*
18. Dorian Gray	*The Picture of Dorian Gray*
19. Clym Yeobright	*Return of the Native*
20. Robinson Crusoe, Friday	*Robinson Crusoe*
21. Silas Marner	*Silas Marner*
22. Alice	*Alice's Adventures in Wonderland*
23. Prince Manfred	*The Castle of Otranto*
24. David Copperfield	*David Copperfield*
25. Emma Wodehouse	*Emma*

ANSWERS TO ENVELOPE PLEASE!

CHARACTER	NOVEL
1. Ahab	*Moby Dick*
2. Gene Forrester and Phineas	*A Separate Peace*
3. Scarlett O'Hara	*Gone with the Wind*
4. Wolf Larsen	*The Sea-Wolf*
5. Atticus Finch	*To Kill a Mockingbird*
6. Thomas Sutpen	*Absalom, Absalom!*
7. Juniper	*Bridge of San Luis Rey*
8. Clyde Griffiths	*An American Tragedy*
9. Billy Budd	*Billy Budd*
10. George Babbitt	*Babbitt*
11. Newland Archer	*The Age of Innocence*
12. Elmer Gantry	*Elmer Gantry*
13. Jay Gatsby	*The Great Gatsby*
14. Wang Lung	*The Good Earth*
15. John Grimes	*Go Tell It on the Mountain*
16. Robert Jordan	*For Whom the Bell Tolls*
17. Ethan Frome and Zeena	*Ethan Frome*
18. Sam Spade	*The Maltese Falcon*
19. Tom Joad	*The Grapes of Wrath*
20. Pyncheon	*The House of the Seven Gables*
21. Forrester	*A Lost Lady*
22. Lennie Small	*Of Mice and Men*
23. William Bligh	*Mutiny on the Bounty*
24. Santiago, Manolin	*The Old Man and the Sea*
25. Philip Nolan	"The Man Without a Country"
26. Ichabod Crane	"The Legend of Sleepy Hollow"
27. Antonia Shimerda	*My Antonia*
28. Carrie Meeber	*Sister Carrie*
29. Hester Prynne and Pearl	*The Scarlet Letter*
30. Huckleberry Finn	*The Adventures of Huckleberry Finn*

ANSWERS TO LETTERS AROUND THE WORLD

CHARACTER	LITERARY WORK
1. Anna Karenina	*Anna Karenina*
2. Dmitry Karamazov	*The Brothers Karamazov*
3. Edmond Dantes	*The Count of Monte Cristo*
4. Rodion Raskolnikov	*Crime and Punishment*
5. Cyrano de Bergerac	*Cyrano de Bergerac*
6. Don Quixote	*Don Quixote*
7. Boris Godunov	*Boris Godunov*
8. Count Dracula	*Dracula*

9.	Madame Ranevsky	*The Cherry Orchard*
10.	Nora Helmer	*A Doll's House*
11.	Thomas Stockman	*An Enemy of the People*
12.	Don Juan	*Don Juan*
13.	Dante Alighieri	*The Divine Comedy*
14.	Penelope, Odysseus	*Odyssey*
15.	Wife of Bath	*Canterbury Tales*
16.	Oedipus	*Oedipus Rex or Oedipus at Colonus*
17.	Charles and Emma Bovary	*Madame Bovary*
18.	Quasimodo	*The Hunchback of Notre Dame*
19.	King Priam	*Iliad*
20.	Halvard Solness	*The Master Builder*

ANSWERS TO THEIR OTHER NAMES

1. F . . . from James Hilton's *Goodbye, Mr. Chips*
2. I . . . from Thomas Hardy's *Jude the Obscure*
3. B . . . from Theodore Dreiser's *Sister Carrie*
4. N . . . from Sinclair Lewis's *Babbitt*
5. M . . . from Gustave Flaubert's *Madame Bovary*
6. L . . . from *Frankenstein* by Mary Shelley
7. C . . . from *Mrs. Dalloway* by Virginia Woolf
8. H . . . from *My Antonia* by Willa Cather
9. A . . . from *Gulliver's Travels* by Jonathan Swift
10. E . . . from *The Emperor Jones* by Eugene O'Neill
11. K . . . from *The Great Gatsby* by F. Scott Fitzgerald
12. J . . . from *Lady Chatterley's Lover* by D. H. Lawrence
13. D . . . from *Dr. Faustus* by Christopher Marlowe
14. O . . . from *Emma* by Jane Austen
15. G . . . from *Doctor Zhivago* by Boris Pasternak

ANSWERS TO CHARACTERS IN LITERATURE WRITTEN BEFORE THE YEAR 1600

1. *The Epic of Gilgamesh:* a 2000 B.C. Babylonian poem.
2. *The Iliad:* a ninth-century B.C. Greek epic poem attributed to Homer.
3. *The Odyssey:* a ninth-century B.C. Greek epic poem attributed to Homer.
4. *Oedipus Rex:* the fifth-century B.C. Greek drama by Sophocles.
5. *Antigone:* the fifth-century B.C. Greek drama by Sophocles.
6. *Agamemnon:* the fifth-century B.C. Greek drama by Aeschylus.
7. *The Bacchae:* Euripedes' fifth-century B.C. Greek tragedy set in Thebes dealing with the death of Pentheus by his own mother during an orgy.
8. *Aeneid:* Vergil's epic poem concerning the origin of the Roman people.
9. *Beowulf:* the Anglo-Saxon epic of the early eighth-century.
10. *The Song of Roland* (Chanson de Roland): a French *chanson de geste*, written in the middle to the end of the eleventh century.
11. *The Nibelungenlied:* German epic poem of the late twelfth century.

12. *The Divine Comedy:* Dante's epic poem of the early fourteenth century. The three sections of this major work include Inferno, Purgatorio, and Paradiso.
13. *The Canterbury Tales:* Chaucer's unfinished poetic work of the late fourteenth century.
14. *The Decameron:* Giovanni Boccaccio's 1351–1353 collection of tales.
15. *Sir Gawain and the Green Knight:* 1375–1400 Medieval poem.
16. *Piers Plowman:* Middle English poem (1377) attributed to William Langland.
17. *The Second Shepherd's Play:* 1385 medieval mystery play.
18. *Morte d'Arthur:* late fifteenth-century Sir Thomas Malory version of the King Arthur legends.
19. *The Arabian Nights' Entertainment (A Thousand and One Nights):* collection of tales set in India, China, Persia, and Arabia. Scheherazade is the narrator of these stories.
20. *Everyman:* morality play of the late fifteenth and early sixteenth centuries.
21. *Orlando Furioso:* 1516 romantic epic by Lodovico Ariosto.
22. *Utopia:* philosophical romance written in Latin (1516) by Sir Thomas More. It was translated into English by Ralph Robinson in 1551.
23. *Ralph Roister Doister:* Nicholas Udall's 1553 dramatical farce.
24. *The Spanish Tragedy:* the late sixteenth-century Thomas Kyd revenge drama.
25. *Dr. Faustus:* Christopher Marlowe's 1588 play.
26. *The Faerie Queene:* 1590–1596 allegorical epic poem by Edmund Spenser.

ANSWERS TO
COUPLES, THEIR LITERARY TITLES, AND THEIR AUTHORS

1. h-pp	6. q-ff	11. n-jj	16. s-rr
2. j-dd	7. k-ee	12. l-nn	17. b-ss
3. c-qq	8. i-oo	13. t-bb	18. g-ii
4. r-kk	9. e-mm	14. m-tt	19. a-ll
5. d-hh	10. p-aa	15. o-gg	20. f-cc

ANSWERS TO FAMOUS PAIRS AND THEIR LAST NAMES

ANSWER . . . CHARACTERS . . . LITERARY WORK . . . AUTHOR

1. K . . . Henry Jekyll and Edward Hyde . . . *The Strange Case of Dr. Jekyll and Mr. Hyde* . . . Robert Louis Stevenson
2. G . . . Lennie Small and George Milton . . . *Of Mice and Men* . . . John Steinbeck
3. A . . . Romeo Montague and Juliet Capulet . . . *Romeo and Juliet* . . . William Shakespeare
4. O . . . Scarlett O'Hara and Rhett Butler . . . *Gone with the Wind* . . . Margaret Mitchell
5. E . . . Edgar Linton and Catherine Earnshaw . . . *Wuthering Heights* . . . Emily Brontë
6. M . . . Hester Prynne and Arthur Dimmesdale . . . *The Scarlet Letter* . . . Nathaniel Hawthorne
7. C . . . Ma and Pa (Tom) Joad . . . *The Grapes of Wrath* . . . John Steinbeck

8. I . . . Nora and Torvald Helmer . . . *A Doll's House* . . . Henrik Ibsen
9. H . . . Anna Karenina and Aleksei Vronski . . . *Anna Karenina* . . . Leo Tolstoy
10. B . . . Don Quixote and Sancho Panza . . . *Don Quixote* . . . Miguel de Cervantes
11. N . . . Leopold and Molly Bloom . . . *Ulysses* . . . James Joyce
12. D . . . Finny (no last name given) and Gene Forester . . . *A Separate Peace* . . . John Knowles
13. L . . . Cyrano de Bergerac and Roxanne Robin . . . *Cyrano de Bergerac* . . . Edmond Rostand
14. J . . . Stanley and Stella Kowalski . . . *A Streetcar Named Desire* . . . Tennessee Williams
15. F . . . Jane Eyre and Edward Rochester . . . *Jane Eyre* . . . Charlotte Brontë

ANSWERS TO WOMEN'S NAMES IN TITLES

A. Leo Tolstoy
B. John Greenleaf Whittier
C. Sinclair Lewis
D. Henry James
E. Jane Austen
F. Erica Jong
G. Clare Darcy
H. Henrik Ibsen
I. Euripedes
J. Charlotte Brontë
K. Sigrid Undset
L. R. D. Blackmoor
M. Daniel Defoe
N. Emile Zola
O. George Griffith
P. Samuel Richardson
Q. Aleksandr Pushkin
R. Daphne Du Maurier
S. Alphonse Daudet
T. Thomas Hardy
U. Honoré de Balzac
V. Hugh Walpole
W. A. A. Milne
X. Orlando Villas
Y. Guy de Maupassant
Z. Nancy Mitford

ANSWERS TO MEN'S NAMES IN LITERARY TITLES

1. Lew Wallace
2. Miguel de Cervantes
3. Edmond Rostand
4. Chaim Potok
5. Robert Sherwood
6. Harriet Beecher Stowe
7. William Styron
8. James Thurber
9. Mark Twain
10. Kurt Vonnegut
11. Edith Wharton
12. Thornton Wilder
13. James Barrie
14. James Boswell
15. Mark Twain
16. Lord Byron
17. Lord Byron
18. Joseph Conrad
19. Charles Dickens
20. Mark Twain
21. Charles Dickens
22. George Eliot
23. Henry Fielding
24. Ben Jonson
25. Thomas Hughes
26. William Golding
27. Henry Fielding
28. Thomas Hardy
29. Horatio Alger
30. Mary Chase
31. Paddy Chayefsky
32. Mary Mapes Dodge

33. Howard Fast
34. Alex Haley (collaboration)
35. William Dean Howells
36. Sinclair Lewis
37. David Mamet

38. Herman Melville
39. Herman Melville
40. John O'Hara
41. George Eliot
42. Athol Fugard

ANSWERS TO LADIES OF LITERATURE

1. Anne
2. Annie
3. Antonia
4. Maggie
5. Carrie

6. Rosemary
7. Lolita
8. Anna
9. Sophie
10. Alice

11. Emma
12. Jane
13. Alice
14. Rebecca
15. Barbara

16. Julie
17. Tess
18. Joan
19. Jean
20. Anna

Section 3

TIMING IS EVERYTHING

(Pages 311–322)

ANSWERS TO THE START OF CIVILIZATION . . .
3500 B.C.–1 B.C.

1. Homer
2. Socrates
3. Aesop
4. Tutankhamen
5. Hammurabi
6. Caesar
7. Hippocrates
8. Pericles

9. Cleopatra
10. Aristophanes
11. Aeschylus
12. Pindar
13. Moses
14. Sophocles
15. Alexander the Great
16. Vergil

ANSWERS TO THE MISSING LINK . . . 1 A.D.–999

1. 79
2. 425
3. 700
4. 984

5. 800
6. 5
7. c. 300
8. 891

9. 175
10. 68
11. 360
12. 285

13. 625
14. 391
15. 760

ANSWERS TO THE HEADLINES OF THE TIME . . . 1000–1400

1. Leif Ericson
2. Macbeth

3. Hastings
4. Domesday

5. Crusade
6. Song of Roland
7. Omar Khayyám
8. Canterbury
9. Lion Hearted
10. Nibelungenlied
11. Genghis Khan

12. Magna Carta
13. Dante
14. 1456
15. Black Death
16. Laura
17. Geoffrey Chaucer
18. Decameron

ANSWERS TO
FRAUDULENT FRED'S FACT OR FICTION? . . . 1400–1599

1.	Fiction	The printing press was invented by Gutenberg.
2.	Fiction	The Hundred Years War was fought between England and France.
3.	Fact	
4.	Fiction	Leonardo da Vinci drew a flying machine.
5.	Fiction	The *Santa Maria* was the ship of Christopher Columbus.
6.	Fact	
7.	Fiction	The *Mona Lisa* was painted by Leonardo da Vinci.
8.	Fiction	The Sistine Chapel is located in the Vatican.
9.	Fact	
10.	Fiction	Martin Luther posted 95 theses.
11.	Fiction	Magellan was killed by natives before he completed his trip.
12.	Fiction	Henry VIII married Anne Boleyn.
13.	Fact	
14.	Fact	
15.	Fact	
16.	Fact	
17.	Fiction	Shakespeare was born in Stratford-upon-Avon.
18.	Fiction	Mary Queen of Scots was imprisoned by Elizabeth I.
19.	Fiction	Drake reached the Pacific Ocean.
20.	Fiction	Richard Burbage opened *The Theatre.*
21.	Fiction	The English fleet defeated the Spanish Armada.
22.	Fact	
23.	Fiction	London theatres closed because of the plague.
24.	Fiction	Christopher Marlowe was killed in a tavern brawl.
25.	Fiction	Shakespeare's plays were performed in the *Globe Theatre.*

ANSWERS TO VOICES FROM LONG AGO . . . THE 1600s

1. James I of Scotland
2. Lope de Vega
3. Miguel de Cervantes
4. Ben Jonson
5. El Greco
6. Sir Walter Raleigh
7. Francis Bacon

8. Sir Anthony Van Dyck
9. William Harvey
10. Harmensz van Rijn Rembrandt
11. René Descartes
12. John Milton
13. Puritans
14. Giovanni Bernini

15. Oliver Cromwell
16. Molière
17. Charles II
18. Sir Christopher Wren
19. John Dryden
20. Peter the Great
21. Sir Isaac Newton
22. Jean de La Fontaine

ANSWERS TO THE CONFUSED TOWN CRIER . . . THE 1700s

1. Samuel Pepys wrote diaries.
2. Richard Steele and Joseph Addison wrote *The Spectator.*
3. David Garrick was a popular thespian and stage manager of the day.
4. Voltaire was imprisoned in the Bastille.
5. Daniel Defoe wrote *Moll Flanders* and *Robin Crusoe.* Jane Austen wrote *Emma.*
6. Catherine succeeded Peter the Great in 1725.
7. Jonathan Swift wrote *Gulliver's Travel's.*
8. Roger Williams settled in Rhode Island. James Oglethorpe founded Savannah, Georgia.
9. Benjamin Franklin wrote *Poor Richard's Almanack.*
10. Stravinsky composed during the twentieth century.
11. William Hogarth painted *"The Rake's Progress."*
12. John Peter Zenger won a freedom of the press trial.
13. A papal bull is an official document by the pope. It is not an animal.
14. Thomas Gray wrote "Elegy Written in a Country Churchyard."
15. As an editor, Thomas Bowdler was famous for deleting words or expressions that he felt lacked propriety.
16. These men were all philosophers.
17. Jane Austen was born in 1775.
18. William Blake wrote *"Songs of Experience."*
19. Marie Antoinette was executed.
20. Napoleon married Josephine de Beauharnais.
21. Samuel Taylor Coleridge wrote *"Kubla Khan."*
22. George Washington died in 1799.

ANSWERS TO THE SPORTING LIFE . . . THE 1800s

Game 1

1. K
2. G
3. N
4. B
5. R
6. P
7. E
8. T
9. A
10. O
11. C
12. D

Game 2

1. E
2. R
3. L
4. J
5. B
6. N
7. G
8. T
9. M
10. C
11. D
12. H

13. S

14. M

15. H

16. F

17. Q

18. I

19. L

20. J

Bonus: Emily Dickinson

13. O

14. A

15. Q

16. K

17. I

18. S

19. P

20. F

Bonus: William Butler Yeats

ANSWERS TO
THE CENTURY OF COMMUNICATIONS . . . THE 1900s

1. Theodore Dreiser
2. Anton Chekhov
3. Friedrich Nietzsche
4. Sigmund Freud
5. Max Planck
6. Beatrix Potter
7. Orville and Wilbur Wright
8. Jack London
9. George Bernard Shaw
10. Albert Einstein
11. E. M. Forster
12. Florence Nightingale
13. Edith Wharton
14. Jim Thorpe
15. Marie Curie
16. Henry Ford
17. Archduke Francis Ferdinand
18. Edgar Lee Masters
19. Jack Dempsey
20. Eugene O'Neill
21. James Joyce
22. Robert Frost
23. Will Rogers
24. F. Scott Fitzgerald
25. Sinclair Lewis

26. A. A. Milne
27. Babe Ruth
28. D. H. Lawrence
29. Herbert Hoover
30. Winston Churchill
31. Jesse Owens
32. John Steinbeck
33. Orson Wells
34. Joe DiMaggio
35. Adolf Hitler
36. Tennessee Williams
37. Harry Truman
38. J. D. Salinger
39. Ernest Hemingway
40. John Fitzgerald Kennedy
41. Harper Lee
42. Edward Albee
43. William Faulkner
44. Martin Luther King, Jr.
45. Cassius Clay (Muhammad Ali)
46. Neil Simon
47. Carl Bernstein and Bob Woodward
48. Alex Haley
49. Toni Morrison
50. John Grisham

ANSWERS TO ENGLISH LITERATURE
TIME PERIODS . . . PART ONE

1. G   The novel was published in 1891.
2. C   Dryden was England's poet laureate from 1668 to 1688.
3. E   Lord Byron's narrative poem was published in cantos from 1812 to 1818.
4. D   The essay was published in 1711.
5. F   The poem was completed in 1854.

6. D He wrote this in the late 1700s.

7. F The dramatic monologue was written in 1842.

8. E These odes were written by John Keats.

9. D Joseph Addison and Richard Steele were essayists who published their works in a series of essays called *The Tattler* and *The Spectator* from 1709 to 1712.

10. A This was a poetic work authored by Geoffrey Chaucer featuring a pilgrimage to Becket's shrine at Canterbury and stories that were to be told by the pilgrims. Chaucer supposedly began this effort in 1387.

11. B *Utopia* was a 1516 literary work written in Latin.

12. F "Dover Beach" was an 1867 poem expressing Matthew Arnold's pessimistic outlook of the world's future.

13. G This play, written by T. S. Eliot and performed in 1935, deals with the assassination of St. Thomas à Becket, Canterbury's Archbishop.

14. C This is the first line of John Donne's 1633 poem entitled "Song."

15. D *The Pilgrim's Progress* is a two-part allegory written by John Bunyan between 1678 and 1684.

16. G This is Shaw's 1913 play about Eliza Doolittle, a flower girl, and Professor Henry Higgins, a phonetics teacher.

17. G These three were poets of the twentieth century.

18. A *Sir Gawain and the Green Knight* is a poem about the ideal knight. It was written sometime between 1375 and 1400.

19. B This poem, written by the famous explorer and poet, is the response to Christopher Marlowe's 1599 poem, "The Passionate Shepherd to His Love."

20. A *Morte d'Arthur* is a splendid piece of Arthurian romance completed about 1469 while Malory was imprisoned.

21. G Here is a 1960 novel about a leper colony in the Congo.

22. G James Joyce's 1916 novel's protagonist is Stephen Dedalus.

23. G W. H. Auden's 1940 poem's title refers to the Museum of Fine Arts in Brussels.

24. C John Milton's works were written in 1637, 1645, and 1667 respectively.

25. F This writing was published in 1864.

ANSWERS TO ENGLISH LITERATURE
TIME PERIODS . . . PART TWO

1. F These were Fitzgerald's 1857 and later translations of the work of Omar Khayyám, a Persian who composed the four line epigrams.

2. C Bacon's 1605 philosophical treatise addressed learning and knowledge.

3. C These men were poets of this age.

4. F "Jabberwocky" is a poem from Lewis Carroll's 1872 *Through the Looking Glass*, the sequel to *Alice's Adventures in Wonderland*.

5. E Coleridge and Shelley were two of the most famous British Romantic poets.

6. B *The Faerie Queene* was Edmund Spenser's epic allegory begun in 1589 featuring characters that included Gloriana, The Faerie Queene, Duessa, and Una.

7. A Here is a Middle English poem that supposedly was composed by William Langland (or Langley).

8. A "Barbara Allan," "Lord Randall," and "Sir Patrick Spens" were popular ballads of the Medieval Age.

9. E   These were two poems written by Romantic poet William Blake.

10. B Christopher Marlowe was an English dramatist and poet who wrote *The Tragical History of Dr. Faustus* (performed in 1588) and *The Jew of Malta* (performed in 1589).

11. F They were brother and sister English poets of Italian parentage.

12. G Here is Joseph Conrad's 1902 symbolic novella set in the Belgian Congo.

13. G A. E. Housman's 1896 poem celebrates the memory of the town's athletic champion.

14. C This is the age pertaining to the reign of James I of England (James VI of Scotland) from 1603 to 1625.

15. D Jonathan Swift's 1726 satirical work includes the four voyages made by Lemuel Gulliver, a ship's doctor.

16. D This is a 1700 play by William Congreve.

17. G Rudyard Kipling's 1894 collection of animal stories for children is entitled *The Jungle Book*.

18. F Charles Darwin's 1859 work concerns his theory of evolution by natural selection.

19. G J. M. Barrie's 1904 play is about the Darling children and Peter Pan, the boy who never grew up.

20. F Charles Dickens is a British author who lived from 1812–1870 and wrote many novels including *David Copperfield* (1849–1850), *A Tale of Two Cities* (1859), and *Hard Times* (1845).

21. B These 154 sonnets composed between 1593 and 1601 were printed in 1609.

22. G Samuel Beckett's 1955 tragicomedy features two tramps, Didi and Gogo.

23. F *Idylls of the King* is Tennyson's long series of poems about King Arthur's life. They were published in twelve parts.

24. F This is an 1848 novel by William Makepeace Thackeray.

25. A Bede was an English historian who wrote *The Ecclesiastical History of the English People* in 731.

ANSWERS TO ENGLISH LITERATURE
TIME PERIODS . . . PART THREE

1. E   *Lyrical Ballads* is a collection of Romantic poems by William Wordsworth and Samuel Taylor Coleridge. Editions were published in 1798, 1800, and 1802.

2. G   *Brideshead Revisited,* a novel subtitled *The Sacred and Profane Memories of Captain Charles Ryder,* was written in 1945 by Evelyn Waugh.

3. F   Charlotte Brontë's 1847 novel tells of governess Jane Eyre's falling in love with the estate owner, Edward Rochester.

4. A   *Beowulf* is an Anglo-Saxon epic poem supposedly composed anonymously around 700. It recounts the brave deeds of its hero, Beowulf, who conquers the monster, Grendel.

5. A   This was a 1086 Latin recorded publication requested by William the Conqueror. It was a census and survey record of England's land and people.

6. C   *Macbeth* was a 1606 Shakespearean tragedy that traces the downfall of the Scotsman, Macbeth, the man possessing "vaulting ambition."

7. A Tradition has it that around 1040 Lady Godiva, the wife of Earl Leofric of Mercia, rode naked through the town to protest the high taxes Leofric imposed on the citizens of Coventry.

8. F George Eliot's novel was published in 1859.

9. F *Bleak House* was written by Charles Dickens during the years 1852 and 1853.

10. G E. M. Forster's 1924 novel is set in India.

11. G John Millington Synge's 1907 play precipitated Dublin's "Playboy riots."

12. G The 1940 collection of stories written by Dylan Thomas concerns his childhood. The title is reminiscent of James Joyce's (whom Thomas greatly admired) autobiographical novel.

13. E Austen's 1814 novel relates the story of destitute Fanny Price who is sent to live with her rich relatives at Mansfield Park.

14. D In his 1742 novel, a parody of the novel *Pamela, or Virtue Rewarded* by Samuel Richardson, Henry Fielding introduces his readers to the virtuous Joseph Andrews.

15. D *The School for Scandal,* Richard Brinsley Sheridan's comedic play, was written in 1777. *She Stoops to Conquer* is a comedy written four years earlier by Oliver Goldsmith.

16. B This is Christopher Marlowe's 1598 unfinished poem, based on the earlier poem by Musaeus. Marlowe's poem was completed by George Chapman.

17. G *Women in Love* is D. H. Lawrence's 1920 novel.

18. D Though the *Diary* was written in shorthand between 1660 and 1669, it was not deciphered until 1825.

19. F H. G. Wells' 1895 science-fiction novel is entitled *The Time Machine.*

20. G Hornblower was a heroic British naval officer in several C. S. Forester novels published in the late 1930s.

21. G Here is J.R.R. Tolkien's 1937 novel whose hero is Bilbo Boggins. A hobbit is a creature who inhabits Middle Earth.

22. E This is Romantic poet William Wordsworth's 1807 poem.

23. E Sir Walter Scott's 1819 novel's hero is Wilfred, knight of Ivanhoe. The work is set during the time of Richard the Lion-Hearted.

24. C Shakespeare's 1606 tragedy is concerned with Lear, who desires to divide his kingdom among his three daughters. This division is contingent upon their declaration of love for him.

25. G Sean O'Casey's play, initially presented in 1924, tells the story of Juno Boyle's struggle to keep her family together during tough times in Ireland.

ANSWERS TO ENGLISH LITERATURE
TIME PERIODS . . . PART FOUR

1. F Stevenson's historical 1886 novel deals with David Balfour's difficulties after being sent to sea by his cruel uncle. Fortunately for Balfour, he meets up with Alan Breck.

2. G The ban on D. H. Lawrence's controversial novel (thought obscene) was lifted in America in 1959 and in England a year later.

3. C In this 1651 treatise Hobbes presents his theory regarding the sovereign state in which he advocates a strong authoritative government.
4. G The story was released in 1959.
5. C A group of poets who wrote during the early seventeenth century was called the Metaphysical Poets. This group included Andrew Marvell, George Herbert, John Donne, and Richard Crashaw among others.
6. D Swift published this satirical work in 1729.
7. B Shakespeare's comedy with characters Beatrice, Benedict, Hero, and Claudio was performed in 1598 or 1599.
8. G George Orwell's futuristic, satirical novel about Oceania and Big Brother was published in 1949.
9. G In 1915 W. Somerset Maugham completed his story about Philip Carey, the clubfooted orphan who desires to become a doctor.
10. F The essay was published in 1859.
11. F The story was published in 1842.
12. C The first poet laureate appointment was given to Ben Jonson, who held the position and performed the required duties of the office from 1619 until 1637. Sir William Davenant was the first poet laureate to officially have the title of poet laureate, 1638–1668, followed by John Dryden, 1668–1688.
13. F In this 1878 work by Hardy, Clem Yeobright of Wessex marries Eustacia Vye.
14. D This 1719–1720 novel by Daniel Defoe has for its full title *The Life and Strange Surprising Adventures of Robinson Crusoe, of York, Mariner.*
15. F Eliot's novel was published in 1861.
16. G This 1955 work by Lessing tells the story of a young boy named Jerry who needs to prove something to himself.
17. B William Shakespeare was born there in the year 1564. He died 52 years later.
19. F In his 1859 novel entitled *A Tale of Two Cities,* Charles Dickens explores the people and happenings surrounding the French Revolution. The two cities, incidentally, are London and Paris.
19. F The novel was published in 1844.
20. D The novel was published in 1749.
21. G Dylan created this 1954 play depicting a spring day in a Welsh village.
22. F William Makepeace Thackeray wrote *Vanity Fair* and *The Memoirs of Barry Lyndon.* George Eliot wrote *Middlemarch, Silas Marner, Mill on the Floss,* and *Adam Bede.* Thomas Hardy wrote *Tess of the D'Urbervilles, Jude the Obscure, The Return of the Native, The Mayor of Casterbridge,* and *Far from the Madding Crowd.*
23. G The characters Mr. Toad, Water Rat, and Mole come to life in this 1908 classic.
24. B This is an English comedy written by Nicholas Udall and performed in 1553.
25. G This poem was written in 1927.

ANSWERS TO AMERICAN LITERATURE
TIME PERIODS . . . COLONIALUTIONARY PERIOD

1. G	4. J	7. I	9. F
2. B	5. D	8. C	10. E
3. H	6. A		

ANSWERS TO AMERICAN LITERATURE TIME PERIODS . . . THE NINETEENTH CENTURY
THE AUTHORS SPEAK FOR THEMSELVES

1. Washington Irving
2. William Cullen Bryant
3. Noah Webster
4. Ralph Waldo Emerson
5. James Fenimore Cooper
6. The Concord Group
7. The Fireside Poets
8. Henry Wadsworth Longfellow
9. John Greenleaf Whittier
10. Oliver Wendell Holmes
11. The Cambridge Scholars
12. Edgar Allan Poe
13. Henry David Thoreau
14. Walt Whitman
15. Emily Dickinson
16. Nathaniel Hawthorne
17. Herman Melville
18. Harriet Beecher Stowe
19. Mark Twain
20. William Dean Howells
21. Henry James
22. Kate Chopin
23. Edith Wharton
24. Bret Harte
25. Ambrose Bierce
26. Sarah Orne Jewett
27. Frederick Douglass
28. Stephen Crane
29. Frank Norris
30. Theodore Dreiser

ANSWERS TO AMERICAN LITERATURE TIME PERIODS . . . 1900–1950
THE WRIGHT WAR DEPRESSION WAR

1. Naturalism
2. The Octopus
3. Jack London
4. John Steinbeck
5. The Age of Innocence
6. O. Henry
7. Ezra Pound
8. Willa Cather
9. Robert Frost
10. Carl Sandburg
11. Sinclair Lewis
12. Sherwood Anderson
13. Gertrude Stein
14. e. e. cummings
15. Edna Ferber
16. John Dos Passos
17. Amy Lowell
18. The Great Gatsby
19. Thomas Wolfe
20. Nathanael West
21. Ernest Hemingway
22. William Faulkner
23. Henry James
24. Pearl S. Buck
25. Eugene O'Neill
26. Tennessee Williams
27. Carson McCullers
28. Thornton Wilder
29. Lillian Hellman
30. Robert Penn Warren
31. James Thurber

ANSWERS TO AMERICAN LITERATURE TIME PERIODS . . . 1951–PRESENT
THE FAX OF MODERN AMERICAN LITERATURE

1. William Styron
2. Samuel Beckett
3. Marianne Moore
4. Archibald MacLeish

 5. Saul Bellow
 6. Theodore Roethke
 7. MacKinlay Kantor
 8. John Fitzgerald Kennedy
 9. Richard Wilbur
10. Dr. Seuss
11. Jack Kerouac
12. Ayn Rand
13. Norman Mailer
14. Lorraine Hansberry
15. Philip Roth
16. Harper Lee
17. J. D. Salinger
18. Joseph Heller
19. Edward Albee
20. Bernard Malamud
21. William Carlos Williams

22. Truman Capote
23. James Michener
24. Langston Hughes
25. Alice Walker
26. Toni Morrison
27. Tom Wolfe
28. August Wilson
29. Neil Simon
30. John Cheever
31. John Updike
32. Sylvia Plath
33. Anne Sexton
34. Dorothy Parker
35. Chaim Potok
36. Kurt Vonnegut
37. Richard Wright
38. Ralph Ellison

ANSWERS TO THROUGH THE YEARS

1. 1910–1919
2. 1780–1789
3. 1620–1629
4. 1870–1879
5. 1720–1729

 6. 1820–1829
 7. 1850–1859
 8. 1840–1849
 9. 1810–1819
10. 1890–1899

ANSWERS TO THE EVENTS OF THE YEARS

Year	Literary Events	Historical and Political Events	Other Events
1791	F	DD	BBB
1815	I	AA	DDD
1850	C	JJ	AAA
1870	J	EE	GGG
1890	B	CC	III
1907	H	HH	KKK
1922	K	KK	EEE
1941	A	II	HHH
1959	G	BB	CCC
1977	E	GG	FFF
1988	D	FF	JJJ

ANSWERS TO
LITERATURE WRITTEN DURING THE 1600s AND THE 1700s

1. *Don Quixote de la Mancha:* Spaniard Miguel de Cervantes' 1605 (Part I) and 1615 (Part II) romantic novel about the man who took on windmills and dreamed the impossible dream.

2. *The Duchess of Malfi:* John Webster's early seventeenth-century Jacobean romantic tragedy.

3. *Comus:* John Milton's 1634 pastoral masque first performed by children in the Ludlow castle of the Earl of Bridgewater.

4. *The School for Wives:* a social satire and one of Molière's most successful plays, was written in 1622.

5. Molière's comedy, *Tartuffe:* the story of the religious hypocrite, was first presented in 1664.

6. The Frenchman Molière (Jean Baptiste Poquelin) wrote the contemporary comedy of manners play, *The Misanthrope,* which was first presented in 1666.

7. *Paradise Lost:* John Milton's 1667 epic poem of man's first disobedience in the Garden of Eden. It was written "to justify the ways of God to man."

8. *Samson Agonistes:* John Milton's 1671 tragedy that focuses on the biblical story of Samson.

9. Neo-classicist Jean Racine's French tragedy, *Phedre:* based on the play by the Greek playwright, Euripedes, it was initially presented in 1677.

10. *The Pilgrim's Progress* was written by John Bunyan. The first part of this 1678 religious allegory deals with man's progress through his worldly existence to the life hereafter. The first part of this literary piece far exceeds the literary merit of the second part.

11. *Absalom and Achitophel:* John Dryden's 1681 satirical poem, written in heroic couplets, that addresses the possible exclusion of James, Duke of York, from his just ascendancy to the throne of England due to his Catholic faith.

12. *The Way of the World:* the 1700 comedy of manners play by William Congreve that so depressed him following its poor public reception that he abandoned stage writing.

13. *The Rape of the Lock* by Alexander Pope: This mock-heroic, epic poem, written in cantos and published in 1712, is based on a true story in which two families feuded after Lord Petre cut off a lock of Arabella Fermor's hair.

14. *Robinson Crusoe:* Daniel Defoe's 1719 novel.

15. Moll Flanders: Daniel Defoe's 1722 picaresque, social novel. The complete title of this novel is a beauty: *The Fortunes and Misfortunes of the Famous Moll Flanders, and who was Born at Newgate, and during a Life of continued Variety for Threescore Years, besides her Childhood, was Twelve Year a Whore, five times a Wife (whereof once to her own Brother), Twelve Year a Thief, Eight Year a Transported Felon in Virginia, at last grew rich, liv'd Honest, and died a Penitent. Written from her own Memorandums.*

16. *A Journal of the Plague Year:* Daniel Defoe's work, published in 1722, recounting the bubonic plague in England during the year 1665.

17. *Gulliver's Travels,* completed in 1726: Jonathan Swift's social satire, written in journal form, can be read on several levels—satire, bitter denunciation, adventure, and fantasy. Lemuel Gulliver voyages to four lands—Lilliput, Brobdingnag, Laputa, and Houyhnhnmland.

18. *Pamela:* Samuel Richardson's 1740–1742 pioneer romantic novel. The form of this literary work, considered by many to be the first modern English novel, is epistolary.

19. *Joseph Andrews:* Henry Fielding's 1742 novel that parodies Richardson's Pamela. The title is a shortened form of the full title—*The History of the Adventures of Joseph Andrews, and of his Friend, Mr. Abraham Adams, written in Imitation of the Manner of Cervantes.*

20. *Tom Jones:* the 1749 satiric Henry Fielding novel is the shortened title of the full title, *The History of Tom Jones, a Foundling,* an advanced novel for its time.

21. It was Henry Fielding's mission to introduce to his readers the ideas of prison and legal reform and to portray a loving and virtuous wife, the titular character, in his 1751 novel: *Amelia.*

22. *Candide:* Voltaire's 1759 socially satirical novel that questions Leibnitz's statement, "All is for the best in this best of all possible worlds."

23. *Tristram Shandy:* amusing novel by Laurence Sterne, published in several books (1759–1767). Some of the techniques and ideas presented by the author, including a completely blank page, are quite odd.

24. *The Castle of Otranto:* 1764 Gothic romance by Horace Walpole.

25. *The Vicar of Wakefield:* the 1766 pastoral novel by the candid and witty Oliver Goldsmith whose other works include *She Stoops to Conquer, The Good Natur'd Man,* and *The Citizen of the World.*

26. *She Stoops to Conquer:* lively and witty 1773 comedy of situation written by Oliver Goldsmith.

27. *Humphrey Clinker:* Tobias Smollett's 1771 humorous novel written in the form of letters by the various characters. Its full title is *The Expedition of Humphrey Clinker.*

28. *The Rivals:* Richard Brinsley Sheridan's 1775 satirical comedy of manners. Our word *malapropism* is taken from the character, Mrs. Malaprop, who appears in this play.

29. *The School for Scandal:* Richard Brinsley Sheridan's 1777 comedic play, famous for its screen scene.

30. *The Rime of the Ancient Mariner:* 1798 masterpiece poem by Samuel Taylor Coleridge, a romantic poet. The famous line "Water, water, everywhere / Nor any a drop to drink" is from this poem.

Section 4

NOVELS—TALES TO REMEMBER

(Pages 322–334)

ANSWERS TO JUST FOR STARTERS (PART ONE)

TITLE   **AUTHOR**

1. *Little Women* . . . Louisa May Alcott
2. *Pride and Prejudice* . . . Jane Austen
3. *Go Tell It on the Mountain* . . . James Baldwin
4. *Peter Pan* . . . J. M. Barrie
5. *Fahrenheit 451* . . . Ray Bradbury
6. *Jane Eyre* . . . Charlotte Brontë
7. *Wuthering Heights* . . . Emily Brontë
8. *The Good Earth* . . . Pearl S. Buck
9. *The Last Days of Pompeii* . . . Edward Bulwer-Lytton

10. *Tobacco Road* . . . Erskine Caldwell
11. *The Stranger* . . . Albert Camus
12. *Alice's Adventures in Wonderland* . . . Lewis Carroll
13. *My Antonia* . . . Willa Cather
14. *Don Quixote* . . . Miguel de Cervantes
15. *The Awakening* . . . Kate Chopin
16. *Heart of Darkness* . . . Joseph Conrad
17. *The Red Badge of Courage* . . . Stephen Crane
18. *Robinson Crusoe* . . . Daniel Defoe
19. *A Christmas Carol* . . . Charles Dickens
20. *David Copperfield* . . . Charles Dickens
21. *Great Expectations* . . . Charles Dickens
22. *Oliver Twist* . . . Charles Dickens
23. *A Tale of Two Cities* . . . Charles Dickens
24. *The Brothers Karamazov* . . . Fyodor Dostoyevsky
25. *Crime and Punishment* . . . Fyodor Dostoyevsky
26. *An American Tragedy* . . . Theodore Dreiser
27. *The Count of Monte Cristo* . . . Alexander Dumas
28. *Rebecca* . . . Daphne Du Maurier
29. *Silas Marner* . . . George Eliot
30. *Invisible Man* . . . Ralph Ellison
31. *As I Lay Dying* . . . William Faulkner
32. *The Sound and the Fury* . . . William Faulkner
33. *Tom Jones* . . . Henry Fielding
34. *The Great Gatsby* . . . F. Scott Fitzgerald
35. *Tender Is the Night* . . . F. Scott Fitzgerald

ANSWERS TO JUST FOR STARTERS (PART TWO)

TITLE   **AUTHOR**

1. *A Passage to India* . . . E. M. Forster
2. *Lord of the Flies* . . . William Golding
3. *Brighton Rock* . . . Graham Greene
4. *The Maltese Falcon* . . . Dashiell Hammett
5. *Jude the Obscure* . . . Thomas Hardy
6. *The House of the Seven Gables* . . . Nathaniel Hawthorne
7. *The Scarlet Letter* . . . Nathaniel Hawthorne
8. *Catch-22* . . . Joseph Heller
9. *For Whom the Bell Tolls* . . . Ernest Hemingway
10. *The Old Man and the Sea* . . . Ernest Hemingway
11. *The Sun Also Rises* . . . Ernest Hemingway
12. *A Bell for Adano* . . . John Hersey
13. *Siddhartha* . . . Herman Hesse
14. *The Hunchback of Notre Dame* . . . Victor Hugo
15. *Les Misérables* . . . Victor Hugo
16. *Brave New World* . . . Aldous Huxley

17. *A Portrait of the Artist as a Young Man* . . . James Joyce
18. *Ulysses* . . . James Joyce
19. *A Separate Peace* . . . John Knowles
20. *Sons and Lovers* . . . D. H. Lawrence
21. *To Kill a Mockingbird* . . . Harper Lee
22. *Babbitt* . . . Sinclair Lewis
23. *Main Street* . . . Sinclair Lewis
24. *The Call of the Wild* . . . Jack London
25. *The Sea Wolf* . . . Jack London
26. *The Assistant* . . . Bernard Malamud
27. *Of Human Bondage* . . . W. Somerset Maugham
28. *Billy Budd* . . . Herman Melville
29. *Moby Dick* . . . Herman Melville
30. *Gone with the Wind* . . . Margaret Mitchell
31. *Beloved* . . . Toni Morrison
32. *Song of Solomon* . . . Toni Morrison
33. *Animal Farm* . . . George Orwell
34. *Nineteen Eighty-Four* . . . George Orwell
35. *Cry, the Beloved Country* . . . Alan Paton

ANSWERS TO JUST FOR STARTERS (PART THREE)

TITLE   **AUTHOR**
1. *The Bell Jar* . . . Sylvia Plath
2. *The Yearling* . . . Marjorie Kinnan Rawlings
3. *All Quiet on the Western Front* . . . Erich Maria Remarque
4. *The Catcher in the Rye* . . . J. D. Salinger
5. *Frankenstein* . . . Mary Shelley
6. *On the Beach* . . . Neville Shute
7. *The Jungle* . . . Upton Sinclair
8. *One Day in the Life of Ivan Denisovich* . . . Alexander Solzhenitsyn
9. *The Grapes of Wrath* . . . John Steinbeck
10. *Of Mice and Men* . . . John Steinbeck
11. *The Pearl* . . . John Steinbeck
12. *Dracula* . . . Bram Stoker
13. *Uncle Tom's Cabin* . . . Harriet Beecher Stowe
14. *Gulliver's Travels* . . . Jonathan Swift
15. *Anna Karenina* . . . Leo Tolstoy
16. *The Adventures of Huckleberry Finn* . . . Mark Twain
17. *The Adventures of Tom Sawyer* . . . Mark Twain
18. *Fathers and Sons* . . . Ivan Turgenev
19. *Dinner at the Homesick Restaurant* . . . Anne Tyler
20. *Rabbit, Run* . . . John Updike
21. *Twenty Thousand Leagues Under the Sea* . . . Jules Verne
22. *Slaughterhouse-Five* . . . Kurt Vonnegut
23. *The Color Purple* . . . Alice Walker
24. *All the King's Men* . . . Robert Penn Warren

25. *Brideshead Revisited* . . . Evelyn Waugh
26. *The Time Machine* . . . H. G. Wells
27. *Delta Wedding* . . . Eudora Welty
28. *The Age of Innocence* . . . Edith Wharton
29. *Ethan Frome* . . . Edith Wharton
30. *The Picture of Dorian Gray* . . . Oscar Wilde
31. *The Bonfire of the Vanities* . . . Tom Wolfe
32. *Mrs. Dalloway* . . . Virginia Woolf
33. *To the Lighthouse* . . . Virginia Woolf
34. *Native Son* . . . Richard Wright

ANSWERS TO NOVEL FITNESS TEST (PART ONE)

NOVEL	AUTHOR
1. *Adam Bede*	George Eliot
2. *The Adventures of Huckleberry Finn*	Mark Twain
3. *The Adventures of Tom Sawyer*	Mark Twain
4. *The African Queen*	C. S. Forster
5. *All Quiet on the Western Front*	Erich Maria Remarque
6. *All the King's Men*	Robert Penn Warren
7. *An American Tragedy*	Theodore Dreiser
8. *And Then There Were None (Ten Little Indians)*	Agatha Christie
9. *The Andromeda Strain*	Michael Crichton
10. *Animal Farm*	George Orwell
11. *Anna Karenina*	Leo Tolstoy
12. *Around the World in Eighty Days*	Jules Verne
13. *Arrowsmith*	Sinclair Lewis
14. *As I Lay Dying*	William Faulkner
15. *Atlas Shrugged*	Ayn Rand
16. *Babbitt*	Sinclair Lewis
17. *The Bell Jar*	Sylvia Plath
18. *Beloved*	Toni Morrison
19. *Billy Budd*	Herman Melville
20. *Bleak House*	Charles Dickens
21. *The Bonfire of the Vanities*	Tom Wolfe
22. *Brave New World*	Aldous Huxley
23. *The Bridge of San Luis Rey*	Thornton Wilder
24. *Brighton Rock*	Graham Greene
25. *The Brothers Karamazov*	Fyodor Dostoyevsky

ANSWERS TO NOVEL FITNESS TEST (PART TWO)

NOVEL	AUTHOR
1. *The Call of the Wild*	Jack London
2. *Captains and the Kings*	Taylor Caldwell
3. *Catch-22*	Joseph Heller
4. *The Catcher in the Rye*	J. D. Salinger

5.	*Cat's Cradle*	Kurt Vonnegut, Jr.
6.	*The Chosen*	Chaim Potok
7.	*The Citadel*	A. J. Cronin
8.	*The Color Purple*	Alice Walker
9.	*The Confessions of Nat Turner*	William Styron
10.	*The Count of Monte Cristo*	Alexandre Dumas
11.	*Crime and Punishment*	Fyodor Dostoyevsky
12.	*Cry, the Beloved Country*	Alan Paton
13.	*David Copperfield*	Charles Dickens
14.	*The Day of the Jackal*	Frederick Forsyth
15.	*Dead Poet's Society*	N. H. Kleinbaum
16.	*The Death of Ivan Ilyich*	Leo Tolstoy
17.	*Death in Venice*	Thomas Mann
18.	*The Deerslayer*	James Fenimore Cooper
19.	*Demian*	Herman Hesse
20.	*Doctor Zhivago*	Boris Pasternak
21.	*Don Quixote*	Miguel de Cervantes
22.	*Dracula*	Bram Stoker
23.	*Dubliners* (short story "The Dead")	James Joyce
24.	*Elmer Gantry*	Sinclair Lewis
25.	*Fahrenheit 451*	Ray Bradbury

ANSWERS TO NOVEL FITNESS TEST (PART THREE)

NOVEL	**AUTHOR**
1. *The Fall*	Albert Camus
2. *Far from the Madding Crowd*	Thomas Hardy
3. *The Fixer*	Bernard Malamud
4. *For Whom the Bell Tolls*	Ernest Hemingway
5. *The Fountainhead*	Ayn Rand
6. *Go Tell It on the Mountain*	James Baldwin
7. *Gone with the Wind*	Margaret Mitchell
8. *The Good Earth*	Pearl S. Buck
9. *Goodbye, Mr. Chips*	James Hilton
10. *The Grapes of Wrath*	John Steinbeck
11. *Great Expectations*	Charles Dickens
12. *The Great Gatsby*	F. Scott Fitzgerald
13. *The Great Santini*	Pat Conroy
14. *Gulliver's Travels*	Jonathan Swift
15. *The Heart Is a Lonely Hunter*	Carson McCullers
16. *Heart of Darkness*	Joseph Conrad
17. *The Heart of the Matter*	Graham Greene
18. *The Hound of the Baskervilles*	Agatha Christie
19. *The House of the Seven Gables*	Nathaniel Hawthorne
20. *How Green Was My Valley*	Richard Llewellyn
21. *The Hunchback of Notre Dame*	Victor Hugo
22. *Invisible Man*	Ralph Ellison

23. *Jane Eyre*	Charlotte Brontë
24. *Jaws*	Peter Benchley
25. *The Jungle*	Upton Sinclair

ANSWERS TO NOVEL FITNESS TEST (PART FOUR)

NOVEL	AUTHOR
1. *The Keys of the Kingdom*	A. J. Cronin
2. *The Last Hurrah*	Edwin O'Connor
3. *The Last of the Mohicans*	James Fenimore Cooper
4. *Les Misérables*	Victor Hugo
5. *Lillies of the Field*	William Barrett
6. *Light in August*	William Faulkner
7. *Look Homeward, Angel*	Thomas Wolfe
8. *Lord Jim*	Joseph Conrad
9. *Lord of the Flies*	William Golding
10. *Madame Bovary*	Gustave Flaubert
11. *Main Street*	Sinclair Lewis
12. *Member of the Wedding*	Carson McCullers
13. *Moby Dick*	Herman Melville
14. *A Moveable Feast*	Ernest Hemingway
15. *Mutiny on the Bounty*	Charles Nordoff and James Norton Hall
16. *My Ántonia*	Willa Cather
17. *Nineteen Eighty-Four*	George Orwell
18. *The Octopus*	Frank Norris
19. *Of Human Bondage*	W. Somerset Maugham
20. *Of Mice and Men*	John Steinbeck
21. *O Pioneers!*	Willa Cather
22. *The Old Man and the Sea*	Ernest Hemingway
23. *Old Yeller*	Fred Gipson
24. *Oliver Twist*	Charles Dickens
25. *One Flew Over the Cuckoo's Nest*	Ken Kesey

ANSWERS TO NOVEL FITNESS TEST (PART FIVE)

NOVEL	AUTHOR
1. *The Ox-Bow Incident*	Walter Van Tilburg Clark
2. *A Passage to India*	E. M. Forster
3. *A Patch of Blue*	Elizabeth Kata
4. *The Pearl*	John Steinbeck
5. *Peter Pan*	J. M. Barrie
6. *The Phantom of the Opera*	Gaston Laroux
7. *The Picture of Dorian Gray*	Oscar Wilde
8. *The Portrait of the Artist as a Young Man*	James Joyce
9. *The Power and The Glory*	Graham Greene
10. *Pride and Prejudice*	Jane Austen
11. *The Prince of Tides*	Pat Conroy

12. *Rebecca*	Daphne Du Maurier
13. *The Red Badge of Courage*	Stephen Crane
14. *Redburn*	Herman Melville
15. *The Return of the Native*	Thomas Hardy
16. *Robinson Crusoe*	Daniel Defoe
17. *A Room with a View*	E. M. Forster
18. *The Scarlet Letter*	Nathaniel Hawthorne
19. *The Sea Wolf*	Jack London
20. *A Separate Peace*	John Knowles
21. *Siddhartha*	Herman Hesse
22. *Silas Marner*	George Eliot
23. *Slaughterhouse-Five*	Kurt Vonnegut
24. *Sophie's Choice*	William Styron
25. *Sons and Lovers*	D. H. Lawrence

ANSWERS TO NOVEL FITNESS TEST (PART SIX)

NOVEL	AUTHOR
1. *The Sound and the Fury*	William Faulkner
2. *Steppenwolf*	Herman Hesse
3. *The Strange Case of Doctor Jekyll and Mr. Hyde*	Robert Louis Stevenson
4. *The Stranger*	Albert Camus
5. *Stranger in a Strange Land*	Robert A. Heinlein
6. *The Sun Also Rises*	Ernest Hemingway
7. *A Tale of Two Cities*	Charles Dickens
8. *Tender Is the Night*	F. Scott Fitzgerald
9. *The Trial*	Franz Kafka
10. *To Kill a Mockingbird*	Harper Lee
11. *Treasure Island*	Robert Louis Stevenson
12. *A Tree Grows in Brooklyn*	Betty Smith
13. *Ulysses*	James Joyce
14. *Uncle Tom's Cabin*	Harriet Beecher Stowe
15. *Up the Down Staircase*	Bel Kaufman
16. *Washington Square*	Henry James
17. *White Fang*	Jack London
18. *Winesburg, Ohio*	Sherwood Anderson
19. *The World According to Garp*	John Irving
20. *Wuthering Heights*	Emily Brontë
21. *The Yearling*	Marjorie Kinnan Rawlings
22. *Zorba the Greek*	Nikos Kazantzakis

ANSWERS TO NOVELS IN OTHER WORDS

1. *A Tale of Two Cities*
2. *Little Women*
3. *The Stranger*
4. *Pride and Prejudice*
5. *Tarzan of the Apes*
6. *Jaws*
7. *Silent Spring*
8. *Murder on the Orient Express*
9. *In Cold Blood*
10. *Ten Little Indians*

11. *Invisible Man*
12. *The Citadel*
13. *Alice's Adventures in Wonderland*
14. *Death Comes for the Archbishop*
15. *The Awakening*
16. *Hard Times*
17. *An American Tragedy*
18. *Tender Is the Night*
19. *The Three Musketeers*
20. *A Passage to India*
21. *Deliverance*
22. *Crime and Punishment*
23. *The Secret Sharer*
24. *Bleak House*
25. *Sister Carrie*
26. *Adam Bede*
27. *Absalom, Absalom!*
28. *So Big*
29. *A Room with a View*
30. *Seize the Day*
31. *Giant*
32. *Light in August*
33. *The Idiot*
34. *The Sound and the Fury*
35. *The Red Badge of Courage*
36. *Oliver Twist*
37. *Heart of Darkness*
38. *The Illustrated Man*
39. *Dandelion Wine*
40. *Tobacco Road*
41. *Go Tell It on the Mountain*
42. *This Side of Paradise*
43. *Brave New World*
44. *Green Mansions*
45. *Jude the Obscure*
46. *Lost Horizon*
47. *The Scarlet Letter*
48. *The Old Man and the Sea*
49. *Return of the Native*
50. *Lord of the Flies*

ANSWERS TO MORE NOVELS IN OTHER WORDS

1. *The Turn of the Screw*
2. *Dubliners*
3. *From Here to Eternity*
4. *Ship of Fools*
5. *Captains Courageous*
6. *On the Road*
7. *One Flew Over the Cuckoo's Nest*
8. *Salem's Lot*
9. *Sons and Lovers*
10. *Main Street*
11. *The Heart Is a Lonely Hunter*
12. *White Fang*
13. *Of Human Bondage*
14. *Gone with the Wind*
15. *Cry, the Beloved Country*
16. *The Bell Jar*
17. *1984*
18. *Wise Blood*
19. *Mutiny on the Bounty*
20. *The Octopus*
21. *The Call of the Wild*
22. *To Kill a Mockingbird*
23. *A Separate Peace*
24. *Death in Venice*
25. *The Assistant*
26. *Billy Budd*
27. *The Trial*
28. *A Portrait of the Artist as a Young Man*
29. *Daisy Miller*
30. *The Fixer*

ANSWERS TO THE NOVEL TOWN CRIER (PART ONE)

1. *And Then There Were None*
2. *An American Tragedy*
3. *All Quiet on the Western Front*
4. *The Adventures of Huckleberry Finn*
5. *The Adventures of Tom Sawyer*
6. *Billy Budd*
7. *Catcher in the Rye*
8. *Call of the Wild*
9. *The Chosen*
10. *Jaws*
11. *Crime and Punishment*
12. *The Grapes of Wrath*

13. *The Hound of the Baskervilles*
14. *Heart of Darkness*
15. *How Green Was My Valley*
16. *Lord of the Flies*
17. *Dead Poets Society*
18. *Nineteen Eighty-Four*
19. *The Old Man and the Sea*
20. *Peter Pan*
21. *Siddhartha*
22. *A Tale of Two Cities*
23. *The Scarlet Letter*
24. *To Kill a Mockingbird*
25. *Sons and Lovers*
26. *A Separate Peace*

27. *The Bridge of San Luis Rey*
28. *Winesburg, Ohio*
29. *Pride and Prejudice*
30. *Go Tell It on the Mountain*
31. *Fahrenheit 451*
32. *Jane Eyre*
33. *The Good Earth*
34. *Captains and the Kings*
35. *The Stranger*
36. *My Ántonia*
37. *O Pioneers!*
38. *Don Quixote*
39. *The Ox-Bow Incident*
40. *The Prince of Tides*

ANSWERS TO THE NOVEL TOWN CRIER (PART TWO)

1. *The Red Badge of Courage*
2. *The Andromeda Strain*
3. *David Copperfield*
4. *Great Expectations*
5. *Oliver Twist*
6. *The Return of the Native*
7. *The House of the Seven Gables*
8. *For Whom the Bell Tolls*
9. *The Brothers Karamazov*
10. *Sister Carrie*
11. *Rebecca*
12. *The Count of Monte Cristo*
13. *Silas Marner*
14. *As I Lay Dying*
15. *The Sound and the Fury*
16. *A Passage to India*
17. *The Natural*
18. *White Fang*
19. *A Farewell to Arms*
20. *The Day of the Jackal*

21. *One Flew Over the Cuckoo's Nest*
22. *The Heart of the Matter*
23. *Babbitt*
24. *Ulysses*
25. *Arrowsmith*
26. *The Sea Wolf*
27. *Tender Is the Night*
28. *Up the Down Staircase*
29. *The Fixer*
30. *Being There*
31. *Main Street*
32. *Finnegan's Wake*
33. *The Sun Also Rises*
34. *Absalom, Absalom!*
35. *The Metamorphosis*
36. *A Room with a View*
37. *A Portrait of the Artist as a Young Man*
38. *Zorba the Greek*
39. *Far from the Madding Crowd*
40. *Howards End*

ANSWERS TO THE NOVEL TOWN CRIER (PART THREE)

1. *The Portrait of a Lady*
2. *Madame Bovary*
3. *Catch-22*
4. *Flowers for Algernon*
5. *Gone with the Wind*
6. *Death in Venice*
7. *The Heart Is a Lonely Hunter*
8. *The Member of the Wedding*

9. *Moby Dick*
10. *Beloved*
11. *Song of Solomon*
12. *The Octopus*
13. *Wise Blood*
14. *Animal Farm*
15. *Doctor Zhivago*
16. *Cry, the Beloved Country*

17. *The Bell Jar*
18. *The Fountainhead*
19. *Atlas Shrugged*
20. *Summer of '42*
21. *The Yearling*
22. *Wide Sargasso Sea*
23. *Franny and Zooey*
24. *Shane*
25. *Frankenstein*

ANSWERS TO THE NOVEL TOWN CRIER (PART FOUR)

1. *On the Beach*
2. *The Jungle*
3. *Of Mice and Men*
4. *The Pearl*
5. *The Strange Case of Dr. Jekyll and Mr. Hyde*
6. *Dracula*
7. *Uncle Tom's Cabin*
8. *Sophie's Choice*
9. *The Confessions of Nat Turner*
10. *Anna Karenina*
11. *The Hobbit*
12. *The Fellowship of the Rings*
13. *Watership Down*
14. *Around the World in Eighty Days*
15. *Slaughterhouse-Five*
16. *The Color Purple*
17. *All the King's Men*
18. *The Time Machine*
19. *Miss Lonelyhearts*
20. *The Day of the Locust*
21. *Ethan Frome*
22. *The Picture of Dorian Gray*
23. *Look Homeward, Angel*
24. *The Bonfire of the Vanities*
25. *You Can't Go Home Again*

ANSWERS TO A NOVEL WORLD WITHOUT VOWELS

1. *Alice's Adventures in Wonderland*
2. *The Red Badge of Courage*
3. *The Great Gatsby*
4. *Invisible Man*
5. *Crime and Punishment*
6. *Don Quixote*
7. *Jane Eyre*
8. *Robinson Crusoe*
9. *The Adventures of Huckleberry Finn*
10. *Gulliver's Travels*
11. *Animal Farm*
12. *Frankenstein*
13. *The Grapes of Wrath*
14. *The Color Purple*
15. *Native Son*
16. *Pride and Prejudice*
17. *Go Tell It on the Mountain*
18. *Tom Jones*
19. *Sons and Lovers*
20. *A Portrait of the Artist as a Young Man*
21. *The Scarlet Letter*
22. *A Farewell to Arms*
23. *Babbitt*
24. *Death in Venice*
25. *Brave New World*
26. *Their Eyes Were Watching God*
27. *The Catcher in the Rye*
28. *Ivanhoe*
29. *Vanity Fair*
30. *Fathers and Sons*
31. *The Portrait of a Lady*
32. *Moby Dick*
33. *Wuthering Heights*
34. *Adam Bede*
35. *Joseph Andrews*
36. *David Copperfield*
37. *A Tale of Two Cities*
38. *Winesburg, Ohio*
39. *Madame Bovary*
40. *Anna Karenina*
41. *Uncle Tom's Cabin*
42. *Of Mice and Men*
43. *The Bell Jar*
44. *The Stranger*
45. *Northanger Abbey*
46. *Cry, the Beloved Country*
47. *The Brothers Karamazov*
48. *All the King's Men*
49. *Mrs. Dalloway*
50. *Heart of Darkness*

ANSWERS TO PULITZER PRIZE-WINNERS' GRID

YEAR	AUTHOR	NOVEL
1921	Edith Wharton	*The Age of Innocence*
1925	Edna Ferber	*So Big*
1932	Pearl S. Buck	*The Good Earth*
1937	Margaret Mitchell	*Gone with the Wind*
1939	Marjorie Kinnan Rawlings	*The Yearling*
1940	John Steinbeck	*The Grapes of Wrath*
1945	John Hersey	*A Bell for Adano*
1947	Robert Penn Warren	*All the King's Men*
1948	James Michener	*Tales of the South Pacific*
1952	Herman Wouk	*The Caine Mutiny*
1953	Ernest Hemingway	*The Old Man and the Sea*
1958	James Agee	*A Death in the Family*
1961	Harper Lee	*To Kill a Mockingbird*
1963	William Faulkner	*The Reivers*
1965	Shirley Ann Grau	*The Keepers of the House*
1967	Bernard Malamud	*The Fixer*
1968	William Styron	*The Confessions of Nat Turner*
1969	N. Scott Momaday	*House Made of Dawn*
1972	Wallace Stegner	*Angle of Repose*
1973	Eudora Welty	*The Optimist's Daughter*
1975	Michael Shaara	*The Killer Angels*

ANSWERS TO PULITZER PRIZE ANNOUNCEMENTS

1. *The Old Man and the Sea*   (1953)
2. *Bridge of San Luis Rey*   (1928)
3. 1939
4. John Updike
5. *All the King's Men*   (1947)
6. Norman Mailer   (1980)
7. Edith Wharton   *The Age of Innocence*   (1921)
8. William Faulkner   (1963)
9. *Beloved*   (1988)
10. Margaret Mitchell   (1937)
11. Anne Tyler
12. MacKinlay Kantor   (1956)
13. *To Kill a Mockingbird*   (1961)
14. John Steinbeck   *The Grapes of Wrath*   (1940)
15. John Hersey   (1945)
16. Sinclair Lewis   (1926)
17. Bernard Malamud
18. *The Confessions of Nat Turner*
19. James Michener   (1948)

20. Pearl S. Buck   (1920)
21. Eudora Welty   (1973)
22. Alice Walker   (1983)
23. John Cheever   *The Stories of John Cheever*
24. Upton Sinclair   (1943)
25. 1920, 1941, 1946, 1954, 1957, 1964, 1971, 1974, 1977

ANSWERS TO
ENGLISH AND IRISH NOVELISTS' EARLIEST WRITINGS

1. Jane Austen
2. Edward Bulwer-Lytton
3. Agatha Christie
4. Wilkie Collins
5. Joseph Conrad
6. Daniel Defoe
7. Charles Dickens
8. George Eliot
9. Henry Fielding
10. Ford Madox Ford
11. C. S. Forester
12. E. M. Forster
13. John Galsworthy
14. Graham Greene
15. Sir Henry Rider Haggard
16. Thomas Hardy
17. W. H. Hudson
18. Aldous Huxley
19. Charles Kingsley
20. D. H. Lawrence
21. C. S. Lewis
22. W. Somerset Maugham
23. A. A. Milne
24. Jean Rhys
25. William Makepeace Thackeray
26. Evelyn Waugh
27. Virginia Woolf
28. Charlotte Brontë
29. Emily Brontë
30. Samuel Butler
31. Lewis Carroll
32. Sir Arthur Conan Doyle
33. William Golding
34. Samuel Richardson
35. Mary Shelley
36. Laurence Sterne
37. Bram Stoker
38. H. G. Wells
39. Oscar Wilde

ANSWERS TO IMPORTANT AMERICAN NOVELS

1. F. Scott Fitzgerald
2. Ernest Hemingway
3. Mark Twain
4. Ralph Ellison
5. Nathaniel Hawthorne
6. William Faulkner
7. John Steinbeck
8. Harper Lee
9. John Steinbeck
10. Herman Melville
11. Ernest Hemingway
12. James Baldwin
13. Richard Wright
14. Kate Chopin
15. Stephen Crane
16. William Faulkner
17. Zora Neale Hurston
18. Nathaniel Hawthorne
19. J. D. Salinger
20. Sinclair Lewis
21. Herman Melville
22. Toni Morrison
23. Mark Twain
24. Edith Wharton
25. Alice Walker
26. John Knowles

27. Ray Bradbury
28. Pearl S. Buck
29. Toni Morrison
30. Harriet Beecher Stowe
31. Willa Cather
32. Theodore Dreiser
33. Jack London
34. Ernest Hemingway
35. Henry James
36. Jack Kerouac
37. Thornton Wilder
38. Sinclair Lewis

39. Edith Wharton
40. John Updike
41. Booth Tarkington
42. William Faulkner
43. Betty Smith
44. Upton Sinclair
45. William Saroyan
46. Joseph Heller
47. Marjorie Kinnan Rawlings
48. Margaret Mitchell
49. Bernard Malamud
50. Jack London

ANSWERS TO IMPORTANT ENGLISH NOVELS

1. Emily Brontë
2. Joseph Conrad
3. Jane Austen
4. James Joyce
5. E. M. Forster
6. Aldous Huxley
7. William Golding
8. George Eliot
9. Charles Dickens
10. Mary Shelley
11. Virginia Woolf
12. Jonathan Swift
13. Daniel Defoe
14. Thomas Hardy
15. George Orwell
16. James Joyce
17. Joseph Conrad
18. Charlotte Brontë
19. Charles Dickens
20. E. M. Forster
21. Joseph Conrad
22. Henry Fielding
23. D. H. Lawrence
24. (Sir) Arthur Conan Doyle
25. Richard Llewellyn

26. Charles Dickens
27. George Orwell
28. Lewis Carroll
29. Thomas Hardy
30. W. Somerset Maugham
31. (Sir) Walter Scott
32. Jane Austen
33. Henry Fielding
34. Ford Madox Ford
35. James Joyce
36. Oscar Wilde
37. Thomas Hardy
38. Charles Dickens
39. John Galsworthy
40. Laurence Sterne
41. Jane Austen
42. Charles Dickens
43. D. H. Lawrence
44. Henry Fielding
45. John le Carre
46. Anthony Burgess
47. D. H. Lawrence
48. Joseph Conrad
49. Thomas Hardy
50. E. M. Forster

Section 5

SHORT STORIES—MASTERS AND MASTERPIECES

(Pages 334–339)

ANSWERS TO SHORT-STORY TERMS

1. protagonist
2. symbol
3. denouement
4. tone
5. theme
6. framework story
7. satire
8. style
9. antagonist
10. rising action
11. in medias res
12. suspense
13. climax
14. exposition
15. verbal irony
16. locale
17. incident
18. dialect
19. character
20. flashback

ANSWERS TO SCRAMBLED SHORT-STORY WRITERS

1. Aleichem
2. Bierce
3. Poe
4. Updike
5. Kafka
6. O'Connor
7. Welty
8. London
9. Gogol
10. Salinger
11. Caldwell
12. Wharton
13. Porter
14. Mann
15. Maugham
16. Woolf
17. Chekhov
18. Lardner
19. Sillitoe
20. Doyle
21. Runyon
22. James
23. Turgenev
24. Dreiser
25. de Maupassant
26. Munro
27. Kipling
28. Mansfield
29. Hemingway
30. Hawthorne

ANSWERS TO ROLL CALL FOR SHORT-STORY WRITERS . . . PART ONE

1. Mark Twain
2. Leo Tolstoy
3. James Thurber
4. Isaac B. Singer
5. J. D. Salinger
6. Edgar Allan Poe
7. Katherine A. Porter
8. Tillie Olsen
9. Flannery O'Connor
10. Guy de Maupassant

11. Herman Melville
12. Thomas Mann
13. Katherine Mansfield
14. Bernard Malamud
15. Jack London

16. D. H. Lawrence
17. Franz Kafka
18. James Joyce
19. Sarah Orne Jewett
20. O. Henry

ANSWERS TO ROLL CALL FOR SHORT-STORY WRITERS . . . PART TWO

1. Washington Irving
2. Shirley Jackson
3. Ernest Hemingway
4. Henry James
5. Nathaniel Hawthorne
6. Nikolai Gogol
7. Nadine Gordimer
8. F. Scott Fitzgerald
9. William Faulkner
10. Stephen Crane

11. Sir A. C. Doyle
12. Joseph Conrad
13. Anton Chekhov
14. John Cheever
15. Conrad Aiken
16. Sherwood Anderson
17. James Baldwin
18. Ann Beattie
19. Ambrose Bierce
20. Ray Bradbury

ANSWERS TO WORLD SHORT-STORY WRITERS WORD FIND

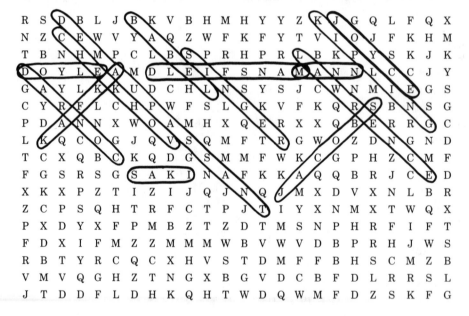

STORY

ARABY
CAPTAINS ALL
DISORDER AND EARLY SORROW
HER FIRST BALL

AUTHOR

JOYCE
JACOBS
MANN
MANSFIELD

METAMORPHOSIS	KAFKA
ODESSA TALES	BABEL
THE DEAD FIDDLER	SINGER
THE KISS	CHEKHOV
THE MAN WHO WOULD BE KING	KIPLING
THE NECKLACE	de MAUPASSANT
THE OPEN WINDOW	SAKI
THE RED-HEADED LEAGUE	DOYLE
THE ROCKING HORSE WINNER	LAWRENCE
THE SECRET SHARER	CONRAD

ANSWERS TO AMERICAN SHORT-STORY WRITERS

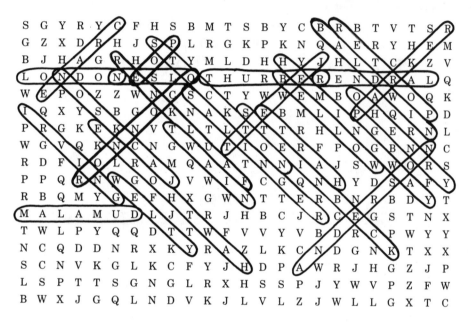

SHORT STORY (or collection)	AUTHOR
1. A Father To Be	BELLOW
2. A Good Man Is Hard to Find	O'CONNOR
3. A Perfect Day for Banana Fish	SALINGER
4. After Twenty Years	O. HENRY
5. Barn Burning	FAULKNER
6. Deep Haven	JEWETT
7. Flight	STEINBECK
8. Haircut	LARDNER
9. Sonny's Blues	BALDWIN
10. Tell Me a Riddle	OLSEN
11. The Big Blonde	PARKER
12. The Bride of Innisfallen	WELTY
13. The Celebrated Jumping Frog of Calaveras County	TWAIN

14. *The Jilting of Granny Weatherall*   *PORTER*
15. *The Lady or the Tiger*   *STOCKTON*
16. *The Legend of Sleepy Hollow*   *IRVING*
17. *The Lottery*   *JACKSON*
18. *The Luck of Roaring Camp*   *HARTE*
19. *The Open Boat*   *CRANE*
20. *The Pit and the Pendulum*   *POE*
21. *The Prison*   *MALAMUD*
22. *The Secret Life of Walter Mitty*   *THURBER*
23. *The Short Life of Francis Macomber*   *HEMINGWAY*
24. *To Build a Fire*   *LONDON*
25. *Winesburg, Ohio*   *ANDERSON*
26. *Young Goodman Brown*   *HAWTHORNE*

ANSWERS TO
THE CHARACTERS OF SHORT STORIES

1. I	6. Q	11. O	16. K
2. J	7. B	12. L	17. F
3. P	8. N	13. E	18. T
4. A	9. C	14. H	19. M
5. G	10. R	15. D	20. S

ANSWERS TO
MORE CHARACTERS OF SHORT STORIES

1. D	6. I	11. E	16. O
2. N	7. S	12. H	17. M
3. Q	8. P	13. B	18. G
4. L	9. R	14. T	19. J
5. A	10. C	15. K	20. F

ANSWERS TO
SHORT-STORY WRITERS CRYPTOLOGY

1. IJS	1. POE
2. JFJWWJM	2. O'CONNOR
3. VOEOVKR	3. MALAMUD
4. QSNSPP	4. JEWETT
5. ZSVDWTNOL	5. HEMINGWAY
6. PZKMXSM	6. THURBER
7. BOKEAWSM	7. FAULKNER
8. ZOMPS	8. HARTE
9. JEGSW	9. OLSEN
10. J.ZSWML	10. O. HENRY

11. IOMASM
12. GPJFAPJW
13. XOERNDW
14. PNODW
15. FMOWS
16. IJMPSM
17. EJWRJW
18. GPSDWXSFA
19. EOMRWSM
20. OWRSMGJW

11. PARKER
12. STOCKTON
13. BALDWIN
14. TWAIN
15. CRANE
16. PORTER
17. LONDON
18. STEINBECK
19. LARDNER
20. ANDERSON

Letter Substitution Code Used:

Letter: A B C D E F G H I J K L M N O P Q R S T U V W X Y Z

Substitute: O X F R S B T Z D Q A E V W J I H M G P K Y N C L U

ANSWERS TO
POE'S CHALLENGE . . . THE SHORT-STORY QUOTES

1. X	9. A	17. K	24. U
2. Z	10. Q	18. O	25. C
3. AA	11. I	19. P	26. DD
4. W	12. R	20. E	27. Y
5. F	13. J	21. N	28. V
6. D	14. G	22. S	29. BB
7. H	15. L	23. T	30. CC
8. B	16. M		

ANSWERS TO
WORLD SHORT-STORY WRITERS

D → 1. *The Man Who Would Be King*
    A. Mann B. Mansfield C. Saki D. Kipling

B → 2. *Captains All*
    A. Singer B. Jacobs C. Chekhov D. Conrad

A → 3. *The Red-Headed League*
    A. Doyle B. Lawrence C. Mansfield D. Joyce

C → 4. *The Secret Sharer*
    A. Lawrence B. Kipling C. Conrad D. Joyce

B → 5. *Metamorphosis*
    A. Saki B. Kafka C. Mann D. Chekhov

A → 6. *The Dead Fiddler*
    A. Singer B. Doyle C. Conrad D. Mann

B → 7. *Odessa Tales*
    A. Kafka B. Babel C. Joyce D. Conrad

B → 8. *Araby*
  A. Chekhov B. Joyce C. Kipling D. Babel
D → 9. *The Kiss*
  A. Mansfield B. Babel C. Singer D. Chekhov
A → 10. *The Necklace*
  A. de Maupassant B. Singer C. Chekhov D. Kipling
C → 11. *The Open Window*
  A. Kafka B. Babel C. Saki D. Mann
B → 12. *The Rocking Horse Winner*
  A. Mansfield B. Lawrence C. de Maupassant D. Chekhov
D → 13. *Her First Ball*
  A. Joyce B. Lawrence C. Babel D. Mansfield
A → 14. *Disorder and Early Sorrow*
  A. Mann B. Singer C. Kipling D. Mansfield

Section 6

THE POET'S CORNER

(Pages 340–342)

ANSWERS TO THE WORDS OF POETRY (PART ONE)

1. D	6. A	11. O	16. R
2. S	7. G	12. E	17. I
3. M	8. B	13. F	18. Q
4. P	9. C	14. T	19. K
5. J	10. L	15. H	20. N

ANSWERS TO THE WORDS OF POETRY (PART TWO)

1. C	6. M	11. G	16. Q
2. J	7. E	12. F	17. R
3. K	8. N	13. O	18. A
4. B	9. D	14. P	19. I
5. S	10. H	15. L	20. T

ANSWERS TO THE WORDS OF POETRY (PART THREE)

1. H	6. S	11. J	16. F
2. R	7. A	12. K	17. Q
3. G	8. O	13. M	18. I
4. D	9. C	14. T	19. L
5. B	10. P	15. N	20. E

ANSWERS TO THE WORDS OF POETRY (PART FOUR)

1. L	6. P	11. D	16. I
2. C	7. A	12. K	17. M
3. F	8. J	13. G	18. N
4. E	9. H	14. B	19. O
5. T	10. R	15. S	20. Q

ANSWERS TO LOVE POEMS

1. I	4. A	7. D	9. B
2. H	5. C	8. E	10. J
3. F	6. G		

ANSWERS TO WAR POEMS

1. I	4. B	7. C	9. J
2. D	5. A	8. F	10. H
3. G	6. E		

ANSWERS TO NATURE POEMS

1. C	4. B	7. A	9. G
2. F	5. D	8. H	10. I
3. E	6. J		

ANSWERS TO DEATH POEMS

1. D	4. C	7. E	9. I
2. G	5. F	8. J	10. B
3. H	6. A		

ANSWERS TO ANIMAL POEMS

1. G	4. E	7. A	9. J
2. H	5. C	8. I	10. D
3. F	6. B		

ANSWERS TO POEMS WITH ALLUSIONS IN TITLES

1. E	4. H	7. G	9. F
2. D	5. I	8. C	10. J
3. B	6. A		

ANSWERS TO POEMS OF CHILDHOOD AND ADOLESCENCE

1. G	4. B	7. A	9. C
2. J	5. D	8. E	10. I
3. H	6. F		

ANSWERS TO POEMS WITH MEN'S NAMES IN THEIR TITLES

1. E
2. I
3. J

4. H
5. F
6. G

7. B
8. C

9. D
10. A

ANSWERS TO PLACES IN POEMS

1. C
2. G
3. A

4. I
5. J
6. D

7. H
8. E

9. B
10. F

ANSWERS TO
POEMS WITH WOMEN'S NAMES IN THEIR TITLES

1. I
2. A
3. D

4. G
5. B
6. E

7. C
8. F

9. J
10. H

ANSWERS TO THE HALF OF IT

1. Edmund Spenser
2. Christopher Marlowe
3. John Donne
4. Ben Jonson
5. Robert Herrick
6. John Milton
7. John Dryden
8. Alexander Pope
9. Thomas Gray
10. William Blake
11. Robert Burns
12. William Wordsworth
13. Samuel Taylor Coleridge
14. George Gordon, Lord Byron
15. Percy Bysshe Shelley
16. John Keats
17. Elizabeth Barrett Browning
18. Alfred, Lord Tennyson
19. Robert Browning
20. Matthew Arnold
21. Lewis Carroll
22. Thomas Hardy
23. Gerard Manley Hopkins
24. A. E. Housman
25. D. H. Lawrence

ANSWERS TO THE OTHER HALF OF IT

1. Edwin Arlington Robinson
2. Robert Frost
3. Amy Lowell
4. Carl Sandburg
5. Wallace Stevens
6. William Carlos Williams
7. Ezra Pound
8. Siegfried Sassoon
9. Marianne Moore
10. John Crowe Ransom
11. Edna St. Vincent Millay
12. e. e. cummings
13. Langston Hughes
14. Ogden Nash
15. Countee Cullen
16. Theodore Roethke

17. Elizabeth Bishop	22. Robert Lowell
18. Muriel Rukeyser	23. Richard Wilbur
19. Karl Shapiro	24. Allen Ginsberg
20. Randall Jarrell	25. Maya Angelou
21. Gwendolyn Brooks	

Section 7

THE PLAY'S THE THING

(Pages 342–349)

ANSWERS TO PLAYS . . . FRONT AND CENTER (PART ONE)

TITLE	AUTHOR
1. *Agamemnon*	Aeschylus
2. *All My Sons*	Arthur Miller
3. *Amadeus*	Peter Shaffer
4. *Antigone*	Sophocles
5. *Arsenic and Old Lace*	Joseph Kesselring
6. *The Bald Soprano*	Eugene Ionesco
7. *Barefoot in the Park*	Neil Simon
8. *The Barretts of Wimpole Street*	Rudolph Besier
9. *The Birds*	Aristophanes
10. *The Birthday Party*	Harold Pinter
11. *Brighton Beach Memoirs*	Neil Simon
12. *Butterflies Are Free*	Leonard Gershe
13. *Caesar and Cleopatra*	George Bernard Shaw
14. *Candida*	George Bernard Shaw
15. *Cat on a Hot Tin Roof*	Tennessee Williams
16. *Charley's Aunt*	Brandon Thomas
17. *The Cherry Orchard*	Anton Chekhov
18. *Children of a Lessor God*	Mark Medoff
19. *The Children's Hour*	Lillian Hellman
20. *The Cocktail Party*	T. S. Eliot
21. *Come Back, Little Sheba*	William Inge
22. *The Country Girl*	Clifford Odets
23. *The Crucible*	Arthur Miller
24. *Cyrano de Bergerac*	Edmond Rostand
25. *Death of a Salesman*	Arthur Miller
26. *Desire Under the Elms*	Eugene O'Neill
27. *The Diary of Anne Frank*	Frances Goodritch and Albert Hackett
28. *A Doll's House*	Henrik Ibsen
29. *Don Juan*	Molière

30.	*The Effect of Gamma Rays on Man-in-the-Moon Marigolds*	Paul Zindel
31.	*The Elephant Man*	Bernard Pomerance
32.	*The Emperor Jones*	Eugene O'Neill
33.	*An Enemy of the People*	Henrik Ibsen
34.	*Equus*	Peter Shaffer
35.	*Eumenides*	Aeschylus

ANSWERS TO
PLAYS . . . FRONT AND CENTER (PART TWO)

	TITLE	**AUTHOR**
1.	*Exiles*	James Joyce
2.	*Ghosts*	Henrik Ibsen
3.	*The Glass Menagerie*	Tennessee Williams
4.	*Glengarry Glen Ross*	David Mamet
5.	*Golden Boy*	Clifford Odets
6.	*The Great White Hope*	Howard Sackler
7.	*The Hairy Ape*	Eugene O'Neill
8.	*Heartbreak House*	George Bernard Shaw
9.	*Hedda Gabler*	Henrik Ibsen
10.	*Mourning Becomes Electra*	Eugene O'Neill
11.	*The Homecoming*	Harold Pinter
12.	*The Hostage*	Brendan Behan
13.	*I Remember Mama*	John Van Druten
14.	*The Iceman Cometh*	Eugene O'Neill
15.	*The Importance of Being Earnest*	Oscar Wilde
16.	*Inherit the Wind*	Jerome Lawrence and Robert E. Lee
17.	*Juno and the Paycock*	Sean O'Casey
18.	*Krapp's Last Tape*	Samuel Beckett
19.	*Lady Windermere's Fan*	Oscar Wilde
20.	*Little Foxes*	Lillian Hellman
21.	*Long Day's Journey into Night*	Eugene O'Neill
22.	*Look Back in Anger*	John Osborne
23.	*Lysistrata*	Aristophanes
24.	*Major Barbara*	George Bernard Shaw
25.	*Man and Superman*	George Bernard Shaw
26.	*A Man for All Seasons*	Robert Bolt
27.	*The Master Builder*	Henrik Ibsen
28.	*The Matchmaker*	Thornton Wilder
29.	*Medea*	Euripedes
30.	*The Miracle Worker*	William Gibson
31.	*Mister Roberts*	Thomas Heggen and Joshua Logan
32.	*The Mousetrap*	Agatha Christie
33.	*Mrs. Warren's Profession*	George Bernard Shaw
34.	*Murder in the Cathedral*	T. S. Eliot
35.	*No Time for Sergeants*	Max Hyman

ANSWERS TO
PLAYS . . . FRONT AND CENTER (PART THREE)

TITLE	AUTHOR
1. *The Odd Couple*	Neil Simon
2. *Oedipus at Colonus*	Sophocles
3. *Oedipus the King*	Sophocles
4. *Our Town*	Thornton Wilder
5. *Peter Pan*	J. M. Barrie
6. *The Playboy of the Western World*	J. M. Synge
7. *Pygmalion*	George Bernard Shaw
8. *A Raisin in the Sun*	Lorraine Hansberry
9. *The Rivals*	Richard Brinsley Sheridan
10. *Rosencrantz and Guildenstern Are Dead*	Tom Stoppard
11. *Saint Joan*	George Bernard Shaw
12. *The Seagull*	Anton Chekhov
13. *The Skin of Our Teeth*	Thornton Wilder
14. *That Championship Season*	Jason Miller
15. *The Time of Your Life*	William Saroyan
16. *Twelve Angry Men*	Reginald Rose
17. *Uncle Vanya*	Anton Chekhov
18. *A View from the Bridge*	Arthur Miller
19. *Waiting for Godot*	Samuel Beckett
20. *Who's Afraid of Virginia Woolf?*	Edward Albee
21. *Whose Life Is It Anyway?*	Brian Clark
22. *The Wild Duck*	Henrik Ibsen
23. *The Winslow Boy*	Terence Rattigan
24. *The Zoo Story*	Edward Albee

ANSWERS TO THE CHARACTERS STEP FORWARD

1. L	8. F	14. X	20. H
2. E	9. J	15. G	21. U
3. M	10. S	16. N	22. V
4. C	11. A	17. O	23. D
5. K	12. P	18. B	24. W
6. R	13. Q	19. I	25. T
7. Y			

ANSWERS TO PLAYWRIGHTS' CRYPTOLOGY

1. YCPBJNJ	1. MOLIÈRE
2. VSQUUJN	2. SHAFFER
3. VLCRRQNW	3. STOPPARD
4. VSQF	4. SHAW
5. VQNLNJ	5. SARTRE

6. RBKLJN	6. PINTER
7. QJVMSZPHV	7. AESCHYLUS
8. YBPPJN	8. MILLER
9. JPBCL	9. ELIOT
10. NQMBKJ	10. RACINE
11. BGVJK	11. IBSEN
12. SQKVGJNNZ	12. HANSBERRY
13. SJPPYQK	13. HELLMAN
14. VSQDJVRJQNJ	14. SHAKESPEARE
15. XCKVCK	15. JONSON
16. OPGJJ	16. ALBEE
17. YQNPCFJ	17. MARLOWE
18. VCRSCMPJV	18. SOPHOCLES
19. GNJMSL	19. BRECHT
20. QNBVLCRSQKJV	20. ARISTOPHANES

Letter Substitution Code Used:

Letter: A B C D E F G H I J K L M N O P Q R S T U V W X Y Z
Substitute: Q G M W J U T S B X D P Y K C R I N V L H A F E Z O

ANSWERS TO PLAYWORDS

1. *All My Sons*
2. *Antigone*
3. *Arms and the Man*
4. *Cat on a Hot Tin Roof*
5. *The Cherry Orchard*
6. *The Children's Hour*
7. *The Cocktail Party*
8. *Come Back, Little Sheba*
9. *The Crucible*
10. *Cyrano de Bergerac*
11. *The Death of a Salesman*
12. *The Diary of Anne Frank*
13. *A Doll's House*
14. *The Emperor Jones*
15. *An Enemy of the People*
16. *The Glass Menagerie*
17. *The Hairy Ape*
18. *Hedda Gabbler*
19. *The Iceman Cometh*
20. *Inherit the Wind*
21. *The Little Foxes*
22. *Long Day's Journey into Night*
23. *Major Barbara*
24. *Man and Superman*
25. *A Man for All Seasons*
26. *The Master Builder*
27. *The Matchmaker*
28. *The Miracle Worker*
29. *Mister Roberts*
30. *Murder in the Cathedral*
31. *No Time for Sergeants*
32. *Oedipus Rex*
33. *Our Town*
34. *Pygmalion*
35. *A Raisin in the Sun*
36. *The Rivals*
37. *Saint Joan*
38. *The Skin of Our Teeth*
39. *A Streetcar Named Desire*
40. *A View from the Bridge*
41. *The Winslow Boy*

ANSWERS TO NAME THAT PLAYWRIGHT

D → 1. *Rosencrantz and Guildenstern Are Dead*
    A. Ibsen B. Shaffer C. Marlowe D. Stoppard

B → 2. *The Zoo Story*
    A. Shaw B. Albee C. Racine D. Pinter

D → 3. *The Birds*
    A. Shaffer B. Sartre C. Aeschylus D. Aristophanes

D → 4. *Mother Courage and Her Children*
    A. Pinter B. Miller C. Eliot D. Brecht

B → 5. *The Little Foxes*
    A. Shaffer B. Hellman C. Pinter D. Jonson

D → 6. *The Oresteia*
    A. Racine B. Miller C. Hansberry D. Aeschylus

A → 7. *The Birthday Party*
    A. Pinter B. Miller C. Racine D. Albee

A → 8. *Major Barbara*
    A. Shaw B. Jonson C. Pinter D. Eliot

C → 9. *Romeo and Juliet*
    A. Shaffer B. Ibsen C. Shakespeare D. Miller

C → 10. *The Misanthrope*
    A. Jonson B. Shakespeare C. Molière D. Hellman

C → 11. *Volpone*
    A. Miller B. Racine C. Jonson D. Sartre

C → 12. *Doctor Faustus*
    A. Sophocles B. Pinter C. Marlowe D. Miller

A → 13. *Murder in the Cathedral*
    A. Eliot B. Stoppard C. Miller D. Jonson

D → 14. *No Exit*
    A. Brecht B. Euripedes C. Shakespeare D. Sartre

D → 15. *An Enemy of the People*
    A. Aristophanes B. Albee C. Sartre D. Ibsen

B → 16. *Medea*
    A. Sophocles B. Euripedes C. Stoppard D. Miller

D → 17. *Phedre*
    A. Aristophanes B. Sophocles C. Albee D. Racine

C → 18. *Oedipus Rex*
    A. Shaffer B. Euripedes C. Sophocles D. Ibsen

A → 19. *All My Sons*
    A. Miller B. Sophocles C. Hellman D. Stoppard

A → 20. *Equus*
    A. Shaffer B. Sophocles C. Molière D. Shakespeare

ANSWERS TO
A TRIP TO BROADWAY

1. I	3. N	5. B	7. R
2. U	4. E	6. J	8. S

9. T	14. F	18. K	22. V
10. M	15. G	19. O	23. P
11. W	16. C	20. Y	24. Q
12. A	17. H	21. L	25. X
13. D			

ANSWERS TO
MUSIC TO YOUR EARS

1. P	8. A	14. S	20. K
2. M	9. O	15. Y	21. R
3. G	10. V	16. T	22. N
4. U	11. C	17. Q	23. X
5. W	12. I	18. B	24. F
6. L	13. D	19. J	25. H
7. E			

ANSWERS TO THE PLAYWRIGHT MEETS HIS CREATION

I → 1.	C → 6.	O → 11.	N → 16.
F → 2.	J → 7.	T → 12.	P → 17.
M → 3.	D → 8.	L → 13.	Q → 18.
G → 4.	K → 9.	A → 14.	E → 19.
S → 5.	R → 10.	B → 15.	H → 20.

ANSWERS TO THE PLAYWRIGHT PROBLEM

1. Hellman
2. Jonson
3. Albee
4. Shakespeare
5. Eliot
6. Shaw
7. Racine
8. Hansberry
9. Aeschylus
10. Ibsen
11. Aristophanes
12. Miller
13. Brecht
14. Shaffer
15. Molière
16. Marlowe
17. Sophocles
18. Pinter
19. Sartre
20. Euripedes

ANSWERS TO CAN YOU FIND ME?

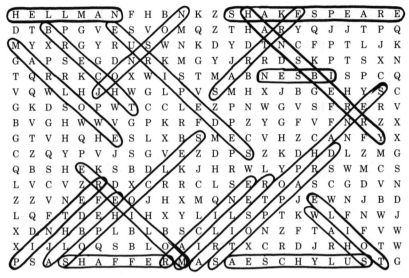

AESCHYLUS	HANSBERRY	MOLIÈRE	SHAW
ALBEE	HELLMAN	PINTER	SOPHOCLES
ARISTOPHANES	IBSEN	RACINE	STOPPARD
BRECHT	JONSON	SARTRE	
ELIOT	MARLOWE	SHAFFER	
EURIPEDES	MILLER	SHAKESPEARE	

ANSWERS TO PULITZER PRIZE-WINNING PLAYWRIGHTS

1. I	6. R	11. J	15. A
2. H	7. C	12. M	16. G
3. Q	8. B	13. O	17. L
4. K	9. F	14. D	18. P
5. E	10. N		

Section 8

SHAKESPEARE—WHERE THERE'S WILL, THERE ARE WORDS

(Pages 349–353)

ANSWERS TO A SHAKESPEARE PRIMER

1. 1564
2. Stratford-upon-Avon
3. Christopher Marlowe
4. Elizabeth
5. Raphael Holinshed
6. Globe
7. Francis Drake
8. Walter Raleigh
9. Mary Arden
10. Anne Hathaway
11. Mary, Queen of Scots
12. 3 (two girls and a boy)
13. Spanish Armada
14. New Place
15. plague
16. Earl of Southampton
17. 1603
18. 0 (women were not permitted to be in plays)
19. 154
20. burned down
21. tragedies
22. 0 (His son, Hamnet, had died.)
23. 1616
24. April 23
25. bones

ANSWERS TO WHAT'S IN A NAME? (PART ONE)

1. Desdemona
2. Cleopatra
3. Bassanio
4. Julius Caesar
5. Edgar
6. Fortinbras
7. Gaunt
8. Banquo
9. Aufidius
10. Cordelia
11. Achilles
12. Antonio
13. Ariel
14. Cressida
15. Coriolanus
16. Nick Bottom
17. Titus Andronicus
18. Apothecary
19. Brutus
20. Sir John Falstaff
21. Cassio
22. Claudio
23. Antony
24. Bianca
25. Sir Toby Belch

ANSWERS TO WHAT'S IN A NAME? (PART TWO)

1. Hippolyta
2. Iago
3. Hamlet
4. Earl of Gloucester
5. Henry VIII
6. Mercutio
7. Katharina Minola
8. Macbeth

9. Octavia
10. King Lear
11. Isabella
12. Othello
13. Macduff
14. Juliet
15. Gertrude
16. Goneril
17. Horatio

18. Henry, Prince of Wales
19. Imogen
20. Helena
21. Laertes
22. Nurse
23. Oberon
24. Ophelia
25. Lorenzo

ANSWERS TO WHAT'S IN A NAME? (PART THREE)

1. Shylock
2. Romeo
3. Priam
4. Pistol
5. Puck
6. Theseus
7. Regan
8. Portia
9. Polonius
10. Petruchio

11. Touchstone
12. Titania
13. Mistress Quickly
14. Proteus
15. Viola
16. Tybalt
17. Christopher Sly
18. Paris
19. Prospero
20. Rosencrantz

ANSWERS TO HOW TRAGIC OF YOU, WILL!

1. C	10. D	19. F	28. A
2. F	11. C	20. J	29. B
3. E	12. B	21. E	30. A
4. D	13. C	22. A	31. J
5. I	14. G	23. D	32. I
6. C	15. D	24. G	33. B
7. I	16. I	25. F	34. F
8. C	17. E	26. H	35. H
9. G	18. B	27. H	

ANSWERS TO WILL PAIRS THEM UP

The answers also include the play that includes each pair.

1. G *Hamlet*
2. S *Romeo and Juliet*
3. H *Macbeth*
4. R *Love's Labour's Lost*
5. B *Two Gentlemen of Verona*
6. J *A Midsummer Night's Dream*
7. P *The Merchant of Venice*

8. F *The Taming of the Shrew*
9. I *Much Ado About Nothing*
10. A *Romeo and Juliet*
11. Q *Twelfth Night*
12. L *Measure for Measure*
13. M *The Winter's Tale*
14. D *Henry IV, Part I*

15. O   *Julius Caesar*   18. C   *Othello*
16. K   *Hamlet*   19. N   *Macbeth*
17. T   *Troilus and Cressida*   20. E   *The Tempest*

ANSWERS TO WILL SETS THE SCENE

1. J   *Love's Labour's Lost*   14. F   *Cymbeline*
2. D   *The Comedy of Errors*   15. Y   *The Winter's Tale*
3. X   *Two Gentlemen of Verona*   16. T   *The Tempest*
4. N   *A Midsummer Night's Dream*   17. U   *Titus Andronicus*
5. M   *The Merchant of Venice*   18. R   *Romeo and Juliet*
6. S   *The Taming of the Shrew*   19. H   *Julius Caesar*
7. O   *Much Ado About Nothing*   20. G   *Hamlet*
8. C   *As You Like It*   21. P   *Othello*
9. W   *Twelfth Night*   22. I   *King Lear*
10. V *Troilus and Cressida*   23. K   *Macbeth*
11. A *All's Well That Ends Well*   24. B   *Antony and Cleopatra*
12. L *Measure for Measure*   25. E   *Coriolanus*
13. Q *Pericles*

ANSWERS TO SHAKESPEARE STAGES A BRAWL

The answers also include the play associated with each "storm."

1. B   *Henry IV, Part I*   9. N   *King Lear*
2. G   *Henry V*   10. C   *Macbeth*
3. M   *Titus Andronicus*   11. I   *Antony and Cleopatra*
4. H   *Romeo and Juliet*   12. D   *Coriolanus*
5. E   *Julius Caesar*   13. J   *The Merchant of Venice*
6. F   *Troilus and Cressida*   14. O   *Measure for Measure*
7. A   *Hamlet*   15. K   *Henry VI, Part II*
8. L   *Othello*

ANSWERS TO SHAKESPEARE'S SENSATIONAL SALES

The answers also include the play associated with each item.

1. S   *The Tempest*   12. V   *Two Gentlemen of Verona*
2. F   *Cymbeline*   13. D   *The Comedy of Errors*
3. K   *Measure for Measure*   14. E   *Coriolanus*
4. A   *All's Well That Ends Well*   15. T   *Timon of Athens*
5. N   *A Midsummer Night's Dream*   16. B   *Antony and Cleopatra*
6. U   *Twelfth Night*   17. G   *Hamlet*
7. C   *As You Like It*   18. J   *Macbeth*
8. O   *Much Ado About Nothing*   19. I   *King Lear*
9. M   *The Merry Wives of Windsor*   20. P   *Othello*
10. L *The Merchant of Venice*   21. H   *Julius Caesar*
11. R *The Taming of the Shrew*   22. Q   *Romeo and Juliet*

ANSWERS TO THE END JUSTIFIES THE SCENES

The answers also include the play associated with the actions.

1. G *Henry VI, Part I*
2. P *Richard II*
3. F *Henry IV, Part I*
4. H *Henry VIII*
5. Q *Romeo and Juliet*
6. I *Julius Caesar*
7. E *Hamlet*
8. O *Othello*
9. J *King Lear*
10. K *Macbeth*

11. B *Antony and Cleopatra*
12. S *Timon of Athens*
13. D *Coriolanus*
14. T *Two Gentlemen of Verona*
15. R *The Taming of the Shrew*
16. M *A Midsummer Night's Dream*
17. L *The Merchant of Venice*
18. N *Much Ado About Nothing*
19. C *As You Like It*
20. A *All's Well That Ends Well*

ANSWERS TO THE BARD'S BUNGLES

1. Romeo and Juliet are teenagers.
2. Caesar was victorious over Pompey.
3. The ghost of Hamlet's father urges him to seek revenge.
4. Othello chooses Cassio instead of Iago for the position of lieutenant.
5. Each of the men receives three prophecies.
6. Antony and Cleopatra will be buried together.
7. The citizens are angry about the famine.
8. Timon dies in a cave.
9. Cordelia is hanged and Lear, who has been in prison, dies broken-hearted.
10. The plot involves the Trojan War.
11. The marriage of Henry and Katherine is annulled.
12. Richmond kills Richard.
13. Hal is reformed and possesses kinglike qualities.
14. Prince Hal, the son of Henry IV, kills Hotspur.
15. Richard is killed by Sir Pierce of Exton.
16. Prospero's servant, Ariel, has magical powers.
17. Posthumus gives Imogen a beautiful bracelet.
18. The setting is France.
19. Claudio's foil is Benedick.
20. Bianca cannot marry until Katherina is married.

ANSWERS TO LOVE—SHAKESPEAREAN STYLE

1. E
2. L
3. K
4. T
5. A

6. D
7. J
8. B
9. N
10. M

11. S
12. C
13. H
14. P
15. F

16. Q
17. I
18. G
19. O
20. R

ANSWERS TO WILL'S TRAGIC WORDS

1. H	14. A	27. D	39. K
2. F	15. E	28. C	40. H
3. E	16. G	29. I	41. D
4. G	17. C	30. B	42. C
5. C	18. H	31. H	43. E
6. D	19. H	32. H	44. F
7. A	20. B	33. F	45. H
8. B	21. E	34. K	46. G
9. I	22. F	35. F	47. K
10. D	23. G	36. E	48. B
11. C	24. J	37. I	49. J
12. F	25. I	38. I	50. J
13. I	26. A		

Section 9

POTPOURRI—ACTIVITIES TO PLEASE THE SENSES

(Pages 353–363)

ANSWERS TO
SCRAMBLED AMERICAN AUTHORS . . . PART ONE

1. Ellison	10. Pound	18. Ferber
2. Hansberry	11. Moore	19. Lewis
3. Jewett	12. Roth	20. Oates
4. Anderson	13. Simon	21. Salinger
5. Bradstreet	14. Twain	22. Wright
6. Chopin	15. Ransom	23. Ozick
7. Crichton	16. McCullers	24. Cozzens
8. Grey	17. Caldwell	25. Kerouac
9. Irving		

ANSWERS TO
SCRAMBLED AMERICAN AUTHORS . . . PART TWO

1. Inge	7. Frost	13. Michener
2. Dreiser	8. Potok	14. MacLeish
3. Buck	9. Riley	15. Beattie
4. Bellow	10. Stein	16. Fitzgerald
5. Albee	11. Welty	17. Lardner
6. Hersey	12. Nash	18. Hellman

19. Cather
20. Dickinson
21. London
22. Clancy
23. Knowles
24. Glasgow
25. Odets

ANSWERS TO
SCRAMBLED AMERICAN AUTHORS . . . PART THREE

1. Sexton
2. Stowe
3. O'Neill
4. Longfellow
5. Plath
6. Steinbeck
7. Singer
8. Cheever
9. Jackson
10. Heller
11. Capote
12. Baldwin
13. Hemingway
14. Crane
15. Bierce
16. Runyon
17. Updike
18. Sandburg
19. Pynchon
20. Norris
21. Lowell
22. Thurber
23. Brooks
24. Hughes
25. Kantor

ANSWERS TO
SCRAMBLED AMERICAN AUTHORS . . . PART FOUR

1. Burroughs
2. Baraka
3. Rand
4. Sinclair
5. Rawlings
6. Millay
7. Styron
8. Melville
9. Mitchell
10. Saroyan
11. Faulkner
12. Carver
13. Jarrell
14. Alcott
15. Barth
16. Dodge
17. Conroy
18. Benét
19. Miller
20. Parker
21. Roethke
22. Morrison
23. Porter
24. Robinson
25. Paley

ANSWERS TO
SCRAMBLED BRITISH AND IRISH AUTHORS . . . PART ONE

1. Pepys
2. Goldsmith
3. Browning
4. Byron
5. Marlowe
6. Addison
7. Rossetti
8. Forster
9. Kipling
10. Arnold
11. Jonson
12. O'Connor
13. Maugham
14. Coleridge
15. Behan
16. Eliot
17. Defoe
18. Orwell
19. Potter
20. Rhys
21. Scott
22. Lawrence
23. Donne
24. Chaucer
25. Austen
26. Blake
27. Greene
28. O'Casey
29. Saki
30. Sassoon
31. Lewis
32. Joyce
33. Forester
34. Boswell
35. Thackeray
36. Shakespeare
37. Wilde
38. Wordsworth
39. Steele
40. Sheridan

ANSWERS TO
SCRAMBLED BRITISH AND IRISH AUTHORS . . . PART TWO

1. Pinter
2. Malory
3. Conrad
4. Beckett
5. Shaffer
6. Synge
7. Smollett
8. Waugh
9. Stevenson
10. Golding
11. Pope
12. Dickens
13. Burns
14. Huxley

15. Ruskin
16. Swift
17. Shaw
18. Trollope
19. Sterne
20. Brontë
21. Gray
22. Mansfield
23. Barrie
24. Spenser
25. Woolf
26. Stoppard
27. Yeats

28. Shelley
29. Dryden
30. Carroll
31. Owen
32. Keats
33. Coward
34. Tolkien
35. Sidney
36. Webster
37. Fielding
38. Thomas
39. Spark
40. Tennyson

ANSWERS TO SCRAMBLED WORLD AUTHORS

1. Boccaccio
2. Hesse
3. Euripedes
4. Munro
5. Ibsen
6. Chekhov
7. Pasternak
8. Cervantes
9. Aesop

10. Goethe
11. Mann
12. Kafka
13. Grimm
14. Dostoyevsky
15. Aleichem
16. Kazantzakis
17. Naipaul

18. Garciá Márquez
19. Aeschylus
20. Kosinski
21. Aristophanes
22. Gibran
23. Homer
24. Brecht
25. Gordimer

ANSWERS TO AN ASSORTMENT OF EXCERPTS

1. E
2. H
3. L
4. A
5. O

6. P
7. N
8. F
9. D

10. J
11. K
12. M
13. C

14. I
15. G
16. B
17. Q

ANSWERS TO BODY PARTS IN LITERARY TITLES

1. Ernest Hemingway
2. Nelson Algren
3. Carson McCullers
4. Thornton Wilder
5. Edgar Allan Poe
6. Joseph Conrad

7. George Bernard Shaw
8. Sam Shepard
9. Kenneth Roberts
10. Ursula LeGuin
11. Graham Greene
12. Richard Llewellyn

13. Zora Neale Hurston
14. Dee Brown
15. Toni Morrison
16. Christy Brown
17. Peter Benchley
18. Lewis B. Patten
19. Lewis Thomas
20. Elizabeth Bowen
21. Ken Follett
22. Patrick White
23. Ivy Compton-Burnett
24. Violette Leduc
25. Susanna Rowson

ANSWERS TO COLORS IN LITERATURE

1. Scarlet
2. White
3. White
4. Black
5. Blue
6. Purple
7. Blues
8. White
9. White
10. Red
11. Gold
12. Scarlet
13. Black
14. Blue
15. Purple
16. White
17. Red
18. Green
19. Red
20. Green
21. Red . . . Black
22. Green
23. Black
24. White
25. Gold
26. Gray
27. Black
28. Orange
29. Red
30. Black
31. Yellow

ANSWERS TO THE COMMON DENOMINATOR

Group 1: Relatives

Anton Chekhov—*Uncle Vanya*
Fyodor Dostoyevsky—*The Brothers Karamazov*
Ivan Turgenev—*Fathers and Sons*
Bertolt Brecht—*Mother Courage and Her Children*

Group 2: Body parts

George Bernard Shaw—*Arms and the Man*
Zora Neale Hurston—*Their Eyes Were Watching God*
Thornton Wilder—*The Skin of Our Teeth*
Graham Greene—*The Heart of the Matter*

Group 3: Animals

John Updike—*Rabbit, Run*
Tennessee Williams—*Cat on a Hot Tin Roof*
Eugene O'Neill—*The Hairy Ape*
C. S. Lewis—*The Lion, the Witch, and the Wardrobe*

Group 4: Fruits

J. D. Salinger—*A Perfect Day for Bananafish*
Anthony Burgess—*A Clockwork Orange*
John Steinbeck—*The Grapes of Wrath*
Fannie Flagg—*Fried Green Tomatoes*

Group 5: Commands

William Faulkner—*Go Down, Moses*
Thomas Wolfe—*Look Homeward, Angel*
James Baldwin—*Go Tell It on the Mountain*
William Styron—*Lie Down in Darkness*

Group 6: The word house appears in all the titles.

Edith Wharton—*House of Mirth*
Nathaniel Hawthorne—*The House of the Seven Gables*
Charles Dickens—*Bleak House*
Henrik Ibsen—*A Doll's House*

Group 7: Military ranks

John Fowles—*The French Lieutenant's Woman*
Rudyard Kipling—*Captains Courageous*
Mac Hyman—*No Time for Sergeants*
George Bernard Shaw—*Major Barbara*

Group 8: Birds

Dashiell Hammett—*The Maltese Falcon*
Harper Lee—*To Kill a Mockingbird*
Jack Higgins—*The Eagle Has Landed*
Aristophanes—*The Birds*

Group 9: Men's first names

George Eliot—*Adam Bede*
Joseph Conrad—*Lord Jim*
Charles Dickens—*David Copperfield*
Kingsley Amis—*Lucky Jim*

Group 10: The word last appears in all the titles.

Robert Browning—"My Last Duchess"
Edwin O'Connor—*The Last Hurrah*
James Fenimore Cooper—*The Last of the Mohicans*
Edward Bulwer-Lytton—*Last Days of Pompeii*

Group 11: Bodies of water

Jean Rhys—*Wide Sargasso Sea*
Henry David Thoreau—*A Week on the Concord and Merrimack Rivers*
Rachael Carson—*The Sea Around Us*
Mark Twain—*Life on the Mississippi*

Group 12: The word adventures appears in all the titles.

Mark Twain—*The Adventures of Huckleberry Finn*
Saul Bellow—*The Adventures of Augie March*
Lewis Carroll—*Alice's Adventures in Wonderland*
Walker Percy—*The Adventures of a Bad Catholic at a Time Near the End of the World*

Group 13: Directions

Erich Maria Remarque—*All Quiet on the Western Front*
Kenneth Roberts—*Northwest Passage*
John Millington Synge—*The Playboy of the Western World*
Percy Byshe Shelley—*Ode to the West Wind*

Group 14: Colors

Anna Sewell—*Black Beauty*
Alice Walker—*The Color Purple*
Stendhal—*The Red and the Black*
W. H. Hudson—*Green Mansions*

Group 15: Seasons of the year

Aldous Huxley—*After Many a Summer Dies the Swan*
Rachael Carson—*Silent Spring*
William Shakespeare—*Winter's Tale*
Barbara Pym—*Quartet in Autumn*

Group 16: The word women appears in the titles.

D. H. Lawrence—*Women in Love*
Alberto Moravia—*Two Women*
Euripedes—*The Trojan Women*
Louisa May Alcott—*Little Women*

Group 17: Nationalities

Nikos Kazantzakis—*Zorba the Greek*
Theodore Dreiser—*An American Tragedy*
Thomas Kyd—*The Spanish Tragedy*
Elizabeth Barrett Browning—*Sonnets from the Portuguese*

Group 18: The word light appears in the titles.

Conrad Richter—*The Light in the Forest*
Alfred Lord Tennyson—*The Charge of the Light Brigade*
William Faulkner—*Light in August*
Garrett Hongo—*Yellow Light*

ANSWERS TO CREATURES IN LITERARY TITLES

1. Edgar Rice Burroughs
2. James Clavell
3. Lillian Hellman
4. Ken Kesey
5. Harper Lee
6. Jack London
7. Frank Norris
8. Eugene O'Neill
9. Aristophanes
10. Marjorie Kinnan Rawlings
11. Kurt Vonnegut
12. John Steinbeck
13. Maya Angelou
14. Tennessee Williams
15. John Updike
16. Nathanael West
17. Tennessee Williams
18. William Golding

19. George Bernard Shaw
20. Dylan Thomas
21. William Butler Yeats
22. Hans Christian Andersen
23. Sir Arthur Conan Doyle
24. Dashiell Hammett
25. Jack Higgins
26. C. S. Lewis

27. Irwin Shaw
28. Jerzy Kosinski
29. Colleen McCullough
30. Aristophanes
31. Tennessee Williams
32. Susan Minot
33. David Henry Hwang
34. George Orwell

ANSWERS TO THE FLOW OF LITERATURE

1. D—Sea
2. F—Mississippi
3. M—Mohawk
4. N—Creek
5. E—Boat
6. G—Sea
7. C—Rhine
8. A—Sea

9. O—Lake
10. B—Boat
11. J—Sea
12. H—Mast
13. K—Beach
14. I—Ferry
15. L—River

ANSWERS TO THE DEATHS OF LITERATURE

1. Arthur Miller
2. Agatha Christie
3. Thomas Mann
4. Willa Cather
5. Leo Tolstoy
6. Robert Frost
7. Tom Stoppard
8. James Agee

9. Elizabeth Bowden
10. William Faulkner
11. Wole Soyinka
12. Athol Fugard
13. Emily Dickinson
14. Nikolai Gogol
15. Norman Mailer

ANSWERS TO THE "-ISM'S" OF LITERATURE
PART ONE

1. barbarism
2. spoonerism
3. imagism
4. anachronism
5. realism

6. syllogism
7. didacticism
8. humanism
9. New Criticism
10. existentialism

11. euphemism
12. aphorism
13. transcendentalism
14. pragmatism
15. romanticism

ANSWERS TO THE "-ISM'S" OF LITERATURE
PART TWO

1. symbolism
2. neoclassicism

3. malapropism
4. classicism

5. solecism
6. criticism

7. expressionism
8. empiricism
9. naturalism

10. rationalism
11. regionalism
12. surrealism

13. provincialism
14. archaism
15. plagiarism

ANSWERS TO KIDDIE LIT CHARACTERS

1. E	5. C	9. M	13. L
2. I	6. A	10. O	14. J
3. H	7. D	11. G	15. K
4. B	8. N	12. F	

ANSWERS TO LIT 101 . . . AND OTHER NUMBERS

1. 84	18. Thirty-nine	35. Fourth
2. Two	19. One	36. One Hundred
3. Eighty	20. Nine	37. Eight
4. None	21. Seven	38. One
5. Two	22. Twenty Thousand	39. Eight
6. Three	23. Eight	40. Eight
7. Two	24. Two	41. One
8. One	25. One	42. Nine
9. Two	26. 22	43. Three
10. Fourth	27. Six	44. Three
11. Five	28. 8	45. Four
12. Six	29. Two	46. Twice
13. Four	30. 49	47. Seven
14. Seventeen	31. Seven	48. Seven
15. 451	32. Two	49. First
16. Two	33. Million	50. Twelve
17. Nine	34. Ten	

ANSWERS TO LOCATION . . . LOCATION . . . LOCATION

STATE	TITLE	AUTHOR	STATE	TITLE	AUTHOR
			SET 1		
1. Alabama	D	P	6. Colorado	C	S
2. Alaska	J	N	7. Connecticut	I	K
3. Arizona	F	Q	8. Delaware	B	T
4. Arkansas	A	R	9. Florida	G	O
5. California	E	L	10. Georgia	H	M

SET 2

11. Hawaii	F	L	16. Kansas	D	O
12. Idaho	E	M	17. Kentucky	J	R
13. Illinois	A	Q	18. Louisiana	C	T
14. Indiana	B	S	19. Maine	H	P
15. Iowa	G	K	20. Maryland	I	N

SET 3

21. Mass.	E	P	26. Montana	B	O
22. Michigan	D	Q	27. Nebraska	H	N
23. Minnesota	A	R	28. Nevada	J	K
24. Mississippi	I	L	29. New Hampshire	C	T
25. Missouri	G	S	30. New Jersey	F	M

SET 4

31. New Mexico	C	L	36. Oklahoma	G	N
32. New York	H	O	37. Oregon	I	M
33. No. Carolina	D	T	38. Pennsylvania	J	S
34. North Dakota	A	Q	39. Rhode Island	B	P
35. Ohio	F	R	40. So. Carolina	E	K

SET 5

41. So. Dakota	D	L	46. Virginia	I	N
42. Tennessee	E	K	47. Washington	B	P
43. Texas	J	Q	48. West Virginia	F	R
44. Utah	H	O	49. Wisconsin	C	S
45. Vermont	A	T	50. Wyoming	G	M

POSSIBLE ANSWERS TO ONE-WORD TITLES

The answers that follow are by no means the only acceptable answers. There are quite a few works that the students will name whether it is through research or memory alone.

a. *Arrowsmith* . . . Sinclair Lewis; *Andersonville* . . . MacKinlay Kantor
b. *Babbitt* . . . Sinclair Lewis
c. *Chance* . . . Joseph Conrad
d. *Demian* . . . Herman Hesse; *Dracula* . . . Bram Stoker
e. *Electra* . . . Euripedes
f. *Frankenstein* . . . Mary Shelley
g. *Ghosts* . . . Henrik Ibsen

h. *Hecuba* . . . Euripides
i. *Ivanhoe* . . . Sir Walter Scott
j. *Justice* . . . John Galworthy
k. *Kenilworth* . . . Sir Walter Scott
l. *Lycidas* . . . John Milton
m. *Mother* . . . Maxim Gorki
n. *Nocturne* . . . Frank Swinnerton
o. *Omoo* . . . Herman Melville
p. *Phaedra* . . . Jean Racine; *Pygmalion* . . . George Bernard Shaw
q. *Quarry* . . . Bill Pronzini
r. *Romola* . . . George Eliot
s. *Seventeen* . . . Booth Tarkington
t. *Typee* . . . Herman Melville
u. *Ulysses* . . . James Joyce
v. *Volpone* . . . Ben Jonson
w. *Waverly* . . . Sir Walter Scott
x. *Xaipe* . . . e. e. cummings
y. *Yaqui* . . . Zane Grey
z. *Zadig* . . . Voltaire

ANSWERS TO THE TWO ROADS THAT ARE TRAVELED . . . THE FIRST ROAD

1. Florida (e) *The Yearling*   Marjorie Kinnan Rawlings
2. Georgia (k) *Deliverance*   James Dickey
3. South Carolina (a) *Porgy*   DuBose Heyward
4. North Carolina (g) *Look Homeward, Angel*   Thomas Wolfe
5. Virginia (m) *The Confessions of Nat Turner*   William Styron
6. West Virginia (h) *Up from Slavery*   Booker T. Washington
7. Maryland (l) *The Sot-Weed Factor*   John Barth
8. Pennsylvania (c) *The Autobiography of Ben Franklin*   Benjamin Franklin
9. New York (f) *An American Tragedy*   Theodore Dreiser
10. Vermont (j) *A Day No Pigs Would Die*   Robert N. Peck
11. Massachusetts (b) *The Scarlet Letter*   Nathaniel Hawthorne
12. New York City (d) *The Age of Innocence*   Edith Wharton
13. Long Island (i) *The Great Gatsby*   F. Scott Fitzgerald

ANSWERS TO THE TWO ROADS THAT ARE TRAVELED . . . THE SECOND ROAD

1. Montana (c) *A River Runs Through It*   Norman McLean
2. Wyoming (h) *Shane*   Jack Schaefer
3. South Dakota (n) *Bury My Heart at Wounded Knee*   Dee Brown
4. Nebraska (g) *O Pioneers!*   Willa Cather
5. Kansas (e) *In Cold Blood*   Truman Capote

6. Oklahoma (b) *The Grapes of Wrath*   John Steinbeck
7. Texas (l) *Giant*   Edna Ferber
8. Louisiana (m) *All the King's Men*   Robert Penn Warren
9. Arkansas (k) *I Know Why the Caged Bird Sings*   Maya Angelou
10. Mississippi (j) *As I Lay Dying*   William Faulkner
11. Alabama (i) *To Kill a Mockingbird*   Harper Lee
12. Tennessee (a) *A Death in the Family*   James Agee
13. Illinois (d) *The Jungle*   Upton Sinclair
14. Indiana (o) *The Friendly Persuasion*   Jessamyn West
15. Ohio (f) *Beloved*   Toni Morrison